SCOTLAND'S LIVING COASTLINE

THE NATURAL HERITAGE OF SCOTLAND

This series of books deals with the variety of topics that encompass the natural heritage of Scotland. Some titles will be specially written for the series, whilst others will be based on Scottish Natural Heritage (SNH) conferences. Each year since it was founded in 1992, SNH has organised or jointly organised a conference that has focused attention on a particular aspect of Scotland's natural heritage. The papers read at the conferences, or the specially written manuscripts, all go through a rigorous process of refereeing and editing before being submitted for publication. The titles already published in this series are:

1. *The Islands of Scotland: a Living Marine Heritage*
    Edited by J. M. Baxter and M. B. Usher (1994), x + 286pp.

2. *Heaths and Moorland: Cultural Landscapes*
    Edited by D. B. A. Thompson, A. J. Hester and M. B. Usher (1995), xvi + 400pp.

3. *Soils, Sustainability and the Natural Heritage*
    Edited by A. G. Taylor, J. E. Gordon and M. B. Usher (1996), xvii + 316pp.

4. *Freshwater Quality: Defining the Indefinable?*
    Edited by P. J. Boon and D. L. Howell (1997), xx + 552pp.

5. *Biodiversity in Scotland: Status, Trends and Initiatives*
    Edited by L. V. Fleming, A. C. Newton, J. A. Vickery and M. B. Usher (1997), xviii + 310pp.

6. *Land Cover Change: Scotland from the 1940s to the 1980s*
    E. C. Mackey, M. C. Shewry and G. J. Tudor (1999), xxviii+264pp.

This is the seventh book in the series.

SCOTLAND'S LIVING COASTLINE

Edited by John M. Baxter, Katherine Duncan,
Stephen Atkins and George Lees

SCOTTISH NATURAL HERITAGE

LONDON: THE STATIONERY OFFICE

First published 1999

ISBN 0 11 495856 4

British Library Cataloguing in Publication Data
A catalogue record for this book is available from the British Library.

Published by The Stationery Office and available from:

The Publications Centre
(mail, telephone and fax orders only)
PO Box 276, London SW8 5DT
General enquiries 0171 873 0011
Telephone orders 0171 873 9090
Fax orders 0171 873 8200

The Stationery Office Bookshops
123 Kingsway, London WC2B 6PQ
0171 242 6393 Fax 0171 242 6394
68–69 Bull Street, Birmingham B4 6AD
0121 236 9696   Fax 0121 236 9699
33 Wine Street, Bristol BS1 2BQ
0117 9264306 Fax 0117 9294515
9–21 Princess Street, Manchester M60 8AS
0161 834 7201 Fax 0161 833 0634
16 Arthur Street, Belfast BT1 4GD
01232 238451 Fax 01232 235401
The Stationery Office Oriel Bookshop
18–19 High Street, Cardiff CF1 2BZ
01222 395548 Fax 01222 384347
71 Lothian Road, Edinburgh EH3 9AZ
0131 228 4181   Fax 0131 622 7017

The Stationery Office's Accredited Agents
(see Yellow Pages)

and through good booksellers

Contents

LIST OF PLATES

(between pages 132 and 133)

Photographic credits

FOREWORD

It is my pleasure and privilege, as chairman of Scottish Natural Heritage (SNH), to write the foreword to *Scotland's Living Coastline*. This volume originates in the sixth annual Scottish Natural Heritage conference – one of a series which highlights, year by year, a specific and special aspect of Scotland's diverse natural heritage. Back in 1992, the inaugural conference explored the natural heritage of the sea around the islands of Scotland; since then we have hosted major conferences on heaths and moorland (1993), soils and their sustainability (1994), freshwater quality (1995) and Scotland's biodiversity (1996). In 1997 the focus was on the coast, and in 1998 we hosted a conference, jointly with the Macaulay Land Use Research Institute, on landscape. By the millennium, the conference volumes will be a unique dossier, virtually an encyclopaedia, of Scotland's natural heritage. They will prove of lasting benefit to all – researchers, decision-makers and the interested public alike.

In this book we are returning to our coastal margins to explore some of the critical issues and opportunities we must all address in order to ensure that our coastal environments are properly understood and that appropriate measures for their use, protection and enjoyment are put in place. To my mind, this was the most challenging of the six conferences which have been held so far. Our coastal and marine environments have not yet received a fraction of the attention that has been focused on terrestrial environments. The conference offered a very real opportunity, and a real challenge, to consider the issues in depth and to exchange ideas on how best to improve the situation. Bringing together ideas and expertise is crucial to the future of Scotland's living coastline; this is a very important area for Scottish Natural Heritage to explore in partnership with others – a theme which ran throughout the conference.

I want to acknowledge a particularly important partnership, that between SNH and the Ministry of Defence (MoD). The contribution made by the MoD has been of inestimable value to the natural heritage. So we were delighted to be able to hold the conference on MoD land, at Barry Buddon, with its dune complex. It is a very important unspoilt area whose quality has much to do with its long association with the MoD. Barry Buddon is one of a series of about 1400 Sites of Special Scientific Interest, for both its biological and its geomorphological interest; but more than that, it is also a candidate Special Area of Conservation (SAC) under the Habitats Directive. It is designated for its variety of landforms and habitats: foredune, grey dune, dune slack and, most particularly, the hairpin-shaped parabolic dunes which provide some of the best-preserved examples in Britain of this rare and distinctive landform and habitat.

In total, Scotland has some 11 800 km of coastline. The most tangible recognition of the natural heritage value of our coast is the extent of its protection. We have around 400 SSSIs with a coastal interest, covering some 3.5% of the land area of Scotland. The wider European significance of our coast is amply demonstrated in the 18 candidate SACs which have already been identified for their coastal habitat interest and the 14 candidate SACs so far identified for their marine interest. In addition to this there are more than 30 Special Protection Areas (SPA) around the coast as identified under the Birds Directive; and 26 of our 40 National Scenic Areas include the coastal zone.

Only about 12% of the coastline can be considered as developed, and this is chiefly around the main firths; the remainder is largely unspoilt. The coast offers many benefits for residents and visitors alike, a place for traditional and new economic activity, for harvesting the natural bounty of the sea, for developing new ways of producing food and energy, and for relaxation and enjoyment. It offers some spectacular scenery, from the great sweeping sandy bays of the north-east to the towering cliffs and stacks of Shetland, Rum and St Kilda. It is a place for contemplation and for seeing the forces of nature at their most energetic.

Nevertheless, our scientific knowledge of the maritime zone is still limited. Survey is expensive, and the area to cover is great. The public knowledge of our maritime natural heritage is very limited, too. Access to the coast is often restricted, despite our efforts to develop coastal paths. The coastline is retreating in places, and we continue to use inappropriate engineering techniques which blithely disregard the dynamics of the coastal zone. And we seek, quite reasonably, to exploit the sea for food, energy and other resources.

How do we address the particular challenges posed by the maritime environment? The government has recently established a Scottish Coastal Forum following publication of its consultation paper on the coast. SNH is committed to the partnership approach embodied in the forum and intends to play an active part in the work of this important initiative. SNH is also in the process of reviewing its priorities for the maritime environment. At the core of our strategic thinking lie five high-level objectives:

1. *The protection of the maritime natural heritage through appropriate management of special areas.* Here we have much to build on, particularly the excellent work which is under way on Scotland's major firths through our Focus on Firths Project. The developing work on SACs and SPAs is also important in meeting this first objective.

2. *Maintain and enhance Scotland's natural diversity of habitats, species, landforms and landscapes.* We believe that this natural diversity is greater in Scotland than in other parts of the UK, and it is important that we recognise the challenges afforded by our long and, especially in the west, deeply indented coastline. The Biodiversity Action Plan is an initiative which contributes to this second objective.

3. *Promote responsible access to the maritime natural heritage and improve opportunities for public enjoyment.* The coasts and their adjacent seas are very largely unspoilt, and it is this very character which makes them so appealing and consequently so vulnerable to irresponsible exploitation of various kinds, from big business development to chronic small-scale abuse by individuals. That is where the matter of access comes in; it is my belief that the provision of responsible access is not just an environmental duty but an environmental 'good'. Only if people have the opportunity to see and enjoy these precious areas for themselves can we expect to enthuse them and enlist their support in protecting the coast for the future.

4. *Improve the understanding of the maritime natural heritage and foster positive action by individuals, communities and organisations.* A crusade to win the hearts and minds of people, and to convince them of the value of what to some may appear nothing but a sandy desert or a grey sheet of cold water, depends on providing the right information in the right places. SNH has a wide-ranging programme of publications which I commend with some pride. However, there are other ways of getting the message across, for example through formal training and education. To me it is the individual who matters most.

5. *Develop and advise others on policies and practices for promoting sustainable use of the maritime natural heritage.* This is the central issue, the strand which runs through the whole book. It is also the central theme of our maritime work, and will be reflected in the specific policy papers which SNH is preparing on issues such as energy, fisheries and aquaculture.

SNH's programme for the maritime environment is still in the making, and we make no bones about the fact that we are looking to many people with expertise and enthusiasm to help us and to inform and illuminate our own deliberations. It is important that SNH's vision for the coast is shared by and with our partners. It is my earnest hope that this book will make us all much wiser, and all the more determined to recognise the importance of Scotland's living coastline.

Magnus Magnusson KBE
Chairman, Scottish Natural Heritage

LIST OF CONTRIBUTORS

S. Angus, Scottish Natural Heritage, 27 Ardconnel Terrace, Inverness IV2 3AE

S. M. Atkins, Scottish Natural Heritage, 2 Anderson Place, Edinburgh EH6 5NP

J. M. Baxter, Scottish Natural Heritage, 2 Anderson Place, Edinburgh EH6 5NP

A. H. Brampton, HR Wallingford, Howbery Park, Wallingford, Oxfordshire OX10 8BA

A. B. Bryant, The National Trust for Scotland, Highland Regional Office, Abertarff House, Church Street, Inverness IV1 1EU

T. Collins, English Nature, Northminster House, Peterborough PE1 1UA.

R. Covey, English Nature, Cornwall Office, Trevint House, Strangways Villas, Truro TR1 2PH

T. C. D. Dargie, Loch Fleet View, Skelbo Street, Dornoch, Sutherland IV25 3QQ

A. Davison, Scottish Natural Heritage, 2 Anderson Place, Edinburgh EH6 5NP

J. P. Doody, National Coastal Consultants, 5 Green Lane, Brampton, Huntingdon, Cambridgeshire PE18 8RE

K. Duncan, Scottish Natural Heritage, 2 Anderson Place, Edinburgh EH6 5NP

J. D. Hansom, Department of Geography and Topographic Science, University of Glasgow, Glasgow G12 8QQ

R. Hughes, Scottish Natural Heritage, 2 Anderson Place, Edinburgh EH6 5NP

M. Jennison, The Forth Estuary Forum, 1 Cockburn Street, Edinburgh EH1 1BJ

D. Kay, The Forth Estuary Forum, 1 Cockburn Street, Edinburgh EH1 1BJ

R. Leafe, English Nature, Northminster House, Peterborough PE1 1UA

R. G. Lees, Scottish Natural Heritage, 2 Anderson Place, Edinburgh EH6 5NP

P. Macdonald, 6 Ashgrove, Musselburgh, Midlothian EH21 7LT

J. Pethick, Department of Coastal Management, Ridley Building, University of Newcastle, Newcastle upon Tyne NE1 7RU

D. L. Ramsay, HR Wallingford, Howbery Park, Wallingford, Oxfordshire OX10 8BA

S. Sankey, Royal Society for the Protection of Birds, 17 Regent Terrace, Edinburgh EH7 5BN

M. Scott, Plantlife, Strome House, North Strome, Lochcarron, Ross-shire IV54 8YJ

M. B. Usher, Scottish Natural Heritage, 2 Anderson Place, Edinburgh EH6 5NP

PART ONE

PERSPECTIVES ON THE SCOTTISH COAST

The coastline of Scotland is approximately 11 800 km in length and exhibits a remarkable diversity of form and structure arguably unrivalled in the rest of Europe.

As an introduction to this volume Hughes and Macdonald describe how the rich diversity of the landscape character of the coast is defined by embracing both the physical parameters of a place and one's personal experience and perspective in time and space. They highlight the wide range of forms, from the wide firths and their associated human developments to the most remote and undeveloped areas which convey the concept of 'wildness' which surprisingly few have been privileged to experience.

Hughes and Macdonald place the coast of Scotland in an experiential context which is further elaborated on by Pat Doody, who places it within the wider European context. He highlights the disproportionate length of the Scottish coastline in relation to its land area and those features for which Scotland is particularly significant, such as the fjordic and fjardic landscapes that characterise the west coast and Western Isles, the expansive dune systems and machair plains, and the many spectacular sea cliffs.

Many aspects of all these coastal habitats – their dynamics, management and future protection – are explored in the subsequent chapters of this volume.

1 THE LANDSCAPE CHARACTER OF SCOTLAND'S COASTS

R. Hughes and P. Macdonald

Summary

1. Landscape is essentially an integrated concept which combines an understanding of the natural and cultural components of the place and which demonstrates both physical and experiential qualities and attributes. Landscape character is defined as the combination of the physical resource and the experience of that resource and is a term used to describe that which makes the landscape of one area different from that of another. When biophysical and cultural elements are considered together, distinct, recognisable and consistent patterns can be recognised and defined as landscape character.

2. The first part of this chapter discusses the approach that has been developed in Scottish Natural Heritage (SNH) for describing and assessing landscape character. This approach is one that is now recognised throughout the UK as a methodology that is both integrated and iterative and requires an understanding of physical, ecological and cultural processes. The physical components of geology, geomorphology, soils and climate assist the understanding of landscape derivation while the ecological components provide the basis for understanding natural processes and relationships. Examination of the cultural and experiential aspects assists the analysis of human involvement and interaction with the landscape over time. All these parameters have been examined in various landscape character assessment (LCA) reports of the SNH programme which covers the whole of Scotland as the first attempt at a landscape inventory for the country.

3. The second part of this chapter will examine in more detail the experiential and culturally informed aspects of landscape character, with particular reference to the concept of 'wildness', and the significance of these considerations for decision-making on management priorities. In comparison with the situation in some inland areas of wild land, these aspects may be even more significant for coastal areas of Scotland where human access, both physically and visually, has often been easier because of their location by the sea.

1.1 Introduction

Landscape is essentially an integrated concept that combines an understanding of the natural and the cultural components of the countryside. The physical components and processes of geology, geomorphology, soils and climate assist in the understanding of landscape derivation, while the ecological components provide the basis for understanding natural patterns, processes and relationships. Examination of the cultural and experiential aspects assists the analysis of human involvement and interaction over time.

Landscape *character* is defined as the combination of the physical resource and the experience of that resource and is used to describe that which makes the landscape of one area different from that of another. When biophysical and cultural elements are considered together, distinct, recognisable and consistent patterns are seen as landscape character, which can be identified in the field and mapped (Plates 1, 2 and 3).

The remit of Scottish Natural Heritage includes a responsibility for 'the natural beauty and amenity' of the landscape as a critical aspect of the natural heritage. As part of delivering this remit we have developed a national programme of landscape character assessment in partnership with others who have an interest or concern in the variety, condition and trends of change in our landscapes.

Landscape character assessment (LCA) is a widely recognised technique now used throughout the UK (Countryside Commission for Scotland, 1991; Countryside Commission, 1993). The results of LCA can assist in a greater understanding of the form, state and trends displayed by various landscapes on different scales. This descriptive and analytical methodology can also help to define the ways in which we as a society may wish to see particular landscapes evolve in future, especially through developmental planning processes and the formulation of various land management policies and strategies.

1.2 Landscape character

1.2.1 SNH programme of landscape character assessment

The landscape character assessment programme to cover the whole of Scotland was set up in 1994 with the following objectives:

- to survey and assess the landscapes of Scotland

- to establish a landscape inventory and database

- to provide advice on landscape change and inform planning casework

- to inform the local and structure plan review process

- to inform on future policy formulation for internal and external needs.

The LCA programme has now covered all of Scotland including the Northern and Western Isles at 1:50 000 scale.

1.2.2 *Methodology*

In selecting an approach and methodology to apply to the programme it was decided to adopt aspects of the guidance described by the Countryside Commission for Scotland (1991) and the Countryside Commission (1993).

The method that has been developed for LCA in Scotland (Table 1.1) has evolved during the life of the programme and requires both the consideration of elements particular to the Scottish landscape context and an accepted approach to landscape assessment used elsewhere in the UK. It is essentially a repeatable and defensible method that can be consistently applied on a regional and sub-regional scale. Using a combination of background research, desk study, sieve mapping and verification by extensive fieldwork, the approach identifies landscape character areas, describes key features and attributes and goes on to outline key landscape issues and forces for change, and offers non-prescriptive guidelines for the enhancement and conservation of landscape character and diversity.

One notable aspect of this work is the development of partnerships in working with other organisations. Every LCA report has involved the relevant local author-ity through steering group membership and, in the early part of the programme before local government re-organisation, through financial contribution as well. Other public bodies such as the Forestry Authority, Historic Scotland, Local Enterprise Companies and local offices of the Scottish Office Agriculture Environment and Fisheries Department, have also been involved in consultations if not in steering groups.

Table 1.1 Method of landscape assessment.

1.	Desk exercise	map overlays at consistent scale 1:50 000 e.g. topography and drainage, geology, vegetation cover LCS 88 and aerial photo coverage
2.	Research	published materials, maps and guidebooks physical and human influence shaping the landscape e.g. topographical guides of 19th century
3.	Draft character areas	distinct landscape character identify sense of place
4.	Field survey	minimum two landscape assessment surveyors select number of viewpoints for full coverage structured survey sheets adapted for context
5.	Verification or redefinition of character areas	
6.	Consultations	fieldwork informed questions landscape issues e.g. current initiatives, conservation interests local authorities, other publications, e.g. HS, FA, AFF
7.	Identification of landscape change	field survey work NCMS checks consultations
8.	Develop guidelines	enhancement or conservation of landscape character e.g. opportunities for new planting, farm conservation schemes, housing, etc.

From the consideration of the predominant forces for landscape change, it is possible to derive appropriate non-prescriptive landscape guidelines which are useful in managing or directing future landscape change. These issues can then be pursued by various parties including SNH, through enhancement or conservation measures, policies, or targeting financial incentive schemes towards key aspects of the landscape.

1.2.3 *Future applications of LCA*

One of the most encouraging results of the LCA programme, as a consequence of the partnership approach that SNH has adopted from the beginning, is that there is already a demand to use the results of LCA to develop more detailed land-use decision-making tools. For example, this might be adoption of LCA into the structure plan review process as a working document to assist in local plan policy formulation. Another example would be to use LCA to help develop strategies or local frameworks to address particular sectoral needs such as the application and targeting of grant aid for forestry and woodland; or alternatively to assist local authorities to develop wind farm strategies based on landscape character to identify tolerance or capacity to accommodate new structures such as wind turbines into the landscape.

1.3 Coastal landscape character

The west coast of Scotland and especially the landscapes of Lochaber and North Argyll exhibit considerable diversity of landscape character type (Plate 4). This is due partly to the complex geology, the response of the landscape to particular maritime and climatic conditions and the long human relationship with cultivable, defendable and otherwise useable land.

The following extracts from the Lochaber LCA Report (SNH, 1998) describe:

- the way in which landscape character is deciphered and described

- the identification of pressures, sensitivities and forces for change

- the possible formulation of non-prescriptive guidelines.

To demonstrate the process of LCA the *stepped basalt landscape type* has been selected as an example. It is found in parts of the coasts and islands of Lochaber (Plate 4, type 15) and is also similar to one of the landscape character types identified on Mull in the Argyll and Islands' LCA (SNH, 1997). The second part of this chapter will explore the experience of that coastal landscape character type in more detail in the specific context of Mull.

1.3.1 *Background landscape description of Lochaber*

The two peninsulas of Ardnamurchan and Morvern are striking in their contrast to the highland mass to their north east. With Mull, the Small Isles, Skye and other islands of the Inner Hebrides, they stem from relatively recent volcanic origin, around 60 million years ago. In Ardnamurchan, lava erupted through overlying basalt and schist from three volcanic centres (vents), the last of which gave rise to the distinct weathered ring of igneous rocks that can be seen from the air. Today the landscape (the unique volcanic moorland landscape character type) is a chaotic, rock-strewn landscape divided by curving ridges of gabbro and dolerite that spread like ripples across the land.

Much of the western edge shows the remains of violent upwellings of magma and volcanic intrusions. Plains of lava cover a wide area and these lava sheets may still be seen in the stepped basalt landscape of Morvern, parts of Ardnamurchan and the Small Isles, and in the crofted basalt coast of the Small Isles. High basalt cliffs are the most distinctive element of such a landscape, created by differential erosion of successive lava flows or by exposure of volcanic sills. These are sometimes accentuated where ice and water have lowered surrounding glens, leaving the basalt as isolated stepped tablelands, or 'trap' landscape. The basalt friable soils weathered from this now support a rich resource of agriculture and forestry.

This 'trap' landscape is repeated throughout the Small Isles, although each of the islands exhibits features peculiar to their own volcanic ancestry. The many narrow peninsulas and offshore islands contribute to the miles of coastline in this region. The sea lochs, chains of islands, rocky outcrops, forested ridges and sheltered bays form a diverse coastline. Despite the history of cultivation, grazing and clearance, native land-cover features such as oak (*Quercus robur*), birch (*Betula pubescens*) and pine (*Pinus sylvestris*) woodland, moorland and bog persist throughout. These occur in areas which have been difficult to cultivate, usually due to topography, and are of great value for nature conservation, supporting the rich variety of wildlife native to the area.

1.3.2 The stepped basalt landscapes of Lochaber

The characteristic stepped profile of the stepped basalt landscape is formed by the differential erosion of successive lava flows. These surround the ancient volcanic centres of Mull (Plate 5), Ardnamurchan and Rum. The stepped basalt landscape is repeated along a more or less continuous belt from Mull, across the Morvern peninsula, through Ardnamurchan and on to the Small Isles. The islands have a distinctively terraced form which is clearly seen from the west-coast mainland.

Successive basalt steps rise on to flat or tilted tablelands, each one defined by sheer basalt cliffs, most clearly seen on Eigg but also evident on Canna and the Morvern and Ardnamurchan peninsulas. Successive cliffs are separated by gently sloping terraces; where weathering has been more intense the steps have become indistinct and the hillsides appear riven with ridges.

The tablelands or terraces are covered by bracken (*Pteridium aquilinum*) and grass swards and, where not overgrazed, by heather (*Calluna vulgaris*). The friable surfaces have been weathered into base-rich soils which support extensive forest plantations and which often obscure the unique landform. These soils have accumulated in the wider glens, where there is a lush community of trees, plantations and pockets of farmland. Broadleaf woods line the steeper slopes, often comprising thick hazel (*Corylus avellana*) scrub as well as oak (*Quercus robur*) and ash (*Fraxinus excelsior*).

Scattered crofts or settlements occur in the less exposed glens, often sheltering within the lee of the basalt cliffs. Gentler slopes provide suitable ground for pastures, often enclosed by drystone dykes.

1.3.3 Sensitivities and pressures on the landscape character of stepped basalt landscapes in Lochaber

- The most sensitive part of the landscape is the character of the stepped landform which may be obliterated by land uses that mask the structure of steps and terraces.

- Pressure on the visibility of the landform from expansion and management of commercial forestry plantations can be high due to the fertility of the basaltic soils and accessibility of the region.

- Heather-clad terraces are sensitive to changes in land use and management, large-scale forestry operations and potential wind-farm development.

- Native broadleaf woodland, which clings to the coastal edges, is an important feature of the landscape.

- The moorland character with isolated farmsteads and historic sites is vulnerable to neglect and invasion of vegetation.

- Coastal edges are sensitive to built development and forestry, which masks or interrupts the rhythm of the stepped landforms.

- Views across sounds and narrows are vulnerable to visual impact.

1.3.4 Guidance and specific aims for the stepped basalt landscapes of Lochaber

Aim 1: To conserve the character of the distinctive basalt cliffs and stepped-slope profile.

- Recognise strong landforms that may accommodate bold and simple landscape features, such as small stands of trees or wind farms, which are in scale with and visually blend into the sculptural forms of the landscape.

- Encourage possibilities for planting that reflect the terraced landform and geometric lines.

- Seek to avoid planting of terrace edges in a way which will obscure the stepped profile.

Aim 2: To maintain land-use patterns which will conserve and enhance the diversity of landscape features such as heather-clad terraces, broadleaf coastal woods and green coastal pastures.

- The pattern of exposed, stepped ridges with basalt cliffs and wooded slopes and glens may be maintained by controlling grazing pressure on sheltered foothills and glen slopes which will allow natural regeneration to occur.

- Drystone dykes reinforce the structured landscape pattern; their maintenance will enhance the visual condition of the landscape.

- Careful grazing management will help to control the spread of bracken into areas of pasture and undergrazed land and lessen its homogenising effects.

Aim 3: To preserve the character and scale of built development and settings of historical features.

- The setting and archaeological value of historical features such as forts, castles, churches and standing stones is often best conserved by retaining grazing and discouraging natural woodland regeneration or coniferous planting. Such artefacts often appear in an open context which reveals their form and function more clearly and aids understanding of their historic significance.

- Built development which utilises the natural shelter provided by the steps will integrate more readily within this landscape than that sited on promontories.

Aim 4: To enhance views of the landscape from across the sounds and narrows of the west coast.

- The stepped profiles of these basaltic areas are particularly distinctive when viewed across the sea. These views should be considered in the design of roads, from which they may be experienced, and woodlands which may block the view.

- Infrastructure, e.g. roads and power lines, which follow the horizontal linear pattern of steps, are least intrusive; structures which cut across the grain of the landscape may be disruptive, conflicting with the landscape pattern.

- Wind farms will be prominent but may enhance the dynamic wind-blown character of this landscape. Careful consideration should be given to the design and layout of turbines and to the views affected.

1.4 A national inventory of landscape character

The previous section gives a flavour of the type of landscape character appraisal that has been carried out under the SNH LCA programme covering all landscape types found in Scotland. The various studies which now number 29 are indicating that there will be in excess of 600 individual landscape character units that will amalgamate into over 50 landscape character types. It is not possible to be more specific than that at present as work is still going on in the field, but the final data collation, analysis and map digitising exercise will be completed in 1998.

The first comprehensive inventory of the landscape character of Scotland will soon be complete, although by working at a scale of 1:50 000 it is really only the beginning of the task. Yet it is already possible to see how increased appreciation and understanding of the diversity of the Scottish landscape is giving considerable help in furthering appropriate land-use change and development control decision-making. This in turn will assist the landscape conservation, the management and the enhancement of these immensely impressive and diverse, northern Atlantic seaboard landscapes.

1.5   The experience of landscape character

1.5.1 *Experiential and culturally influenced components*

It is the intention in the second part of this chapter to consider in a little more detail two inter-related aspects discussed in the first part, namely those of the experiential and culturally informed components of landscape character, with particular reference to coastal landscapes.

Landscape character, as defined above, is useful and precise in its own terms; the physical resources can be fairly accurately described and assessed. A problem with the definition, however, is that the 'experience of the resource' is not necessarily consistent between different people, especially people from different backgrounds, or even for a single individual throughout their life, and the 'cultural elements' that are 'recognisable' and 'distinct' are not necessarily the same for all. This is particularly the case in a country that is as diverse within its small area as Scotland is, in terms of both geography and the historical experience of communities and cultural and economic groups.

1.5.2 *The effect of awareness upon experience: an example*

The following is a single personal example from the experience of one of the authors (P. Macdonald), concerning the landscape of the western coast of the island of Mull, in Argyll (Plate 6):

> As a child who spent many summers as a visitor on a farm here, this landscape was for me the archetypal ideal place: a paradise of seas teeming with fish, a romantically rugged coast with a myriad of islands and wonderful wild, bare hills surrounding the idyllic small-scale landscape around the farm itself. Our family's hosts, the tenants of the farm, seemed to me to be the archetypal human family, united in a timeless relationship with the land and all the animals. To my surprise, however, the farming family described themselves as 'incomers', not real Muileachs (Mull-folk) at all, although their arrival on the island had been generations back.
>
> This was the beginning of my own learning process about the reality of this landscape. The deconstruction of my early landscape preferences was continued in the course of botanical studies to post-graduate level and completed by conversations in later life with my husband's crofting relatives from the Western Isles and my reading of the accounts of other Highlanders. This landscape that I had once thought ideal is, rather, a typical example of one of the commonest biocultural situations in the Western Highlands:
>
> • that of a degraded landscape of denuded hills, only bare today, at the lower elevations at least, as a consequence of centuries of mis-management of browsing/grazing animals – as can be clearly seen on the slopes of Ben More, the backdrop to my supposedly 'ideal' landscape, the inaccessible gullies crammed with a rich and varied natural vegetation but surrounded by a waste of purple moor-grass (*Molinia caerulea*) [Plates 7 and 8].
>
> • a landscape cleared of its human inhabitants and evidence of them in the 19th century, in obedience to the landowner's instruction to leave 'not one stone lying above another'.
>
> • a 'landscape of sorrow' re-populated by a small number of shepherds brought from elsewhere to manage the new, larger farms – like 'our' farm – which superseded the older populous settlements.

- a landscape wild and romantic, certainly, in the manner of 19th-century urban Romantic sensibility, and especially in view of its sad history and its changeable weather, but hardly one that could be considered in any way ideal from most other points of view.

It is important to remember that the gloomy, misty 'Celtic twilight' view of the Highlands was itself part of the Romantic movement, and completely unconnected to the positive and practical local, traditional view of human relationships to the land and its creatures, as generally expressed in Celtic story and literature, such the 18th-century Gaelic song, *Eala nan Cuantan* (The Swan of the Seas) (Thomson, 1969):

> Slippery the grip on the salmon's tail,
> or on the hind-leg of the deer'
> or on the fins of the porpoise –
> my grip was most slippery of all.
> To grasp the side of the ship
> were just as easy a thing to do
> as to grasp the hand of the blackhearted girl
> who deceived me for seven years.

or Duncan Ban Macintyre's *Coire a' Cheathaich* (The Misty Corrie), addressing the deer of the Misty Corrie on Ben Dorain (Macleod, 1952):

> Fine is the clothing of Craig Mhor – there is no coarse grass for you [the deer] there, but moss saxifrage of the juiciest covering it on this side and on that; the level hollows at the foot of the jutting rocks, where primroses and delicate daisies grow, are leafy, grassy, sweet and hairy, bristly, shaggy – every kind of growth there is.

My happy childhood experiences on Mull – learning the names of plants and fish and birds, how to milk a cow, make hay and handle a small boat – would have fitted in well to the local tradition, but not my subsequent teenage Romantic involvement with the wilder aspects of 'the mountain and the flood' (Scott, 1805).

1.5.3 Changing historical perspectives on landscape

The landscape preferences of the romantic urban aesthete, which are still very much alive among lovers of 'wild places' and even among some of the more objective analysts of landscape and the environment, are to some extent a projection of inner needs, made more pressing by an urban lifestyle, and should be recognised as such. It is also important to remember that, although 'mixed feelings' (of fascination and horror concerning the 'wild') were expressed by writers in the Western tradition as early as the 1st century with Pliny the Elder (Rackham, 1986), the Romantic attitude has not always formed part of the human psyche, but dates back only to the 18th century (Burnet, 1681–9; Oelschlager, 1991).

In the late 17th century, for instance, Thomas Burnet thought of the wilderness in negative terms, as a consequence of the sins of mankind – God's wrath, expressed in the Great Flood, had brought about the present 'ruined' state of the world, with its mountains and chasms which now scar the surface of the original smooth and beautiful, round Earth (Schama, 1996). But by the early 19th century, Walter Scott (1818) was able to articulate a full-blown Romantic enthusiasm for the darker moods of Nature in the 'gothick' aesthetic terms of:

> ... the land where the clouds love to rest,
> Like the shroud of the dead, on the mountain's cold breast

This is a landscape description 'born from the oxymoron of agreeable horror'

(Schama, 1996), in the spirit of Edmund Burke's principle of 'the Sublime' (Burke, 1756). The other principle identified by Burke, and considered by him to be complimentary to that of 'the Sublime', was that of 'the Beautiful'. This principle also engendered a tradition of aesthetic landscape appreciation which is still very much with us today. This tends to be expressed in a preference for landscapes reminiscent of the landscaped parks planned around many large British country houses of the 18th century. This image of Arcadian parkland has remained so powerful that many people today still prefer, for instance, the appearance of a parkland-like, heavily browsed birchwood of widely spaced geriatric trees, where there is not a young sapling to be seen, to that of a healthy, regenerating woodland with a balanced age structure.

It is necessary to be aware of the origins of aesthetic preferences such as these, so as not to accord one set of preferences inappropriate weight in deciding what kind of landscape is to be desired, and in order to realise how difficult it is to be really objective in any assessment of landscape character because of such preferences. It is also necessary to have in place mechanisms of participation for all the interest groups involved (Vane-Wright, 1995; Pretty and Pimbert, 1995). Unless we are aware of the possible pitfalls of this kind, we may be in danger of managing the landscape as a theme-park fossilised at a particular date.

These concerns are also relevant for planning considerations in settlements, as well as in the countryside. It may be tempting, for example, to try to preserve, for aesthetic and historical reasons, the powerful design elements of linear, 19th-century crofting landscapes, but these themselves were often superimposed on earlier settlement plans of the less formal, traditional 'clachan' pattern and it may be more important to ensure that local communities have a say in the form of new settlements.

1.5.4 *Considerations particular to coastal landscapes*

All of the above considerations apply to the landscape of the currently less populated parts of Scotland in general. Looking at coastal areas in particular, they share, despite their considerable diversity in terms of landscape character, some important features. Most parts of Scotland's coastline have always been accessible to humans from the direction of the sea (Plate 9). Even though certain coastal areas, for example the Knoydart peninsula (Plate 10), may seem 'remote' and 'inaccessible' now when most people travel overland on roads, they were once relatively well populated and accessed by boat. It is therefore unusual to find 'core wild areas' on coasts such as those that can be found deep in inland mountainous country, and there is generally on the coast not the same expectation of experiencing complete isolation.

In some ways the coast is subject to less conflict and in other ways to more conflict in terms of different perceptions and agendas than are inland areas. On the one hand, the romantically minded urban recreational visitor can always find there components of his/her idea of 'wildness' because of the changing and to a large extent 'untameable' aspects of the sea and the shore. Also, there appears to be more shared awareness of the 'wild' qualities of the sea, and therefore of the coast, despite its relative accessibility, between visitors and local residents than is the case with the land.

On the other hand, pressure, and at times, acrimonious debate, from various kinds of development, both recreational and industrial, from caravan sites to fish farms to deep-water accessed superquarries, tends to be concentrated on coastal areas (Plates 11 and 12).

1.6   Experiential qualities and landscape character assessment

The different perceptions of the experiential qualities of the landscape character of the coast are, as for other landscapes, a reality that cannot be evaded. Such qualities are touched upon in existing landscape character assessments, for example the LCA of Skye and Lochalsh (SNH, 1996) (Plate 13). The final section entitled 'Who is experiencing this place, and why' summarises as follows:

> The issues highlighted within this section emphasise that information describing and analysing the landscape character of Skye and Lochalsh provides only a broad base from which to explore the potential impact of landscape change. The full implications of this on the intrinsic quality of a particular place can only be determined by fully examining what the detailed characteristics of that place are, and how, and by whom, they are experienced and valued.

The final section as a whole, however, occupies less than one page in a document 158 pages long.

It is difficult to give sufficient emphasis to these issues in a general planning document, which should aim to represent some sort of consensus and which must be as rational and objective as possible. Experiential matters are rarely objective or the stuff of consensus. Unless these issues are seriously addressed, however, planning guidelines based on, for example, LCAs, however comprehensive and excellent in other respects, will not receive sufficient support from local communities. They will tend to be perceived as imposed, externally formulated rules, and therefore to be circumvented whenever possible.

It is also, as discussed above, impossible to make an overall judgement from a single viewpoint about what is appropriate or inappropriate in landscape terms for a particular Scottish landscape, almost all of which are a result of past human choices and/or necessities, as well as of natural characteristics (Macdonald, 1998).

Landscape character assessments in their present form should therefore be seen as important starting points for the process of guiding future development, rather than definitive manuals. Their usefulness could be greatly increased if they gave more consideration to aspects of ecological dynamics, and to the distinctive cultural preferences and economic concerns of local residents, alongside their treatment of visual concerns. In this respect they could benefit from incorporating into their methods elements of holistic, participatory and partnership approaches currently being developed by non-governmental environmental and community organisations (Vane-Wright, 1995; Pretty and Pimbert, 1995). The

John Muir Trust, for example, recognises the important relationships between all the many aspects that make up Scotland's rural landscapes. It has developed a distinctive style of management with devolved management committees making decisions locally for each estate (John Muir Trust, 1998) (Plate 14). If ways could be found to raise the level of sensitivity of landscape character assessment to the two complex issues of ecological and cultural dynamics, the general acceptance, and therefore usefulness, of the approach would be greatly increased.

References

Burke, E. 1756. *Philosophical Inquiry into the Origin of our Ideas of the Sublime and Beautiful.*

Burnet, T. 1681–9. *Telluris Theoria Sacra (The Sacred Theory of the Earth).*

Countryside Commission for Scotland. 1991. *Landscape Assessment Principles and Practice.* Battleby, Perth.

Countryside Commission. 1993. CCP 243, Landscape Assessment Guidance, Cheltenham.

John Muir Trust. 1998. *Conserving the Wild,* Edinburgh.

Macdonald, P. 1998. *Wild Land in Scotland.* John Muir Trust, Edinburgh.

Macleod, A. 1952. *The Songs of Duncan Ban Macintyre* quoted in: Jackson, K. H. 1971. *A Celtic Miscellany,* Penguin, Harmondsworth.

Oelschlager, M. 1991. *The Idea of Wilderness from Prehistory to the Age of Ecology.* Yale, New Haven.

Pretty, J.N. and Pimbert, M.P. 1995. Beyond conservation ideology and the wilderness myth. *Natural Resources Forum,* 19, No 1, UN/Butterworth Heinemann.

Rackham, H. 1986. Pliny the Elder, *Historia Naturalis (Natural History),* trans. Cambridge, MA.

Schama, S. 1996. *Landscape and Memory. Fontana,* London.

Scott, W. 1805. *The Lay of the Last Minstrel.* Ballantyne, Edinburgh.

Scott, W. 1818. *Rob Roy.* Constable.

Scottish Natural Heritage. 1996. *Skye and Lochalsh Landscape Assessment.* Review 71, Scottish Natural Heritage, Battleby, Perth.

Scottish Natural Heritage. 1997. *Argyll and Islands Landscape Character Assessment.* Review 78, Scottish Natural Heritage, Battleby, Perth.

Scottish Natural Heritage. 1998. *Lochaber Landscape Character Assessment.* Review 97, Scottish Natural Heritage, Battleby, Perth.

Thomson, D. 1969. *An Introduction to Gaelic Poetry.* EUP, Edinburgh.

Vane-Wright, R.I. 1995. Identifying priorities for the conservation of biodiversity: systematic biological criteria within a socio-political framework. *In* Gaston, K.J. (ed.). *Biodiversity, a Biology of Numbers and Difference.* Blackwell, Oxford, 309–344.

2 THE SCOTTISH COAST IN A EUROPEAN PERSPECTIVE

J. P. Doody

Summary

1. Scotland has a coastline which is proportionally longer than most other European countries. The large number of islands and the highly indented nature of the coastal inlets provide a substantial resource at the margin between the land and sea.
2. The hard rock nature of much of the coast and the maritime influence associated with its location in the north and west of Europe, combine to give a west-to-east gradient to its structure and associated vegetation.
3. Relatively low-intensity land use and localised infrastructure development has helped ensure the survival of extensive semi-natural habitats, including transitions to non-tidal vegetation in its coastal wetlands. This is in sharp contrast to the intensive agriculture and highly industrialised areas around the southern North Sea, the major tourist urbanisation of the Mediterranean and the intensive agriculture and other uses of many of the deltas of the Baltic and Mediterranean Seas.
4. The continuing traditional land-management practices and the stress on consensus building in developing integrated approaches to coastal management have important lessons for the rest of Europe.

2.1 Introduction

Europe occupies approximately 10 million km^2, a little less than 7% of the total area of the world land surface. Of this total the UK represents less than 24.5 million ha or 2.4%, and with a surface area of 7.9 million ha Scotland has proportionally less. By contrast, Scotland's coastline, including the islands, represents a little over 8% of the total for Europe (Table 2.1). Thus for its size Scotland has a longer coast than its land area would suggest, reflecting the highly indented nature of the mainland and its numerous islands.

Europe's land mass is bounded by the Atlantic Ocean in the west and includes four major seas – the North Sea, the Baltic Sea, the Mediterranean Sea and the Black Sea. The basic fabric of the coast is formed from rocks which span the whole of the geological timescale from the Precambrian Period (3000–570 million years ago) to the beginning of the ice ages some 2 million years ago. Superimposed on this structure are the effects of the ice ages of the Quaternary Period (2 mil-

Table 2.1. Length of the coastline of Great Britain in relation to Europe [N.B. Because the European figure is derived from a map of 1:3 million scale and the GB figures are from measurements taken at a scale of 1:50 000 the figures are therefore not directly comparable and slightly overestimate the proportion of coastline of Great Britain when compared to Europe.]

Geographical region	Length (km)	% European coast
Europe	143000[a]	
Great Britain (total)	18838[b]	13.0
Scotland (total)	11780[b]	8.2
Scotland (mainland)	6482[b]	4.5
Scottish islands	5298[b]	3.7
England	5496[b]	3.8
Wales	1562[b]	1.1

[a]Stanners and Bourdeau (1995)
[b]Joint Nature Conservation Committee, Coastal Resources Survey

lion–10 000 years ago) and the glacial deposits which were left behind as the ice melted. These landforms have been further moulded by changes in sea level and the action of tides, wind and waves.

A variety of other variables, including the ameliorating effect of the warm Atlantic waters and westerly winds, helps to define a west-to-east climatic gradient which is most clearly seen in the nature of the vegetation. Human activities have also been important, although more recent in their impact, causing modification or loss of habitat and 'squeezing' of the coastal zone. Each of these factors can be seen as a series of layers acting over different timescales and at varying geographical scales. Unravelling the way in which they influence coastal change will help set the Scottish coast in a wider European context.

2.2 The 'nature' of Europe's coast

The coastline and marine waters of Europe are areas of great contrast with a high diversity of wildlife and landscape features. The nature of the coastline is determined by a combination of factors which include the physical structure of the underlying geology, climatic effects, oceanographic factors (such as tides and sea-level change) and human activities. Each of these operates at a variety of temporal and spatial scales, and this brief introduction attempts to bring these factors together to highlight the main features important to the conservation and management of the coasts of Europe.

2.2.1 Physical structures and glaciation

In the north and west the underlying geology and the resistance of exposed rocks to erosion, help to define the coast and its landscape. From Norway to the Atlantic coasts of Ireland and western Britain, harder, more resilient rocks occur and the coastline appears unchanging. In the far north, including Scotland, these help to form a highly indented coast with exposed sea cliffs, coastal inlets (including fjords, fjards and firths and a few, usually small, estuaries), rocky shores and pocket beaches. Hard igneous rocks of Precambrian age (3000–570 million years ago) and resistant granites abound here and in the northern Baltic. The Atlantic coasts of France, northern Spain and Portugal have a predominantly 'softer' limestone geology which is also resistant to erosion and which helps to form a series of cliffs and headlands up to 120 m high.

During the 2 million years or so of the Quaternary Period, which ended about 10 000 years ago, the growth (and retreat) of the ice sheets eroded mountains and scoured river valleys. These ice sheets covered all of Scotland. Their combined effects helped to mould the landscape, exposing some underlying structures and covering others. During periods of retreat, large volumes of sediment were left behind as the ice melted, including sediments deposited at the ends of glaciers. At the southern limits of the ice sheets, in the southern North Sea and the Baltic Sea particularly, major deposits of glacial sediment were left behind as the ice retreated northwards. This material has helped to create the present low-lying landscapes in these areas, providing abundant soft sediments for reworking during the Holocene Period of the last 10 000 years. In the southern North Sea low-lying eroding, glacial, till cliffs, sand dunes and tidal areas are abundant and only limited areas of harder rocks occur. On the southern Baltic shores a similar situation occurs, although within the matrix of sandy spits and bars and tidal flats, promontories of harder limestone rocks help to form bays with sedimentary material.

The Mediterranean Sea also has both hard and soft rocks, although the former predominates as karstic limestone cliffs and shores. Generally the land rises directly from the sea. Cliffs over 150 m high occur on the southern coast of Spain and the 'megacliffs' of Croatia rise to over 1000 m (Lovric, 1993). Large river catchments have delivered sediment to the coast as erosion of the mountains has taken place. Over the last 4000 years or so this has helped to create new coastal habitats. These include the large sedimentary coastal plains, which in micro-tidal areas of the Baltic and Mediterranean Seas have grown, partly in response to deforestation in the hinterland, to form large deltaic systems such as the Ebro Delta in Spain and the Po Delta in Italy.

2.2.2 Sea-level change, tidal range and wave action

Long-term sea-level change has also had a major impact on the nature of the coastline (Figure 2.1). From about 7000 years ago, when sea levels began to stabilise at about their present levels, the coastal formations that are present today began to develop. Their evolution then and now depends on a combination of factors including the availability of sediment and the influence of sea-level change, tidal range and wave action. Relative changes in sea level, resulting from a combination of a continuing sea-level rise and those due to tectonic movement, including isostatic adjustment as a consequence of the effects of glacial activity, act over a relatively long timescale. Today there is a general trend towards erosion and mobilisation of sediments, as global sea levels are thought to be rising at about 1–2 mm per year (Warrick and Oerlemans, 1990). Exceptions occur in areas where

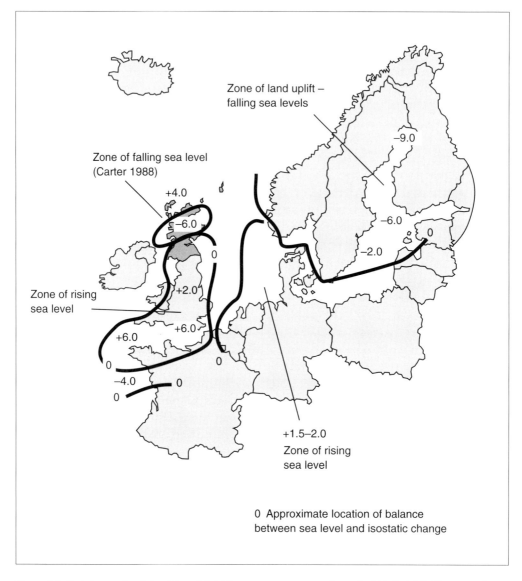

Figure 2.1 Relative sea-level rise (+) or fall (−) in mm per year, over the period 1885–1985 (Emery and Aubrey, 1985).

isostatic rebound of glaciated areas is rising faster than sea level, causing a general rise in the land relative to the sea in areas such as Norway, the Gulf of Bothnia and around the margins of the Central Highlands of Scotland (Carter, 1988). By contrast, the outer islands such as the Hebrides, Orkney and Shetland and parts of the southern lowlands may be experiencing a small relative rise in sea level (Pethick, Chapter 4).

Tides and tidal range are also important, providing a further mechanism for

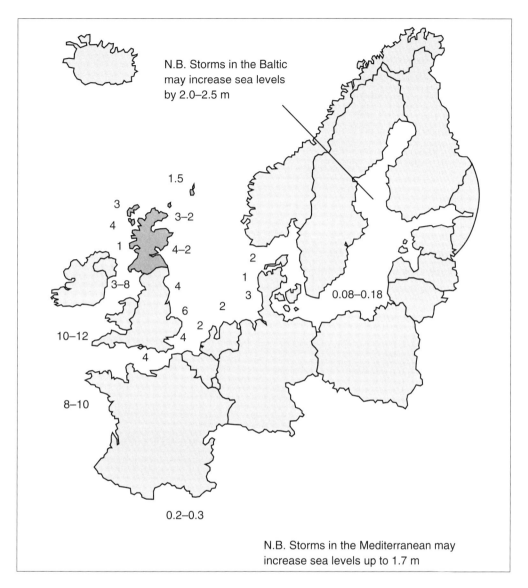

Figure 2.2 Indicative tidal range in north-west Europe (mean spring tides in metres) (taken from various sources, including Barne *et al.*, 1995-98 for UK).

change (Figure 2.2). The amount of material available for transport by tides and wave energy is crucial, helping to create extensive sedimentary habitats in areas of abundance. In the macro-tidal areas (spring tidal range >4 m) of the west, includ- ing the Celtic seas (e.g. Liverpool Bay and the south-west of Great Britain) and the Atlantic coast of France, sediments are moved inland to fill inlets and bays. These can develop into large estuaries with extensive saltmarsh and sand/mud flats. In meso-tidal (spring tidal range 2–4 m) or micro-tidal areas (spring tidal range <2 m) the tides have progressively less influence. In Scotland the combination of reduced sediment supply and the smaller tidal range (largely meso-tidal), partly explain the relative paucity of estuaries in this area (Davidson *et al.*, 1991). In south-east England and the Wadden Sea, by contrast, abundant glacial sediments, combined with an intermediate tidal range, enables spits, bars and barriers, and estuaries with some of the characteristics of deltas, to develop. At the lower end of the tidal range the sediment movement becomes more dependent on waves and wave energy, and the major deltas of the Baltic and the Mediterranean occur in areas with major sediment input, via rivers, from the land.

2.2.3 Climate and sea temperature

The coasts and seas of Europe encompass a wide range of climatic conditions, from the Arctic Circle (e.g. northern Norway, Sweden and Finland) in the north, to the deserts of North Africa in the south. Summer temperatures rarely rise above 10°C in northern latitudes, whilst on the shores of the Mediterranean winter temperature averages 6°C. This gradient is further influenced in the west by the marine waters, which are warmed by the Gulf Stream, and help to create an extreme maritime climate and help to define the Atlantic biogeographical zone which encompasses much of north-west Europe (Polunin and Walters, 1985).

2.3 Scotland's habitats in Europe

For its small size Scotland has a considerable variety of habitats. Its hard-rock geology and northerly location within the Atlantic zone combine to form its characteristically extensive cliffed coast with examples of extreme maritime vegetation. The extent of soft cliffs is, in contrast, limited. Sedimentary habitats, with a few notable exceptions such as the 'machairs' of the west, are restricted to a small number of large estuaries and pocket bays, fjords, fjards and other coastal inlets.

2.3.1 Coastal wetlands

Tidal inlets and bays and their associated sedimentary habitats occur around the whole European coastline. Fjords and fjards are special features which occur in those northern areas where glaciers have worn away depressions in the rocky coastline which were flooded by the rising sea at the end of the last glacial period. These are found extensively in Norway and Scotland and the sea lochs of western Scotland are important European examples. They can contain rich marine flora and fauna, have saltmarshes, especially at the head of the fjordic lochs, and can be surrounded by steep-sided, wooded slopes. The moist climate, exposed conditions, and freedom from air pollution help ensure these woodlands are particularly rich in western Atlantic bryophytes and lichens.

Coastal wetlands are most extensive in the major estuaries of the southern North Sea and the deltas of the southern Baltic and Mediterranean Seas. The associated habitats, including saltmarshes, sand dunes, shingle and coastal marshes are often extensive by comparison with those of the fjords and fjards where sediments are limited. The estuarine sites in Scotland have a total of only 76 642 ha of inter-tidal land (Davidson and Buck, 1997) which is small in comparison with other areas in Europe. The Wadden Sea in Holland alone, for example, has approximately 123 900 ha and the Ebro Delta in Catalonia, one of the five biggest in the Mediterranean/Black Sea area, has some 350 000 ha of inter-tidal and former inter-tidal land.

Saltmarshes occur throughout Europe, differing in plant composition as climatic variation restricts a variety of southern warm-loving species, such as the sea lavenders (*Limonium* spp.), from the marshes of the north. Grazing occurs extensively on marshes throughout much of north-west Europe (Dijkema, 1984). It has a major effect on the structure and species composition of the marsh. In general, as grazing intensity increases and the standing crop is removed, there is a loss of structural diversity. At the same time grazing-sensitive species are removed from the sward. This, combined with the presence of northern species such as narrow blysmus (*Blysmus rufus*) and a variety of small free-living fucoids, has resulted in a distinctive western variant to Europe's saltmarsh vegetation (Adam, 1990), which is especially characteristic of the tidal inlets of western Scotland. As the sward becomes shorter and dominated by tillering grasses (*Puccinellia maritima* and *Festuca rubra*), it is favoured by grazing ducks and geese. The saltmarshes of Scotland also include transitions to other vegetation, which are much more limited in the south and east where land enclosure has truncated the biologically more diverse upper saltmarsh levels.

2.3.2 Sand dunes

Sand dunes border long stretches of the European coastline. They develop wherever there is a suitable supply of sediment which is moved onshore by the tide and then blown inland to form accumulations varying from a few centimetres to 40 m or more thick. In the north the absence of sedimentary material along hard-rock cliffed coasts results in a relatively large number of small sites, many of which are associated with embayments (Doody, 1991). In the west, where the prevailing and dominant winds come from the same direction (in contrast to east-facing coasts where dominant winds are from the north and north-east) large hindshore systems develop where there is an abundant supply of sediment. In Scotland this occurs particularly in the Outer Hebrides which have some of the best and largest examples of the extensive cultivated sandy plain or 'machair' (Ritchie, 1976). This is a distinctive variant of the hindshore dune system, which is also present in the west of Ireland. Together with the dunes in the east, which have developed at the mouths of estuaries of the Moray Firth, Tay and Firth of Forth, the Scottish sand dune resource is large. Earlier estimates (Dargie, 1993) suggest a total of some 31 540 ha of windblown sand in Scotland, but more recent surveys (Dargie and Duncan, Chapter 12) indicate this may have been underestimated.

The vegetation, of the foredunes at least, is remarkably similar throughout Europe due to the over-riding influence of sand mobility, with marram grass (*Ammophila arenaria*) being the principal colonising species. In the north, including parts of Scotland, lyme-grass (*Leymus arenarius*) may become more prominent, whilst further south in the Mediterranean mobile dunes still have marram grass but also include abundant sea medic (*Medicago marina*). Above the foredune zone regional differences are more pronounced and the nature of the vegetation reflects the interaction between the underlying acidity of the sand, climatic variation and human activity. Grazing is ubiquitous on sand dunes throughout Europe. In the north and west the wet climate, coupled with the use for grazing stock (including rabbits), has helped create species-rich calcareous grassland, and heathland. To the south and west (including the 'machair') dunes are generally calcareous and include species-rich dune grasslands with many plants typically found on the richer inland calcareous areas. These may include *Anacamptis pyramidalis* which occurs amongst several other orchid species in the west, e.g. on dunes on Islay. The north and east of Scotland has heathland formed on acid dunes which is dominated by *Calluna vulgaris*, *Empetrum nigrum* or other heathers. This vegetation extends from Scotland and Denmark northwards. There are important examples in eastern Scotland where *Juniper communis* forms a significant component of the vegetation, including the exceptional site of Morrich More which has developed on a coastline which is rising relative to sea level. Here the prograding ridges have become established as a sequence lying 'parallel' to the coast and some are interspersed with damp hollows in which dune slacks develop, another characteristic of the vegetation of the wetter, north and west Europe.

2.3.3 Sea cliffs and seabirds

Wherever high, hard-rock cliffs are exposed to wind and salt spray some of the best examples of maritime cliff vegetation are found. The northwestern coasts of Europe (including those of Scotland) support particularly important examples of Atlantic maritime cliff vegetation. Here communities dominated by rose-root (*Sedum rosea*) and Scots lovage (*Ligusticum scoticum*) occur on the salt-spray drenched cliffs. Above this spray zone the cliffs support rich plant communities which include arctic alpine plants such as purple saxifrage (*Saxifraga oppositifolia*), moss campion (*Silene acaulis*), Scottish primrose (*Primula scotica*) and mountain avens (*Dryas octopetala*), in a matrix of heathland types which are more widely distributed inland. In some areas the extent of the truly maritime zone can be small especially on those cliffs which are east facing and only marginally exposed to the onslaught of the full power of the breaking waves and salt spray.

Because of the close proximity to the rich waters of the North Atlantic and the North Sea these steep cliffs also support large colonies of cliff-nesting seabirds. The most common species are guillemot (*Uria aalge*), kittiwake (*Rissa tridactyla*), fulmar (*Fulmarus glacialis*) and razorbill (*Alca torda*). Large populations of gannet (*Sula bassana*) also occur in Scotland on cliffs and stacks such as Hermaness and Noss in the north, Bass Rock in the south and the granite rocks of Ailsa Craig and Stac Lee and Stac an Armin in the west. On sloping cliffs where soil has accumulated, species such as puffin (*Fratercula arctica*) which nest in burrows are found in high numbers. These cliff and island nesting seabirds only come ashore to breed, remaining at sea for most of the winter.

Spectacular cliffs also occur further south in Europe. Although still exposed to the Atlantic gales, climatic amelioration allows a richer flora to develop. In limestone areas of south-west Britain, northern France and Spain the cliffs may provide important refuges for warm-loving species, such as spider orchid (*Ophrys sphegodes*), typically found in inland grasslands, which have increasingly been destroyed by agricultural intensification. In some areas cliffs provide the most spectacular natural rock gardens such as Cape St Vincent in Portugal, where the endemic *Cistus palinhae* is one of the many species present. Although not so visually impressive the maritime heaths of northern Scotland are also rich in species and have their own endemic, in the aptly named Scottish primrose.

2.4 Scotland's coast as part of a European conservation network

2.4.1 Internationally important sites in Scotland

A map of Scotland showing the areas of protected habitats and species concentrations appears to be dominated by upland sites, including peatlands and mountain areas. However, closer inspection reveals extensive lengths of coast and some large designated coastal areas. Many of these, including the machair of the west coast, will form part of the European series 'Natura 2000'. This series is made up of Special Areas of Conservation (SACs), designated under the European Commission Directive on the Conservation of Natural Habitats and of Wild Fauna and Flora (the 'Habitats Directive') (Council of the European Communities, 1992), and Special Protection Areas (SPAs), designated under the European Commission Directive on the Conservation of Wild Birds (the 'Birds Directive') (Council of the European Communities, 1979). The Solway Estuary, a number of western sea lochs, and other wetlands are included in the list of Ramsar sites designated under the convention concerned with the conservation of internationally important wetlands.

The distribution and type of Scottish sites proposed as Special Areas of Conservation show a heavy bias towards sand dunes and machair sites with six examples of each so far listed. This is not surprising, given the extensive nature of the habitat and the relatively large number (12) of sand dune types included within the Directive from which sites can be selected. Saltmarshes and vegetated shingle structures are only sparsely represented reflecting their relative paucity in the country. Examples of maritime cliff vegetation are under-represented, with only three sites. This partly reflects the uneven distribution of the classification of vegetation community types (only one example has been identified 'Vegetated sea cliffs of the Atlantic and Baltic coasts') which greatly underestimates the importance of the latter habitat. Many other sea cliffs in Scotland are, however, included in the SPA sites network for their nesting sea bird colonies and a number of these also include valuable examples of maritime vegetation.

2.4.2 The pan-European biological and landscape diversity strategy

In 1995 at the ministerial conference 'Environment for Europe' in Sofia, Bulgaria, the 'Pan-European Biological and Landscape Diversity Strategy', submitted by the Council of Europe, was adopted by ministers (Anon., 1996). The strategy is a European response to support the implementation of the Convention on Biological Diversity, agreed at the Earth Summit in Rio in 1992. It 'introduces a co-ordinating and unifying framework for strengthening and building on existing initiatives' across Europe. Over the next 20 years it will attempt to include biological and landscape diversity considerations into social and economic sectors by integrating them with the main human activities. The development of a Pan-European Ecological Network is a crucial part of the strategy. This will build on existing initiatives, such as Natura 2000, but will also link these to a wider appreciation of the extent and complexity of networks especially those involving highly mobile species.

Understanding the nature of the network represents a first stage in determining the significance or otherwise of a single site or group of sites. Examples of many types of species networks could be used to illustrate the contribution, or otherwise, of Scotland to the wider European scene; however, two have been chosen.

1. The puffin (*Fratercula arctica*)
The breeding grounds are concentrated on cliffs and islands around the North Atlantic and North Sea coasts (Figure 2.3). From this it can be seen that Scotland plays a major role in the overall conservation of the species, at least in so far as the breeding populations are concerned. The presence of suitable nesting sites on cliffs and islands free from predators, including introduced species such as rats, is an important consideration. Coupled with this is the close proximity of the rich coastal waters where the abundance of small fish is so crucial to the breeding success of the species.

2. The barnacle goose (*Branta leucopsis*)
By contrast, the barnacle goose, which breeds in the high Arctic, has migration paths and highly specific wintering areas for each of three races (Figure 2.4). Its feeding preferences in the winter include *Zostera* spp. and other plants of salt-marshes, although once this food source is depleted it will move to areas of coastal agricultural pastures. Figure 2.4 shows the core breeding and staging areas ('stepping stones') and autumn arrival points where the birds stay for some time before moving to their wintering areas. For two of the races Scotland clearly has a special significance. The entire population of the race breeding on islands of the Svalbard archipelago winter exclusively on the Solway estuary on the border between Scotland and England.

Having established the nature of the networks and the components which make them up, it is important to establish the needs of the individual species or groups of species at the key locations. The pan-European strategy will attempt to do this and thereby help to integrate conservation strategies for biological networks with

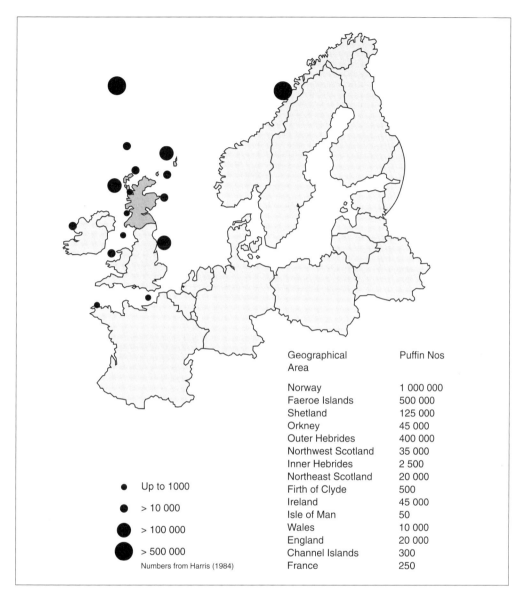

Geographical Area	Puffin Nos
Norway	1 000 000
Faeroe Islands	500 000
Shetland	125 000
Orkney	45 000
Outer Hebrides	400 000
Northwest Scotland	35 000
Inner Hebrides	2 500
Northeast Scotland	20 000
Firth of Clyde	500
Ireland	45 000
Isle of Man	50
Wales	10 000
England	20 000
Channel Islands	300
France	250

● Up to 1000
● > 10 000
● > 100 000
● > 500 000

Numbers from Harris (1984)

Figure 2.3 The distribution and numbers (pairs) of puffins breeding in north-west Europe.

human use and activity. In this context Scotland has much to offer by virtue of its approach to coastal and marine management.

2.5 Conclusion

2.5.1 *The nature of human activities*

The descriptions above have attempted to show the inter-relationships between

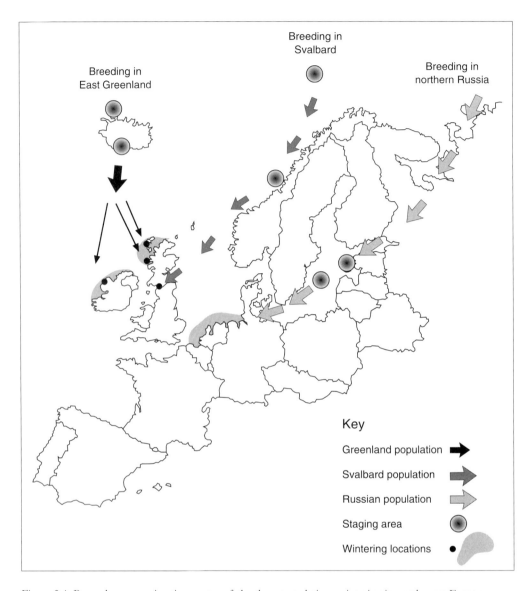

Figure 2.4 Barnacle goose migration routes of the three populations wintering in north-west Europe.

the physical and natural environment. Only passing reference is made to the influence of humankind. However, throughout Europe human activities have had a profound and lasting impact on the coastline. This has followed a similar pattern, where early coastal development was largely in harmony with coastal processes, modifying the habitats rather than destroying them. In some cases, such as the enclosure of saltmarsh, alternative habitats were created which developed their own nature conservation interest. However, as human populations increased and land use intensified, these artificially created or modified habitats in their turn came under pressure. Intensive agriculture, afforestation and infrastructure development, most recently associated with the mass tourism boom in the Mediterranean, have provided the final stage in the destruction of many natural areas. Once-extensive deltas have been reduced to an eroding fringe of sand dunes, protected by groynes and other structures further impeding the natural growth of the systems. An urban fringe replaces the margins of many estuaries, and other tidal lands, including saltmarshes and sand- and mudflats, are increasingly subject to artificial control.

Scotland, by virtue of its location, climate and relatively low population density, has not been subject to the same pressures. In addition, because of the relative fall in sea level along much of the mainland coast and the predominantly hard-rock shores which reduce the incidence of erosion, the need for protective structures are limited. The relative absence, therefore, of enclosure of tidal land also means that Scottish coastal wetlands include a higher proportion of transitions to reed swamp, sand dune, shingle, freshwater marsh and woodland. These can be particularly rich in a wide variety of plants and animals when compared with those in the south, particularly around the southern North Sea, where these transitions are frequently truncated by the construction of sea walls or other coastal defences.

It is important to recognise, however, that although much of Scotland's coast is less affected by infrastructure development (and certainly not on a par with southern North Sea and the Mediterranean coasts), it is nevertheless influenced in one way or another by human action. For example, historical evidence suggests that the greater mobility of sand dunes in the past may be as much a manifestation of mis-management than any natural climatic factors. Ritchie (1967) suggests that the extensive 'machairs' of the Outer Hebrides were 'laid bare' by severe sand erosion and drifting as a result of overgrazing and intensive cultivation since the late 1600s. It is only in this century that traditional farming practices have helped provide an element of stability. Similar examples of large-scale destabilisation due to overuse from activities such as over-grazing, burning and marram grass cutting for bedding and thatch are known from other parts of Europe, e.g. Denmark (Skarregaard, 1989) and the National Park of Doñana, Spain (Garcia Nova, 1979).

Today the combined effects of grazing and exposure maintain open cliff-top habitats and their highly important maritime vegetation. Pastoral use by sheep and cattle is also important in keeping sand dunes free from invasion by scrub and woodland and special variants of saltmarsh vegetation depend on intensive sheep grazing. The fact that pastoral use continues in Scotland today and hence helps to keep these important habitats open is in sharp contrast to other parts of the UK and Europe. The move away from the traditional management of coastal areas, including a reduction in grazing in many areas of north-west Europe, has led to an extension of scrub and woodland cover, at the expense of the richer open vegetation. This has been exacerbated by the wide-scale loss of rabbits as a result of myxomatosis in the early 1950s. Scrub development on coastal cliffs and the loss of open dunes, in particular, has affected many areas. So much so that, in places such as Denmark (the Raabjerg Mile) and Poland (the Leba bar), open mobile dunes are much visited and are features of great general interest.

2.5.2 *Managing Scotland's coast – lessons for Europe*

Protecting areas of highest nature conservation importance from adverse developments has become a major concern for many national governments and European institutions as human pressures have increased. At the same time there is an increasing recognition of the need for the development of a more widely based approach to the conservation of habitats and species. Both Natura 2000 and the development of the European Ecological Network (Theme 1 of the Pan-European Biological and Landscape Diversity Strategy, Anon., 1996) are concerned with the identification and conservation of a comprehensive network of sites across Europe. The former introduces the concept of 'favourable conservation status (of habitats and species) in their natural range' and the latter examines the relationship between site mosaics and the linkages between them, especially along migration corridors.

The traditional sectoral approach to coastal management is also increasingly augmented or replaced by institutional and administrative frameworks which favour management developed through dialogue and agreement between sectors. The mechanism is often referred to as Integrated Coastal Zone Management or Integrated Coastal Management. The European Union Demonstration Programme on integrated management of coastal zones strengthens the approach with its emphasis on 'co-operation' (European Commission Services, 1996). The aim of the programme is to speed up the implementation of sustainable development in coastal zones through the identification of appropriate actions demonstrated by the programme. Amongst these projects is the Firth of Forth in Scotland, which is also one of the project areas in Scottish Natural Heritage's Focus on Firths initiative (see Chapter 7).

Traditional land-use practices continue to play an important role in the conservation of the majority of sites of European importance in Scotland. For many their continued survival is intimately bound up with the social and cultural fabric of the country. The machair of the Western Isles is maintained through cultivation and grazing. Sand dunes, saltmarshes and the maritime vegetation of the sea cliffs require freedom from development and continuing low-level grazing. In addition, the consensus building, which is so much a feature of the Focus on Firths initiative is very much in sympathy with the growing interest throughout Europe on new approaches to conservation such as those being promoted through the EU Demonstration Programme on Integrated Coastal Zone Management (Doody, 1997). In this context the open and informal approach to conflict resolution embodied in Scotland's coastal management initiatives (including the Firth of Forth) may have many important lessons for the rest of Europe.

References

Adam, P. 1990. *Saltmarsh Ecology*. Cambridge Studies in Ecology, Cambridge University Press, Cambridge.

Anon., 1996. *The Pan-European Biological and Landscape Diversity Strategy – a vision for Europe's natural heritage*. Council of Europe, UNEP and the European Centre for Nature Conservation.

Barne, J.H., Robson, C.F., Kaznowska, S.S. and Doody, J.P. 1995. *Coasts and Seas of the United Kingdom. Region 12, Wales: Margam to Little Orme*. Joint Nature Conservation Committee, Peterborough. Subsequent volumes covering 17 UK regions have been published in 1997 and 1998.

Carter, R.W.G. 1988. *Coastal Environments*. Academic Press, London.

Council of the European Communities. 1979. Council Directive 79/409/EEC of 2 April 1979: on the conservation of wild birds.

Council of the European Communities. 1992. Council Directive 92/43/EEC of 21 May 1992: on the conservation of natural habitats and of wild fauna and flora. *Official Journal of the European Communities, L206/7*.

Dargie, T. 1993. *Sand dune vegetation survey of Great Britain, Part 2 – Scotland*. Joint Nature Conservation Committee, Peterborough.

Davidson, N.C. and Buck, A.L. 1997. *An Inventory of UK Estuaries. Volume 1, Introduction and Methodology*. Joint Nature Conservation Committee, Peterborough.

Davidson, N.C., Laffoley, D.d'A., Doody, J.P., Way, L.S., Gordon, J., Key, R., Drake, C.M., Pienkowski, M.W., Mitchell, R. and Duff, K.L. 1991. *Nature Conservation and Estuaries in Great Britain*. Nature Conservancy Council, Peterborough.

Dijkema, K.S. (ed.). 1984. *Saltmarshes in Europe*. Council of Europe, Strasbourg.

Doody, J.P. 1991. *Sand Dune Inventory of Europe*. Joint Nature Conservation Committee/European Union for Coastal Conservation, Peterborough and Leiden.

Doody, J.P. 1997. An unnatural condition. *Journal of the Landscape Institute*, **264**, 17–20.

Emery, K.O. and Aubrey, D.G. 1985. Glacial rebound and relative sea levels in Europe from tide-gauge records. *Tectonophysics*, **120**, 239–255.

European Commission Services. 1996. *Demonstration Programme on Integrated Management of Coastal Zones*. Information document, DG Environment, Nuclear Safety and Civil Protection, DG Fisheries and DG Regional Policy and Cohesion.

Garcia Nova, F. 1979. The ecology of vegetation of the dunes in Doñana National Park (south-west Spain). *In* Jefferies, R.L. and Davy, A.J. (eds) *Ecological Processes in Coastal Environments* (BES Symposium). Blackwell, Oxford, 571–592.

Harris, M.P. 1984. *The Puffin*. T. and A.D. Poyser, Calton, UK.

Lovric, A.Z. 1993. Dry coastal ecosystems of Croatia and Yugoslavia. *In* van der Maarel, E. (ed.) *Ecosystems of the World, Vol. 2A Dry Coastal Ecosystems, Polar Regions and Europe*, Elsevier, Amsterdam, 391–420.

Polunin, O. and Walters, M. 1985. *A Guide to the Vegetation of Britain and Europe*. Oxford University Press, Oxford.

Ritchie, W. 1967. The machair of South West Scotland. *Geographical Magazine*, **83**, 161–165.

Ritchie, W. 1976. The meaning and definition of machair. *Transactions and Proceedings, Botanical Society of Edinburgh*, **42**, 431–440.

Skarregaard, P. 1989. Stabilisation of coastal dunes in Denmark. *In* van der Meulen, F., Jungerius, P.D. and Visser, J.H. (eds) *Perspectives in Coastal Dune Management*, SPB Academic Publishing, The Hague, 151–161.

Stanners, D. and Bourdeau, P. (eds) 1995. *Europe's Environment – The Dobris Assessment*. European Environment Agency, Copenhagen.

Warrick, R.A. and Oerlemans, J. 1990. Sea level rise. *In* Houghton, J.T. *et al.* (eds) *Climate Change: The IPCC Scientific Assessment*. Cambridge University Press, Cambridge, UK, 257–281.

PART TWO

COASTAL PROCESSES

The outstandingly diverse character of the Scottish coastline, and the habitats which exist there, are a direct consequence of variations in the underlying bedrock and the land-forming processes that have shaped this foundation, particularly over the last 10 000 years. Today the same basic processes of erosion, sediment transport and deposition continue to influence the structure and distribution of coastal habitats and exert a profound influence on the nature and location of coastal development and land use.

In the future, with sea levels predicted to rise globally by around 63 cm (Department of the Environment, 1996) over the next century, and the possibility of increased storminess affecting the Scottish coastline, the understanding of these processes and their significance for coastal management is set to become still more important. Indeed, no coastal zone management plan or initiative, particularly if it embraces soft or low-lying coastlines, can be considered sound unless it is founded on an awareness of the nature of the landforming processes which affect the area concerned and the implications of these for all other areas of coastal use and exploitation. Part Two of this book considers these issues, examining the past, present and future evolution of the coastline and the manner in which this has been, and may in the future continue to be, influenced by human intervention.

Jim Hansom provides a succinct summary of the evolution of Scotland's coastline since the close of the last Ice Age and the principal factors which govern the behaviour and distribution of the landforms we witness today. Crucial among these are sediment supply and relative changes in sea level. Most coastlines respond, Hansom argues, to changes in these parameters in a relatively predictable manner. As reasonable confidence exists regarding future trends in sea level (Department of the Environment, 1996), the establishment of sediment budgets for coastlines is clearly fundamental if we are to predict and plan for the changes that Scotland's shorelines will undergo in the course of the next century.

Ironically it is where human intervention has protected the coastline and introduced rigidity into previously dynamic coastal systems that these essentially predictable relationships break down. Hansom describes examples of sites where this has occurred and the potentially damaging effects which ensue. Sustainable management of shorelines in general and coastal erosion specifically will only be achieved, he concludes, when we address the need to conserve sediment sources and transport pathways as part of any defence initiative which we may pursue.

The impacts which sea-level rise might have upon Scotland's coastline in the next half-century and the management options these present are the focus of John Pethick's thought-provoking chapter. Drawing upon examples from north-west and south-east Scotland, Pethick suggests that the isostatic recovery which has affected most of Scotland since the ice retreated, and has led to the emergence of most Scottish coastlines since the post-glacial transgression, may now be gradually declining. Consequently, the rise in global sea levels due to climate change will, over this period, lead to progressive submergence on all Scottish coastlines, at rates of up to 4 mm per year on parts of the mainland. Crucially, Pethick emphasises that this will cause a reversal of the dominant trend of emergence, which has governed most of Scotland over recent millennia, requiring a fundamental change in our thinking on coastal planning and management.

It is on low-lying soft coastlines and in the firths in particular where the effects of this reversal are likely to be most keenly felt. Under natural conditions such shores may be expected to transgress landward as sea level rises. The fact that many of these areas, and the Firth of Forth is a key example of this, are protected by sea walls and flood defences, means that this will not always be feasible. Consequently, coastal squeeze and habitat loss are likely to ensue along with, in the firths, less predictable but no less serious changes elsewhere as tidal regimes readjust to the constraints placed upon them by such barriers. Education and pro-active policies, which facilitate the natural landward transgression of these shores, are the keys to sustainable shoreline management in such areas.

One such example of planning for coastal defence and the pressures which climate change will bring about is the process of Shoreline Management Planning (SMP). These non-statutory plans set out strategies for sustainable coastal defence which take into account natural coastal processes and human and other environmental influences and needs (Ministry of Agriculture, Fisheries and Food, 1995). Under guidance from the Ministry of Agriculture, Fisheries and Food (MAFF), these have been drawn up for most coastlines in England and Wales in the last three years. Richard Leafe and Tim Collins review the basis and preparation of these, highlighting elements of good and bad practice from which we, in Scotland, may learn as sea-level rise exerts its influence upon our coasts.

Like both Hansom and Pethick, Leafe and Collins argue that a good understanding of natural coastal processes is vital for developing the sustainable approaches to coastal defence contained in these plans. A multi-disciplinary approach to plan preparation, involving engineers, environmentalists and geomorphologists, and a thorough public consultation exercise have also proved crucial for plan acceptance and implementation. On the downside, there has been a tendency to date, Leafe and Collins believe, for plans to endorse the *status quo* on the coastlines concerned, avoiding more innovative and potentially more sustainable approaches to coastal defence, such as managed retreat or setback.

A basic tenet of the SMP process in England and Wales is that plan boundaries are based on natural divisions of the coastline – coastal cells – rather than the administrative boundaries of the local authorities concerned. Alan Brampton *et al.* in Chapter 6 describe research undertaken in Scotland over the last three years to identify and describe the coastal cells that exist around the mainland coast and the Northern and Western Isles.

At one level this research seeks to collate the basic information on coastal processes recognised as being essential for understanding the potential environmental impact of proposed coastal defence schemes and the development of sustainable coastal defence initiatives. In so doing, the study has, ironically, highlighted just how little is known at present on sediment movement and budgets around the Scottish coastline. At a more strategic level, however, the research demonstrates which local authorities and landowners need to co-operate with each other if they are to avoid implementing defence schemes which may prove to be mutually harmful in terms of impacts upon sediment budgets and transport. More importantly still, it is the authors' hope that the collation and dissemination of this information will prove to be a catalyst that brings about the fundamental change in our thinking on shoreline management in Scotland which is essential if we are to meet the challenges that climate change and rising global sea levels will bring about.

References

Department of the Environment. 1996. *Review of the Potential Effects of Climate Change in the United Kingdom.* Second report of the UK Climate Change Impacts Review Group. HMSO, London.

Ministry of Agriculture, Fisheries and Food. 1995. *Shoreline Management Plans: A Guide for Coastal Defence Authorities.* MAFF Publications PB 2197.

3   THE COASTAL GEOMORPHOLOGY OF SCOTLAND: UNDERSTANDING SEDIMENT BUDGETS FOR EFFECTIVE COASTAL MANAGEMENT

J. D. Hansom

Summary

1. More than ever Scotland's coastline needs to be managed in a sustainable way. Yet essential to effective management must be an understanding of the nature of the processes and resultant landforms that comprise the Scottish coast.

2. Within certain constraints, it is possible to explain the response of the coast to changes in process, and many unconsolidated coasts are subject to fluctuation that is, or has been, in large part controlled by sediment availability. Phases of sediment surplus and deficit triggered by sea-level changes, glacial/interglacial cycles and in some places land-use changes have resulted in adjustment of the Scottish coast to the shifting phases of the sediment budget.

3. However, human activity both directly and indirectly has been responsible for influencing coastal response and has introduced elements of unpredictability to the coastal system both in relation to sediment budgets and other additional factors such as coastal constructions.

4. Understanding the impacts of such shifts on the natural functioning of the coast remains one of the greatest challenges for the management of Scotland's coastline.

3.1 Introduction

Scotland is fortunate in that most of its coastline remains relatively natural and undisturbed. However, 8–12% of the mainland coast is developed in some way (Ritchie and McLean, 1988; Hughes and Macdonald, Chapter 1), mainly within the firths and close to settlements. These coasts, together with other unconsolidated coasts, are where most of the pressures for management exist. Effective coastal management needs to understand the reciprocal relationships between landforms, processes and sediment supply (an excellent example is the south coast of the Inner Moray Firth). Coastal management is also mainly concerned with recent changes and hence a discussion of geological framework or of long-term sea-level change is largely contextual. For the most part, the likely response of the coast can be understood within certain constraints if factors such as bathymetry, sediment availability and sea-level change are known, together with climatically controlled process variables such as waves and currents. However, human modification of a range of coastal processes and environments has introduced changes to the system that are required to be understood in advance of effective management.

3.2 Structural setting and sea-level changes

The coastline of Scotland is greatly affected by marked geological gradients between the north and west, dominated by hard and ancient rocks, and the south and east, dominated mainly by softer and younger sedimentary strata (Mitchell, 1997). Quaternary glaciation has further enhanced geological differences by differentially subjecting the north and west to intense erosion whereas the south and east suffered less erosion and substantial glacial deposition (Glasser, 1997). Strong west/east environmental gradients result from Scotland's location in the eastern Atlantic, reflected in steep declines in wind and wave energy from the Western and Northern Isles into the relatively sheltered inner west mainland and the North Sea (Carter, 1992). Structurally dominant, high and hard coastal landforms such as cliffs are consequently more prevalent in the north and west (Plate 15), with most of the large-scale depositional coastal features of the Scottish coast found in the east and south (Plate 16).

The effects of glaciation on sea-level change have resulted in a further set of west/east and north/south gradients that affect the modern coast. Isostatic uplift outpacing eustatic sea-level rise has resulted in falling relative sea level (RSL) inside of a line of no change (zero-isobase) and rising RSL outside (Figure 3.1). Although the area enclosed within zero-isobase contracts through time, its boundary takes the form of an elliptical path that includes most of Central Belt and Highlands and excludes most of the outer coast of the Northern Highlands and Isles.

3.3 Contemporary change factors

3.3.1 Coastal processes

Within the general framework of geology, glaciation and sea-level changes, smaller-scale factors influencing coastal change relate primarily to the effects of waves, tides, currents and winds. The effect of incident wave activity on the coast is a function of the wave-energy levels and the nature of the coast. Variations in wave energy on an unconsolidated coast can generate large and rapid responses in beach form with sediment being removed from the upper shoreface and transported in an offshore direction under high wave-energy conditions and brought onshore, leading to beach filling under low-energy conditions (Figure 3.2) (Hansom, 1988). The result of these cycles of cut and fill is a natural envelope of beach positions

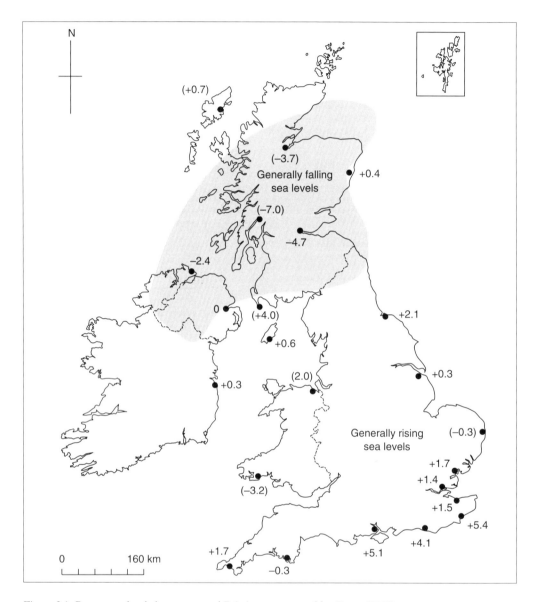

Figure 3.1 Recent sea-level changes around Britain, as presented by Carter (1988).

varying between steeper beach gradients and seawards shoreline migration and flatter gradients and landwards shoreline migration. This simple on/off sediment exchange is modified in areas subject to oblique wave approach and, assuming no barriers such as headlands, can result in the alongshore movement of sediment. Tidal currents have a broadly similar but, in terms of sediment transport along the coastline, less important effect, although they are important for the movement of fine sediment within estuaries and tidal inlets. In the Scottish context the effect of

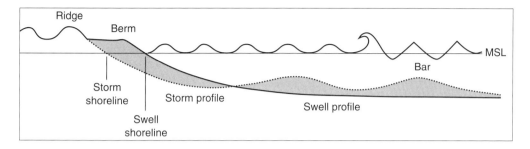

Figure 3.2 Beach changes are usually cyclic and predictable, although variability exists (Hansom, 1988).

wind activity on most sandy shores leads to sand being removed from beaches and accumulated in dunes. According to Birse and Robertson (1970), 63% of the beaches in the Highlands and Islands are 'very exposed', the effect being particularly important in the exposed west where extensive dune plains or machair develop as a result of dune erosion and redeposition by wind (Ritchie, 1979; Gilbertson *et al.*, 1996).

Central to the natural functioning of the coast are interactions that occur between sediment supply and sea level changes. Sediment supply over the late Glacial and Holocene Periods has been controlled by the availability of glacigenic sediment on the continental shelf and by the sense and magnitude of RSL change. Over the early part of this period, rising RSL resulted in the onshore movement of large amounts of first gravel and then sand on to Scottish shores (Firth *et al.*, 1995). The rise in RSL began to slow and although it stabilised around 6500 BP, for most Scottish coasts it subsequently began to fall at a variety of start dates and rates depending on distance from the centre of isostatic uplift. Rising RSL, relative stability and then fall in RSL led to a switch in sediment availability from one of surplus prior to about 6500 BP, to one of deficit (Carter, 1988, 1992), except in those areas of exceptional supply, as at river outlets such as the Tay.

The general switch in sediment supply from surplus to deficit led to a variety of responses forced on Scottish coasts, such as increased offshore sediment losses and reorganisation of sediment budgets into smaller coastal sediment cells. Assuming a relatively constant energy input, under conditions of sediment deficit, sediments from the beach are removed into deeper water in order to maintain a nearshore gradient capable of dissipating wave energy, and this encourages reincorporation of back-beach deposits into the present beach (Carter, 1992). Such erosion is first felt, and so is most advanced, in those areas subject to high-energy conditions and where rising RSL exacerbates the trend. These conditions are met in the north and west of Scotland where tide-gauge evidence shows submergence (Angus and Elliot, 1992). The evidence that out of 466 beaches in the Highlands and Islands, only 32 have progradational edges and that the proportion of beaches with purely erosional edges reaches a maximum in the Western and Northern Isles (Mather and Ritchie, 1977), could be argued to support this hypothesis. Very few dune systems in Scotland are fronted by anything other than eroding sub-vertical, mature dune faces. The positive beach sediment budgets that fed the embryo and fore-dunes, once sited seaward of the mature dunes, have long since been reversed by negative sediment budgets, and the frontal dunes cannibalised (Plate 17) (Hansom, 1988).

Support for such an analysis of declining sediment supply comes from archaeological sites built originally within accreting coastal dunes and now found on eroding coasts. The houses at Rosinish in Benbecula show the onset of sand deposition from 5700 BP (Ritchie, 1979), and Neolithic houses at Skara Brae in Orkney were occupied around 4700 BP. Many other similarly aged sites, such as Bornish and Baleshare in the Uists, and Traigh Varlish in Vatersay, were probably abandoned due to wind blow and instability (Ritchie, 1979; Gilbertson *et al.*, 1996). The relatively recent discovery of many such sites (Skara Brae was uncovered by a storm in 1850) is due to exhumation as the eroding edge of the sand dunes progressively exposes them.

Another repercussion of the decline of sediment supply over the period since 6500 BP was the reorganisation of coastal sediment into smaller and smaller coastal cells (Carter, 1992). In conditions of plentiful sediment supply, sediment is lost to dune building but this may be offset by sediment gains that may result from the alongshore transport of sediment between sections of the coast and by sediment by-passing headlands. However, any reduction in sediment availability and the resultant landward migration of the shoreline post 6500 BP, favoured the emergence of barriers, such as headlands, to alongshore exchanges. As a result, coastal sediment cells emerged which, because they were both smaller and discrete, tended to evolve subsequently by internal reorganisation, erosion and deposition.

A useful case study of the evolution of a coastal sediment cell is the evolution of Culbin Sands in the Moray Firth, a beach and dune system which is intimately linked to the longshore supply of sand and gravel from sources to the east, including both the Findhorn and Spey Rivers. About 6500 BP, sediment accumulation via outward and lateral movement allowed by-passing of the headland of Burghead in its westwards movement from Spey Bay into Burghead Bay and the Culbin area (Comber *et al.*, 1994), and this led to the construction of spectacular raised gravel ridges that underlie large areas on both sides of the River Findhorn (Figure 3.3). However, at some time between 6500 and 4600 BP (Comber *et al.*, 1994), widespread reductions in sediment availability contributed to the emergence of Burghead as a barrier to westerly sediment movement and the sediment supply to Culbin was impeded. Lack of sediment from the west and ongoing westerly tracking waves in the Moray Firth led to up-drift erosion of existing beaches, alongshore westerly sediment transfer, and down-drift deposition in spits which extended into the waters of Findhorn Bay (Figure 3.3). Progressive westward deflection of the exit of the River Findhorn continued until 4600–3300 BP when confinement of the exit by westward extension of the spits and ongoing erosional thinning of the up-drift limb, forced the river to break through the spit at its narrowest point into approximately its present exit location. This process of internal re-organisation of sediment within the cell continued through a series of spits (Figure 3.3) with the present one extending at a rate of 14.6 m per year (Comber, 1995). Similar re-organisation occurred throughout Scottish coasts and led to the establishment of the series of well-organised sediment cells that we see today (Brampton *et al.*, Chapter 6).

What emerges from the above is that with an understanding of the driving process variables, together with a knowledge of sediment availability, a reasonable analysis of the responses of the natural coast to changes can be made. As a result the management of such systems should be a relatively straightforward task, once the direction and magnitude of change is established and the availability of sediment is known. However, this is not usually the case for two reasons. Firstly, the central importance of the sediment budget is rarely fully appreciated and where it is, it may be only imperfectly known. Secondly, experience has shown that effective and wise coastal management is normally neither easy nor straightforward, mainly as a result of human influences on the natural functioning of the coast (Hansom and Kirk, 1991).

3.3.2 Human impact

In many situations the impact of humans on the natural functioning of the Scottish coastline has been to introduce structural rigidity into an inherently dynamic natural system, for example where sea walls have replaced sand dunes. This has led to the introduction of an additional element of unpredictability into the coastal system. Direct and indirect intervention in the operation of coastal processes usually aims to reduce the impact of coastal erosion or flooding of economically valuable land. The construction of seawalls or rock armour represents direct intervention aimed at slowing or halting erosion at specific locations, and whilst many are successful in this aim, they may also be responsible for the drawdown of beach levels by wave reflection and, where applicable, the reduction of sediment input by sterilisation of eroding feeder bluffs (Hansom, 1988; Carter, 1988). For example, the fall in level and reduction in volume of Aberdeen beach resulted in the position of high water of ordinary spring tides migrating 70 m landward from its 1818 position, to reach the seawall in 1962 (Ritchie and Buchan, 1978). At Montrose, the construction of a seawall to protect an industrial site has almost certainly led to reduction in the volume of the intertidal beach (ASH, 1994) and this is likely to have contributed to accelerated erosion of adjacent beach and dune areas to the north which are now subject to further engineering measures. Where there is a substantial component of longshore sediment movement, constructions also lead to the down-drift export of coastal erosion due to reductions in beach sediment supply and volume (Viles and Spencer, 1995). In the conditions of reduced sediment supply that characterise most of the Scottish coast, this may lead to accelerated erosion of down-drift land.

The Morrich More in the Dornoch Firth has been subject to a long history of down-drift erosion which has fed up-drift accretion and coastal progradation

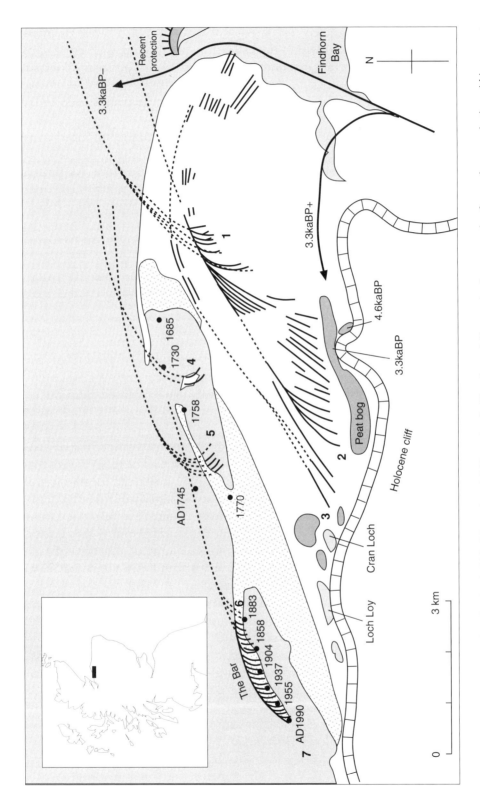

Figure 3.3 The development of Culbin Sands SSSI, Moray, by up-drift erosion fuelling down-drift accretion is an example of coastal re-organisation within a recently created sediment cell. One result of the down-drift extension of the various spits has been the change in exit of the River Findhorn midway in the cycle and a relocation of the axis of accretion.

(Figure 3.4). Using the orientation of truncated beach ridges, it is possible to reconstruct the approximate development of the feature from its inception some 6800 BP. Under the influence of waves from the west, erosion of the western flank close to the present site of Tain released sediment which was moved to the northeast and added to onshore-moving sediment. This resulted in the construction of an 8-km-wide series of beach ridges adorned by low sand dunes that descend from 8.4 m altitude to the present sea level (Firth *et al.*, 1995). However, ongoing erosion of farm and golf course land on the western flank led to a rock bund extension being built in 1990 to bring the total length of protected coast north of Tain to 1.35 km (ASH, 1994). This reduced the amount of erosion over the protected area but at the cost of accelerated erosion at the northern extremity of the structure where an erosional bight has developed (Figure 3.4). This accelerated erosion now affects the Morrich More SSSI, but of more long-term concern is the effect of sediment reduction on the accreting north-eastern flank.

Many such protection schemes can be justified in terms of the economic benefit that they afford to the immediate area. This is particularly the case where urban, industrial and housing areas are affected, but less so where low-intensity 'mobile' land uses, such as golf courses, are concerned. Yet the knock-on effects of intervention are rarely fully costed, if for no other reason than that they may not be evident initially and so cause-and-effect becomes delayed and the linkage unclear. For example, Monifieth has a long history of shore protection using various wooden revetments, gabions, groynes and rock armour. In the mid and late 1980s, erosion of the dune cordon at Monifieth had begun to threaten recreational facilities sited within the original dune system, as well as a municipal rubbish dump similarly located. Rock armour successfully halted erosion of the dune edge but at the expense of sterilising feeder bluffs, which contribute sediment to the down-drift beaches of the southern flank of Buddon Ness/Barry Links SSSI/cSAC. On the northern flank of Buddon Ness/Barry Links at Carnoustie, gabion mattresses and rock armour were emplaced over a 430-m central section of shore in 1989. Extension of the visually intrusive (ASH, 1994) rock armour along a further 3 km of the northern flank of Buddon Ness/Barry Links was undertaken by the MOD in 1992/3 at a cost of c. £3 million. As a result some 75% of the north shore of Buddon Ness/Barry Links has now been effectively sterilised and a potentially large volume of sand prevented from entering the beach sediment budget (Plate 18). This will inevitably affect beach volumes both along this shore and on adjacent down-drift beaches, and may ultimately threaten the stability of Buddon Ness itself. Buddon Ness has been subject in the past to fluctuation as a result of dredging but has maintained dynamic equilibrium of beach and dune throughout. As a result of extensive protection of both of its feeder flanks, there is now a new rigidity to the landform and a commensurate increase in unpredictability of coastal response.

There are also substantial indirect human influences on the coast. Many Scottish coasts, especially those backed by upland and mountainous areas, are

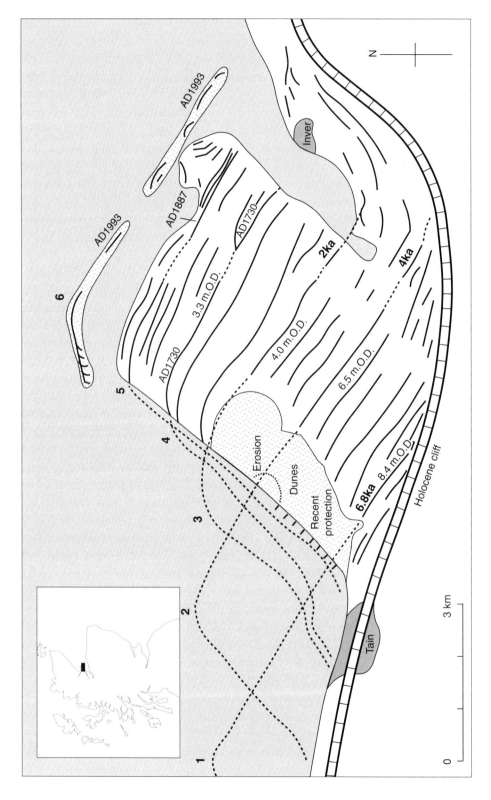

Figure 3.4 The future development of the Morrich More SSSI, Easter Ross, is now affected by shore protection along a part of its western flank resulting in accelerated erosion down-drift.

supplied by significant amounts of river-borne sands and gravels. Although such rivers are largely free of dams and are thus still subject to the extremes of flow that might be important for coastal equilibrium (Carter, 1992), many are subject to the same erosion protection schemes that affect the outer coast. For example, the banks of the River Spey are increasingly being artificially stabilised by rock armour and groynes in an effort to reduce riverbank erosion, especially at bends (Gemmell *et al.*, 1997). Such activity reduces the supply of sediment both to the active channel and to the coast. The 8000 m^3 per year of fluvial sediment supplied by the River Spey is critical to rates of coastal erosion at Spey Bay, any long-term reduction having unpredictable repercussions on beach stability (Gemmell *et al.*, 1997). Reductions in fluvial sediment supply and an already depleted coastal sediment supply are likely to be further exacerbated by losses resulting from any accelerations in RSL rise as a result of human-induced climate change.

3.4   Conclusion

Some clear messages emerge from the above account of the functioning of Scottish coastal sediment budgets. For the most part, the Scottish coast functions predictably within the constraints of the natural spatial and temporal variability that affects all coastal systems. However, over the last 6500 years the marked switch in the coastal sediment economy from one of surplus to one of deficit, combined with changes in sea level, has resulted in a predictable phase of coastal re-organisation. Over the last few hundred years of this cycle, human intervention in the coastal system has introduced a range of physical constraints which have reduced the degrees of freedom under which unconsolidated coastal systems operate. Specifically, 429 km of the 5340 km of mainland coast (Ritchie and McLean, 1988) has become armoured in places that were previously unarmoured. This has reduced the natural capacity of the unconsolidated coast to achieve dynamic equilibrium by translating seawards or landwards, interchanging coastal sediment between beach, backshore and alongshore, and so its buffering capacity against wind, wave and water levels has been constrained. At the same time, the relative predictability of the coastal system has been disrupted as a result of human intervention both at the coast and in the rivers that contribute coastal sediment. Many of these interventions can be justified in terms of the value and quality of the land that they protect but, more often than not, the real impacts on the sediment budget or adjacent coasts are neither fully costed nor appreciated until some time after.

The overarching conclusion is that there is a real need to develop management schemes that are truly sustainable in terms of conservation of coastal sediment and landforms and for national agencies to pursue policies aimed at conserving coastal sediment supplies whatever their provenance. Any human activities that restrict or halt the supply of sediment to the coast need to be regarded as potentially damaging operations, requiring careful control and impact assessment. In parallel, there is a need to mitigate the more serious effects of human intervention in the natural coastal system by employing soft engineering solutions wherever possible, especially those that either allow the wholesale movement of coastal features or enhance the supply of sediment to the coast.

Acknowledgements

I am grateful to Bill Ritchie and John Smith for very helpful and perceptive comments on a draft of this paper.

References

Angus, S. and Elliot, M.M. 1992. Erosion in Scottish machair with particular reference to the Outer Hebrides. *In* Carter, R.W.G., Curtis, T.G.F. and Sheehy-Skeffington, M.J. (eds) *Coastal Dunes*. Balkema, 93–117.

ASH. 1994. Coastal erosion and tourism in Scotland: a review of protection measures to combat coastal erosion related to tourist activities and facilities. *SNH Review Series No. 12*, Scottish Natural Heritage, Edinburgh.

Birse, E.L. and Robertson, L. 1970. *Assessment of Climatic Conditions in Scotland 2. Based on Exposure and Accumulated Frost*. Macaulay Institute for Soil Research, Aberdeen.

Carter, R.W.G. 1988. *Coastal Environments*. Academic Press, London.

Carter, R.W.G. 1992. How the British Coast works: inherited and acquired controls. *In* Stevens, C., Gordon, J.E., Green, C.P. and Macklin, M.G. (eds) *Conserving our Landscape*, Proceedings of the Conference Conserving Our Landscape: Evolving Landforms and Ice-age Inheritance, 63–68.

Comber, D.P.M. 1995. Culbin Sands and the Bar. *Scottish Geographical Magazine*, **111(1)**, 54–57.

Comber, D.P.M., Hansom, J.D. and Fahy, F.M. 1994. *Culbin Sands, Culbin Forest and Findhorn Bay, SSSI: Documentation and management prescription*. Scottish Natural Heritage Research Survey and Monitoring Report No. 14, Edinburgh.

Firth, C.R., Smith, D.E., Hansom, J.D. and Pearson, S.G. 1995. Holocene spit development on a regressive shoreline, Dornoch Firth, Scotland. *Marine Geology*, **124**, 203–214.

Gemmell, S.L.G., Hansom, J.D. and Hoey, T.B. 1997. *The Geomorphology, Conservation and Management of the River Spey and Spey Bay SSSI's, Moray*. Unpublished Report to Scottish Natural Heritage. Dept. of Geography and Topographic Science, University of Glasgow.

Gilbertson, D., Grattan, J., Pyatt, B. and Schwenninger, J.-L. 1996. The Quaternary geology of the coasts of the islands of the Southern Outer Hebrides. *In* Gilbertson, D., Kent, M. and Grattan, J. (eds) *The Outer Hebrides, the last 14,000 years*. Sheffield Academic Press, 59–102.

Glasser, N.F. 1997. The dynamics of ice sheets and glaciers. *In* Gordon, J.E. (ed.) *Reflections on the Ice Age in Scotland*. Scottish Association of Geography Teachers/Scottish Natural Heritage, 37–44.

Hansom, J.D. 1988. *Coasts*. Cambridge University Press, Cambridge.

Hansom, J.D. and Kirk, R.M. 1991. Change on the coast: the need for management. In Johnston, T.R.R. and Flenley, J.R. (eds) *Aspects of Environmental Change*. Massey University Misc. Series, **91/1**, 49–62.

Mather, A.S. and Ritchie, W. 1977. *The Beaches of the Highlands and Islands of Scotland*. Countryside Commission for Scotland, Battleby, Perth.

Mitchell, C. 1997. Geological evolution of Scotland. In Gordon, J.E. (ed.) *Reflections on the Ice Age in Scotland*. Scottish Association of Geography Teachers/Scottish Natural Heritage, 15–30.

Ritchie, W. 1979. Machair development and chronology in the Uists and adjacent islands. *Proceedings of the Royal Society of Edinburgh*, **77B**, 107–122.

Ritchie, W. and Buchan, G.M. 1978. Historical and recent changes in Aberdeen Beach. *Aberdeen University Review*, Vol XLVII, 4, **160**, 313–321.

Ritchie, W. and McLean, L. 1988. UK: Scotland. *In* Walker, H.J. (ed.) *Artificial Structures and Shorelines*. Kluwer, Dordrecht, 127–135.

Viles, H. and Spencer, T. 1995. *Coastal Problems*. Edward Arnold, London.

4 FUTURE SEA-LEVEL CHANGES IN SCOTLAND: OPTIONS FOR COASTAL MANAGEMENT

J. Pethick

Summary

1. The coastline of Scotland appears to be inviolable. Rocky shores, abundant glacial sediment and falling sea levels combine to provide not just a series of natural defences against the sea but also a shoreline which actually advances in its face.

2. However, examination of the long-term Holocene record suggests that this complacent view cannot be held for much longer. The uplift in land levels due to glacial unloading is now slowing rapidly and it seems likely that the predicted sea-level rise caused by global warming will soon dominate the sea-level signal.

3. This may accentuate existing rates of sea-level rise in some areas while, along those shorelines now experiencing sea-level fall, the predictions suggest a reversal in sea-level tendency over the next 50 years which could result in an average rise of 4 mm per year.

4. This chapter shows that such rates have been experienced in the south-east of England for many years and reference to the experience here may be useful in planning coastal management systems in Scotland for the future.

5. The issues raised include beach erosion, the landward transgression of the firths, the loss of intertidal habitat, the reduction in nearshore sediment budgets and the migration of tidal deltas exposing formerly protected shorelines.

6. Management options include increasing the area available for the coast to adjust to these environmental changes, careful use of coastal sediments, compensation packages and, above all, education.

7. The chapter suggests that, unlike many areas of the world which have experienced a steady but increasing rise in sea level over the past century, in Scotland, areas experiencing a reversal from falling to rising sea level may catch coastal managers unawares unless careful consideration is given now to planning for the next 50 years.

4.1 Introduction

Coastal management in Scotland has developed in response to environmental conditions very different from those experienced by the rest of the UK or indeed most of Europe. Much of the Scottish coast is characterised by high, hard-rock cliffs with pocket beaches at the heads of bays, or by glacially deepened inlets which have more in common with fjords than they do with the coastal plain estuaries of south-east England. These shorelines are responding only slowly to the onset of post-glacial conditions, and may be described as fossil coasts whose inherent strength and scale has resisted the relatively low-energy conditions of the post-glacial sea.

In addition to this inherent resistance to change of large parts of the Scottish coast, the approach taken to coastal management here has been profoundly influenced by the fact that, in many areas, sea levels have been falling steadily for the past 5000 years, a result of the isostatic recovery of the land mass from its glacial loading. Thus human use of these areas of the coastal zone has enjoyed a steady reduction in risk, compared to the steady increase experienced by the rest of the UK coastal community.

Despite the generally low level of coastal hazard enjoyed by Scottish coastal sites, the paradox of coastal resource use still applies, that those areas with the highest risk offer the greatest benefits. Access to navigational routes and fisheries, good agricultural land, flat areas for industry that offer waste disposal facilities into sea or estuary, urban development with recreational potential: all these areas are also those which suffer from flooding or erosion, or both, with the additional human-induced hazards of pollution. Thus the high rocky shores and deep fjord-like inlets of Scotland are far less important as a resource base than the low muddy shores of the estuaries which are extremely vulnerable to environmental change whether this be due to natural or human causes. It is these lowland shores, chiefly in the firths, in which industrial, urban and agricultural development will provide the focus for future coastal management in Scotland. These areas are coming under increasing threat from a variety of environmental changes but, perhaps most importantly, from a fundamental change in the rate, and in some places even the directionality, of sea-level change, as the predicted rise in global sea levels augments or offsets existing patterns of sea-level change to give a general pattern of sea-level rise along the Scottish coast over the next few decades.

4.2 Sea-level rise in Scotland

The retreat of the glacial ice from Scotland took place between 14 000 and 10 000 years ago. The effect of this was two-fold: first the decantation of water back into the world oceans from the melting ice caused a massive rise in sea levels of over 100 m within a period of 6000 years, an average rate of global sea-level rise of 0.017 m per year. Second, the removal of the ice load, which had depressed land levels in Scotland during the glacial period, resulted in a rebound, characterised by a general upward movement of the land level in these areas. The rate at which the land level rose varied according to location relative to the maximum ice loading, generally acknowledged in Scotland to be centred around Rannoch Moor. Central areas experienced the highest rates of rebound while areas at increasing distances from the centre rose relatively slowly.

These two effects of the deglaciation: the rise in water level in the world oceans and the rise in land levels in Scotland, combined to give the relative sea level – i.e. the location of the shoreline – around the Scottish coast during the past 14 000 years. If both water level and land levels rose at the same rate then the relative sea level would be constant; if land levels rose faster than water levels the relative sea level would fall and if water levels rose faster than land levels the relative sea level would rise. Work by a variety of authors (e.g. Haggart, 1987; Shennan *et al.*, 1995; Smith *et al.*, 1992) but based mainly on the pioneering work of Sissons and co-workers (Sissons, 1976) has shown that the relative sea-level rates varied not only spatially, according to the distance from the centre of ice loading, but also tem-porally as the rates of change of water level and land level altered. As a consequence, areas peripheral to the uplift centre, such as the Western Isles, Orkney and Shetland, have experienced progressive submergence throughout the Holocene. Areas closer to the uplift centre, however, have experienced a more complex pattern of relative sea-level change in which a fall in relative sea level in the early Holocene was superseded by a period of sea-level rise and more recent-ly by a return to increasing emergence of the shoreline.

In the former, peripheral areas, the predicted rise in global sea levels will aug-ment existing rates of relative sea-level rise and lead to increasing management problems, problems only marginally offset by the nature of the topography and the less intensive land use in these areas. However, it is in those areas characterised by recent sea-level fall where the problems facing future coastal management are considered to be most acute, for here the gradual reduction in the rate of uplift of the land surface and the predicted rise in global sea levels are likely to combine to alter the directionality of sea-level change and lead to relative sea-level rise. It is these areas which form the focus of attention in this chapter: areas characterised by intensive land use, often involving industrial or urban development, where a switch from sea-level fall to sea-level rise will profoundly affect coastal manage-ment systems.

It is not the purpose of this chapter to provide a detailed examination of the spatial variation in predicted sea level in Scotland. Instead, attention is centred on two examples of those areas characterised by sea-level fall at the present time and which are expected to experience a switch to sea-level rise over the next few decades as a result of the interaction discussed above between land-level rise due to glacio-isostasy and predicted sea-level rise due to global warming. These exam-ples are, first, from the north-west coast of Scotland and, second, from the inner estuary of the Forth. Inspection of the sea-level curve for north-west Scotland (Shennan *et al.*, 1995) for the period between 6000 BP and 1000 BP (Figure 4.1A) demonstrates that sea level in this area of the Scottish coast has fallen steadily from 6 m ODN to 1 m ODN (Shennan *et al.*, 1995). If a polynomial regression line is fitted to the entire Holocene data set, i.e. between 12 000 BP and 1000 BP

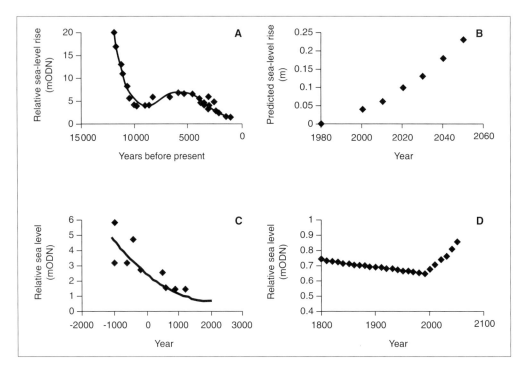

Figure 4.1 (A) Best-fit regression to Holocene sea-level data for north-west Scotland (Shennan *et al.*, 1995). (B) IPCC 'business-as-usual' predictions for sea-level rise to 2050 (Warrick, 1993). (C) Best-fit regression to data in Figure 4.1A for the period 2000 BC to AD 1000 extrapolated to the year 2050. (D) Addition of curves (B) and (C) giving predicted sea-level change in north-west Scotland to the year 2048. A reversal in sea-level tendency is predicted with sea-level rise averaging 4 mm per year over the next 50 years.

(Figure 4.1A), and extrapolated to the present day, the rate of sea-level fall over the last 1000 years begins to flatten out, suggesting that the rate of sea-level fall may have decreased over the recent past to give rates of uplift of less than 1 mm per year at the present time. Such an extrapolation is, of course, entirely based upon past conditions and cannot take into account any recent changes in the controls of sea level; in particular it does not take into account any rise in worldwide sea level due to global warming.

Figure 4.1B shows the predictions of future sea level provided by the Inter-governmental Panel on Climatic Change (IPCC). These predictions are for the 50-year period 1998–2048 and are based upon the so-called, 'business-as-usual scenario' (Warrick, 1993). If the sea levels predicted in the IPCC curve (Figure 4.1B) are now combined with those predicted by the extrapolation of the Holocene sea-level curve (Figure 4.1C), the result (Figure 4.1D) indicates that an abrupt reversal of sea level can be expected over the next few years: a change from sea-level fall to sea-level rise which, for the example given of north-west Scotland, may result in a mean sea-level rise over the next 50 years of 4 mm per year.

The second example of the impact of predicted global sea-level change on the

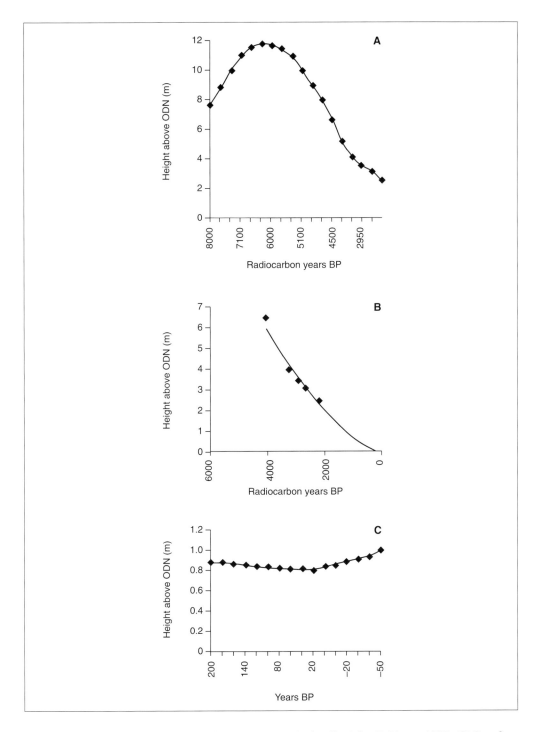

Figure 4.2 (A) Holocene sea-level curve from the eastern Forth valley (after Robinson, 1993). (B) Best-fit regression to most recent data shown in (A). (C) Extrapolated curve from (B) combined with IPCC predicted sea-level rise (see B) for period to 2048. A reversal in sea-level tendency is predicted with sea-level rise averaging 3.4 mm per year over the next 50 years.

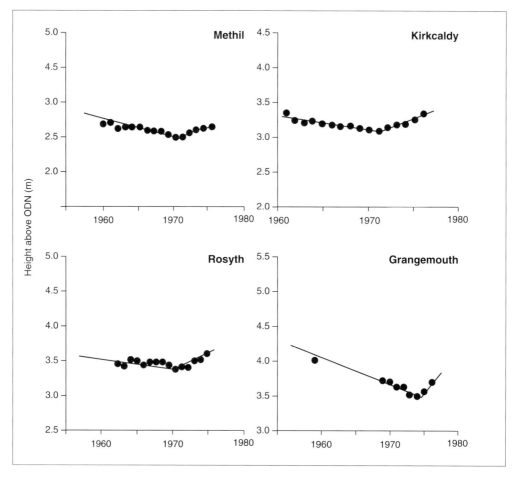

Figure 4.3 Trends in the annual sea-level maxima for the period 1960 to 1980 for stations in south-east Scotland (data from Graff, 1981).

existing rates of change in Scotland is from the inner estuary of the Forth (Plate 19), an area distinct in topography as well as in location from the former example from the north-west coast. Robinson (1993) provides a relative sea-level curve for the eastern Forth valley (Figure 4.2A), which shows a gradual emergence of the shoreline between 6000 and 2000 years BP. No data are available for the period between 2000 BP and the present, but extrapolating a best-fit regression to the available data suggests that uplift over the past 200 years may have decreased to less than 0.5 mm per year (Figure 4.2B). If these predictions are now extrapolated over the next 50 years and combined with those from the IPCC, as in the previous example, the results suggest that the present rate of sea-level fall will be transformed into a sea-level rise averaging 3.4 mm per year over the next 50 years (Figure 4.2C).

Some confirmation of the predicted results shown in Figures 4.1D and 4.2C is provided by the work of Graff (1981), who collated annual sea-level maxima for

UK tidal stations. The data for Scotland vary considerably but, as Figure 4.3 shows, the records for locations such as Rosyth and Grangemouth in the estuary of the Forth and Methil and Kirkcaldy in the outer Firth of Forth bear a strong relationship to the predicted curves. It appears from these data that, by 1980 (the temporal limit of Graff's data set), certain locations in Scotland which are close to the centre of glacial rebound were by that time already exhibiting indications of a reversal of sea-level tendency – from sea-level fall to sea-level rise – with temporal trends very similar to those predicted in Figures 4.1D and 4.2C.

It is emphasised that these predictions are based upon only two examples of Holocene sea-level change and that considerable variation in the rates of future sea-level change may be expected to occur around the coast of Scotland. However, such variations are not considered to alter the main argument presented in this paper, which is that in areas close to the centre of glacio-isostatic rebound a decrease in the rates of land-level uplift over the recent past, together with the predicted increase in global sea levels, will result in a switch from relative sea-level fall to one of sea-level rise.

The implications of this predicted reversal in sea-level tendency in some areas of the Scottish coast and the increase in the existing rate of sea-level rise in others are, of course, fundamental to any approach to coastal management in Scotland. In particular it is emphasised that, while other locations around the UK coast have experienced sea-level rise for centuries, so that the predicted increase in the rate of rise due to global warming is merely an exacerbation of long-standing problems, in Scotland, by contrast, those areas which do experience a reversal in sea-level tendency in the immediate future will require complete re-assessment of management procedures and of the attitudes to coastal resource development. Some of these issues are explored in the following sections.

4.3 Open coasts

The impact of the predicted reversal of sea-level tendency on open-cliffed coasts in Scotland will be significant over the long term but less significant over the short term, foe example over the next 50 years. Rates of erosion of the hard-rock, cliffed coastline are relatively insensitive to changes in sea level, and changes in the erosion rate will be minor, although such erosion will be directed toward a distinct final form: a long-term 'target' which will be constantly changing as sea level rises but may not be attained during the present interglacial period. In areas of southwest England, for example, where hard-rock cliffs have experienced continuous sea-level rise over the entire Holocene Period, cliff and abrasion platform morphology still reflects the sea levels attained during the last interglacial period and can be regarded as fossil features that present-day processes have hardly touched.

In contrast, a predicted reversal in sea-level tendency may have a significant impact on the beaches and dunes of the Scottish coast and this in turn could affect the erosion rates of the softer-rock cliffs, as, for example, along the sandstone cliffs of Fife. It is difficult to provide accurate, quantitative predictions of the impact of sea-level rise on open-coast beaches, as models of beach behaviour under sea-level rise have not developed significantly since the initial Bruun hypothesis was proposed. Bruun (1962) envisaged that a beach profile would respond to sea-level rise by moving the profile location both upward and landward while maintaining its initial morphology. A change in profile location without a change in form allows the profile to maintain its relative position with regard to wave energy and is accomplished by the movement of sediment from the supra-tidal profile, for example the sand dunes or the cliffs backing the beach, to the lower inter- or sub-tidal profile. This exchange of sediment means that erosion of the supra-tidal area is an essential part of the adjustment process and consequently loss of sand dunes, shingle ridges and accelerated erosion of soft-rock cliffs can be expected over the short to medium term.

Such a qualitative model has received considerable criticism, although few critics have provided an adequate quantitative alternative. The criticisms include the failure of the model to incorporate the increases in wave energy at the shore which inevitably occur because sea-level rise causes deeper water in the nearshore zone, and the problems associated with the so-called closure between the lower profile and the nearshore sea bed. The lack of any rigorous quantitative predictions by this model, in particular of the rates of the landward transgression of the profile, means that it is not possible to predict whether the erosion of supra-tidal landforms, such as sand dune complexes in eastern Scotland or the machair systems on the west coast, will result in the complete removal of these forms or whether they will be able to keep pace with the transgression and roll landward as they appear to have done in response to sea-level rise in the past.

The key issue in predicting the response of sand dunes, machair, shingle ridges and other supra-tidal depositional features is the balance between the rate of sea-level rise and the availability of sediment. Although an increase in erosion rates of the soft-rock cliffs may inject some fresh sediment into the coastal system this is unlikely to be adequate to maintain the present coastal morphology. The removal of many of the sources of sediment, mainly of glacial origin, around the Scottish coast has been shown by Hansom (Chapter 3) to be responsible for widespread erosion of these supra-tidal landforms even though the present sea-level trend is negative. It appears that the combination of this general lack of available sediment and a reversal of the sea-level tendency will mean that many of the landforms which we now regard as essential components of the Scottish coastal system will be lost, causing both loss of habitat and in some cases also threatening agriculture and settlements.

In addition to these problems, where cliffs consist of resistant rocks, such as the Old Red Sandstone of Orkney or the Tertiary Volcanics of Skye, sea-level rise may lead to a form of natural 'coastal squeeze'. In these cases, beaches will be eroded at their low-water level due to lack of fresh sediment from cliff erosion and at the same time will not be able to transgress landward due to the physical presence of the cliffs, a combination which may lead to widespread loss of pocket beaches around the Scottish coast.

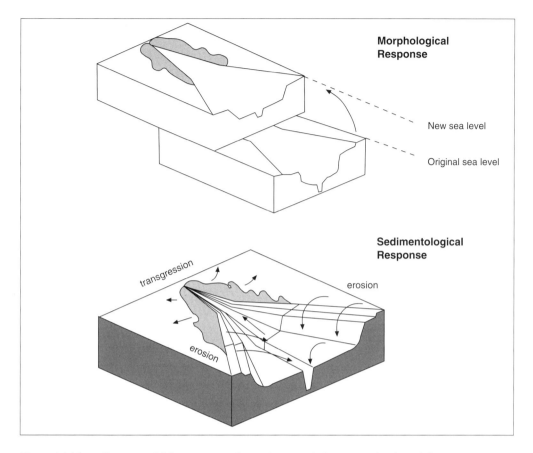

Figure 4.4 The roll-over model for response of estuarine morphology to sea-level rise. The estuary moves both landward and upward (top) as sediment is transferred from the outer to the inner estuary (bottom).

4.4 The firths

The changes in the open coast which may occur as a response to a reversal in sea level are relatively minor compared to the predicted effects on the low coasts, especially those within the firths. Here the experience gained from extensive research carried out in south-east England may be valuable, since, in this region, estuaries have been experiencing rates of sea-level rise of 4 mm per year for several decades, rates which are similar to those predicted above for some areas of the Scottish coast over the next 50 years. There are two major issues of concern; first, the responses to sea-level rise of the estuaries that lie within the firths; and second, the impact of sea-level rise on the interactions between the firths and the adjacent open coasts.

4.4.1 *Impact on the estuaries of the firths*

Many of the firths cannot be regarded as estuaries since, as discussed above, they are best classed as fjords, i.e. tidal inlets in which over-deepening has prevented their morphological response to present-day tidal conditions. Nevertheless, some firths such as the Solway, the Tay and the Dornoch can be classed as sedimentary estuaries, while many of the over-deepened firths have estuaries located within them. The inner Forth above Rosyth and the Beauly and Nigg Bay which lie within the Cromarty Firth are examples in which shallow water at the head of the firths has led to estuarine formation there.

Two aspects of the estuarine response to sea-level rise may be discussed here: the overall response of the estuarine morphology and the response of the mouth of the estuary. Research on English estuaries experiencing rapid sea-level rise (Allen and Rae, 1988; Pethick, 1997) has demonstrated that the general response of estuaries to sea-level rise is similar to that predicted by Bruun for beach profiles, albeit in a three-dimensional rather than a two-dimensional sense. The estuarine response is a landward transgression together with a simultaneous upward movement, described by Allen and Rae (1988) as a 'roll-over' model, so that the initial estuarine morphology is maintained but has been translated in space. In so doing, the estuary appears to maintain its relative position in the energy gradient formed by both tides and waves, a gradient which itself moves landward as water levels increase (Figure 4.4).

This complex movement of the estuary in response to sea-level changes is achieved by two sedimentary processes, the first resulting in a landward movement of the estuary, the second in an upward movement. First, increasing wave action in the outer estuary as water depths increase leads to erosion of the upper intertidal areas, including both upper mudflats and saltmarshes. This releases sediment which moves into the sub-tidal channel and thence landward to the inner estuary where it is deposited in the intertidal zone. In a completely natural estuary this intertidal deposition would result in a landward transgression of the upper intertidal area and its associated saltmarshes, but in most UK estuaries, including many of those in Scotland, this process is inhibited by the presence of flood embankments which protect extensive areas of reclaimed marshes. As a result the estuary is prevented from achieving its landward transgression, and, although sediments are eroded from the outer estuary, they are merely accumulated in the sub-tidal channels further landward so that the estuary in effect becomes 'stubbier', i.e. wider at the mouth and shorter in overall length.

The second sedimentary process accompanying a rise in sea level in estuaries is the import of suspended sediment from adjacent marine sources and its deposition on the upper surface of the saltmarshes and mudflats, so causing the estuary to experience a general rise in elevation. Where marine sources are limited or decreasing, this reliance on an external source of sediment can have a major inhibiting effect on the ability of an estuary to respond to sea-level rise.

The predicted reversal in the sea-level tendency in some areas of the coast of Scotland may be expected to result in similar morphological adaptations as have been observed in southern England and which have been described above. The implications of such a model for the Scottish estuaries are serious; they may be summarised as follows:

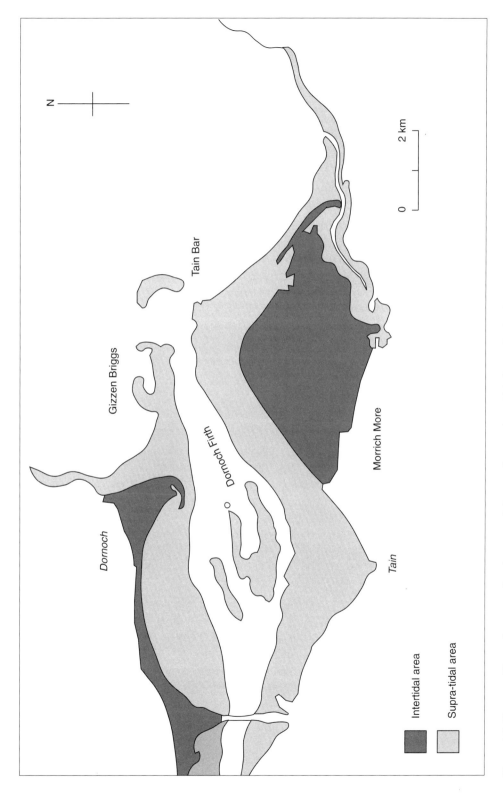

Figure 4.5 The outer Dornoch estuary, showing seaward decrease in estuarine width due to the development of the Dornoch spit and Morrich More.

- erosion of outer estuary intertidal areas with concomitant loss of important coastal habitat

- transfer of eroded sediment to the head of estuaries and its subsequent deposition on the intertidal areas

- inhibition of complete landward transgression due to the presence of flood embankments (e.g. in the Firth of Forth above Grangemouth)

- inhibition of landward transgression due to presence of high ground (e.g. in the Dornoch or Beauly estuaries).

The inhibition of landward transgression due to flood defences or rising ground means that the loss of intertidal habitat in the outer estuaries may not be compensated by the development of similar areas of new marshes or mudflats in the inner estuaries, a loss which may conflict with the Habitats Directive regulations for the maintenance of designated areas. Additionally, in some cases, such an overall loss of intertidal areas within an estuary, could result in an increase in tidal amplitude and consequently in flood risks to low-lying lands, such as those in the inner sections of the estuary of the Firth of Forth (Plate 19).

The deposition rates in the inner estuaries of southern England were shown above to be dependent not only on the transfer of sediment eroded from the outer estuary marshes and mudflats but, critically, on the import of sediment from marine sources. In the southern North Sea, background suspended sediment concentrations are high, ranging from 10 to 50 ppm, and consequently the deposition rates in the estuaries during the recent past have not been limited by sediment availability. In the Scottish case this may not be so; background suspended sediment concentrations in the northern North Sea and Atlantic are low, typically in the region of 2 to 3 ppm and may be decreasing as sea-bed deposits are exhausted, so that estuarine deposition rates may be limited by lack of marine sediment. If this is the case, then the intertidal areas in Scottish estuaries will not be able to keep pace with sea-level rise, and erosion rates of the vulnerable upper mudflats and saltmarshes will be accelerated as wave action is increased in the deeper water, causing not only loss of habitat but also increased risk from erosion and flooding on the adjacent lowlands.

4.4.2 *Impact on the outer firths*

The long period of uninterrupted sea-level fall for much of the Scottish coast has led to a series of morphological adjustments to the coastal morphology, of which one of the more dramatic, although largely unrecognised, has been the adjustment in the location and size of the mouths of the estuaries which are formed in submarine deltaic deposits. This can be seen in the Dornoch estuary where, however, the overall fall in sea level since 6500 BP may have been interrupted by a relatively short period of positive sea-level tendency beginning at 1890 BP (Smith *et al.*, 1992). Since that time relative sea level in the Dornoch appears to have fallen at an average rate of 1 mm per year and this has resulted in two morphological adjustments (Stapleton and Pethick, 1996). First, the gradual reduction in water depth in

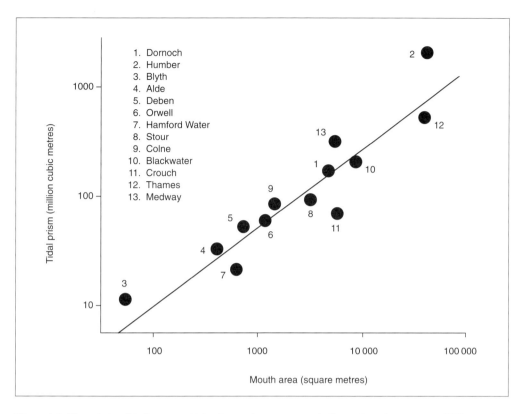

Figure 4.6 The relationship between tidal prism and estuary mouth dimensions for east coast UK estuaries. Note that Dornoch falls on the best-fit regression line, implying morphological adjustment to sea-level fall over the past 5000 years has taken place (from Pethick, 1994).

the nearshore zone, i.e. the region immediately external to the estuary, has allowed the estuarine delta to migrate seaward so that the mouth of the Dornoch now lies some 5 km seaward of the coast. Second, as sea level has fallen, so the volume of tidal water entering the estuary on a flood tide, the tidal prism, has fallen due to the fact that the estuary cross-section is markedly trapezoidal. In response to this reduction in tidal prism, velocities at the mouth have also fallen, resulting in deposition of sediment and a gradual but significant reduction in the width of the mouth. Figure 4.5 shows the effect of this dual process: as the mouth of the estuary has moved further seaward so its width has decreased.

This process of adjustment of an estuary mouth to changes in the tidal prism is well known (e.g. O'Brien, 1931; Gao and Collins, 1994) and a sample of east-coast estuaries between the Dornoch and the Thames (Figure 4.6) shows that a statistical relationship is present which can form the basis of a predictive model (Pethick, 1994). By interpolating the relationship for the east-coast estuaries shown in Figure 4.6, a prediction of the change in the morphology of the mouth of the Dornoch estuary can be made. Using an average sea-level fall of 1 mm per year for the past 2000 years (Smith *et al.*, 1992) to calculate the reduction in tidal prism over this period, the model predicts a reduction in width, from 3900 m at 2000 BP to 1900 m at the present. Inspection of the map of the outer Dornoch (Figure 4.5) demonstrates that the mouth width of 3900 m coincides with the section between the western limits of the Morrich More in the south and the Dornoch spit in the north. It appears from this that both the Morrich More and the Dornoch spit are morphological expressions of the reduction in the size of the estuary mouth, so that their plan shape provides a spatial record of these temporal changes: as the areas of sand dune widened to the east, so the Dornoch mouth was further constricted.

Such a model, connecting sea-level change to estuary mouth dimensions, may also be used to predict future changes under a rising sea level. Assuming a future rate of sea-level rise of around 4 mm per year, significant areas of the outer Dornoch estuary, including both the Dornoch spit and the Morrich More, would be eroded away over the next 50 years and their loss, together with the landward transgression of the outer deltaic sands, would lead to an increase in wave energy at the shore with serious coastal management implications for the defence of settlements such as Inver and Dornoch.

The same general conclusions apply to other Scottish estuaries such as the Ythan, Don and Dee, as well as the larger systems such as Solway and Tay. Perhaps most significant in this context are the changes which could occur in the outer Tay estuary where the deltaic areas and the sand dune areas of Barry and Tentsmuir appear to be exact analogues of the features at the mouth of the Dornoch. Further research is necessary on this and other Scottish estuaries, but the preliminary work outlined here suggests that sea-level rise would result in major erosion of the outer areas of the Tay, threatening the existing sea defences and involving increased hazards to coastal users, both along the open coast and within the outer estuary itself.

4.5 Management options

The predictions of coastal change in response to the reversal in sea-level tendency given in this chapter have necessarily concentrated on those areas where significant changes are likely. In general, however, the Scottish coastline is both undeveloped and geomorphologically resistant, so that sea-level rise is unlikely to have any widespread impact. The coast has responded in the past to changes in sea level of much greater magnitude than those envisaged for the next 50 years: it is only the inappropriate location of human infrastructures in high-risk areas at the coast that renders similar future responses hazardous.

Yet, in some areas of Scotland, major changes in the existing coastline must be anticipated over the next 50 years, and the discussion above has sought to highlight these vulnerable areas. Management must not only anticipate these changes, but also provide some amelioration of their effects on human use of the coast. There are several possibilities. Perhaps the least dramatic, but most useful, is education – i.e. developing an awareness of the problems that are about to be faced.

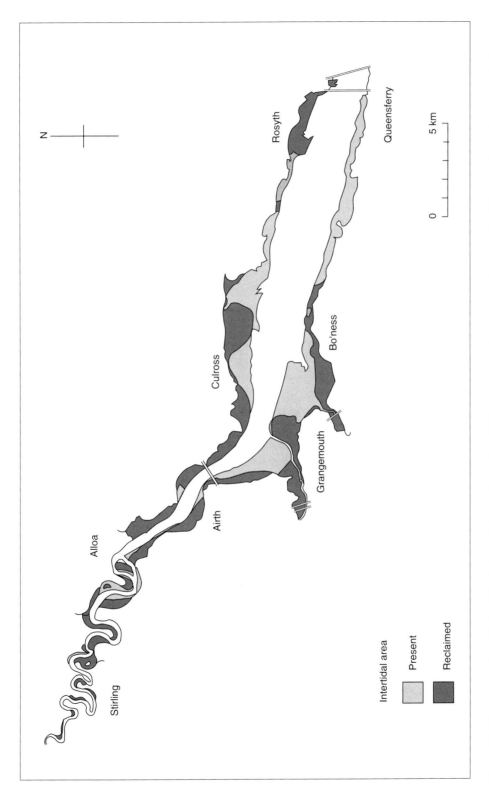

Figure 4.7 The estuary of the Firth of Forth. Intertidal areas formerly available to accommodate transgression as sea level rises have been almost completely reclaimed for agriculture.

A reversal of sea-level tendency in areas of the Scottish coast that have experienced a long period of uninterrupted sea-level fall, would result in coastal changes that will not be understood by many people. Where life or property is not at risk, including those areas with recreational or landscape value, such changes may have to be accepted and the coast allowed to adjust naturally. In other areas with major industrial or urban concentrations, such as Grangemouth, coastal defence may be seen as inevitable (Plate 20). In such cases it is important that coastal managers are aware of the impacts of such defences on the wider coastal system and increase the scale of their plans both spatially and temporally so as to allow the adjoining coast sufficient room to respond both to natural change and the constraints of artificial defences.

On open coasts, the loss of beaches and their associated sand dune and machair systems may be seen as a major negative impact of sea-level rise. One soft engineering approach to such losses is to recharge using dredged sediment from marine sources. While such solutions are to be preferred to the hard-engineering solutions of the past, the source of such recharge sediment must be carefully considered. The Scottish coast is already suffering from a massive loss of sediment inputs (Hansom, Chapter 3); attempts to dredge active sources may merely exacerbate the problems of the coast. Deep-water dredging using inactive sediment deposits is one solution, but the wave climate around the Scottish coast means that most sediment grain sizes are moved in water depths of less than 50 m. In contrast, the expense involved in aggregate dredging in water depths of more than 30 m means that such exploitation is rarely economically justifiable.

Within estuaries, the inhibition of the landward transgression due to flood defences offers one area where active management intervention can be achieved. Managed re-alignment of flood defences in England has now begun and several schemes have been initiated. The estuary of the Firth of Forth provides an excellent example of the potential of such a management intervention. Figure 4.7 shows that west of Grangemouth most of the recent intertidal area of the Forth has been reclaimed. The flood defence of these areas of agricultural land will become increasingly difficult and expensive over the next decade and this will be exacerbated by the inability of the estuary to migrate inland. Re-alignment of these flood defences, in some cases as far back as the cliff in the Carse Clays, would allow the estuary transgression to take place, resulting in lower tidal amplitudes and reduction in erosion of both natural habitat and coastal defences.

Finally, the impact of these predicted changes on the natural habitat of the Scottish coast must provide one of the most crucial issues for management, more especially due to the designation of many of the most vulnerable areas under the EC Habitats Directive. Careful evaluation of those areas most likely to suffer loss due to sea-level rise is the first essential of any management planning. The possibility of provision of alternative areas of similar habitat value must then be considered, either involving active measures such as managed re-alignment of existing defences, or the designation of areas which are considered to develop naturally into intertidal habitat under a sea-level rise. In all cases the maintenance of the integrity of the coastal system is both a Habitats Directive condition and a geomorphological imperative if a sustainable solution to habitat loss is to be evolved.

4.6 Conclusions

The conclusions reached in this review of the future development of the Scottish coast are less than comforting. If the results of the IPCC review of global sea-level changes are accepted, in some areas existing rates of sea-level rise will be augmented, in others the present fall in sea level will be reversed to give rates of sea-level rise predicted in this paper to average around 4 mm per year over the next 50 years. This may have little effect on the cliffed coastline, but it will affect both sand dune/machair systems and open-coast beaches. In conjunction with a dramatic reduction in available sediment around the Scottish coast, sea-level rise is likely to result in erosion of all of these vulnerable systems.

Even more profound would be the effects of sea-level rise on the estuaries. The conclusions reached above are that a landward migration of estuarine morphology will take place causing loss of outer estuary habitat and increased risks to outer estuary lowland areas from flood and erosion. The development of areas of intertidal habitat in the inner estuaries may, however, be impeded due to the presence of flood defences around the large areas of reclaimed land and this will mean a net loss in habitat and a rise in hazard levels.

Coastal management authorities must act to allow coastal users to understand the level of change which is about to affect them. They must also consider methods for amelioration and mitigation, including soft-engineering methods for reduction of risk and coastal re-alignment schemes for restoring estuarine and coastal habitat.

The scale of the changes likely to affect much of the Scottish coast over the next 50 years is not as great as those anticipated in many regions of the UK; it is the reversal from a long period of stability to one of instability that will prove the most difficult aspect with which coastal management in Scotland must contend.

References

Allen, J.R.L. and Rae, J.E. 1988. Vertical salt marsh accretion since the Roman period in the Severn Estuary, southwest Britain. *Marine Geology*, **83**, 225–235.

Bruun, P. 1962. Sea level rise as a cause of shore erosion. *Proceedings, American Society of Civil Engineers. Journal of Waterways and Harbor Division*, **88**, 117–130.

Gao, S. and Collins, M. 1994. Tidal inlet equilibrium, in relation to cross-sectional area and sediment transport patterns. *Estuarine, Coastal and Shelf Science*, **38** (2), 157–172.

Graff, J. 1981. An investigation of the frequency distributions of annual sea level maxima at ports around Great Britain. *Estuarine, Coastal and Shelf Science*, **12**, 389–449.

Haggart, B.A. 1987. Relative sea level changes in the Moray Firth area, Scotland. *In* Tooley, M.J. and Shennan, I. (eds) *Sea-level Changes*. Blackwell, Oxford, 67–108.

O'Brien, M.P. 1931. Estuary tidal prisms related to entrance areas. *Civil Engineering*, **1**(8), 738–739.

Pethick, J.S. 1994. Estuaries and wetlands: function and form. *In* Falconer, R.A. and Goodwin, P. (eds) *Wetland Management.* Institution of Civil Engineers, London, 75–87.

Pethick, J.S. 1997. Coastal management and sea level rise: a morphological approach. *In* Lane, S., Richards, K.S. and Chandler, J. (eds) *Landform Monitoring, Modelling and Analysis.* Wiley, London, 105–421.

Robinson, M. 1993. Microfossil analysis and radiocarbon dating of depositional sequences related to Holocene sea level change in the Forth valley, Scotland. *Transactions of the Royal Society of Edinburgh: Earth Science,* **84**, 1–60.

Shennan, I., Innes, J.B., Long, A.J. and Zong, Y. 1995. Late Devensian and Holocene relative sea level changes in north west Scotland. New data to test existing models. *Quaternary International,* **26**, 97–123.

Sissons, J.B. 1976. *The Geomorphology of the British Isles: Scotland.* Methuen, London.

Smith, D.E., Firth, C.R., Turbayne, S.C. and Brooks, C.L. 1992. Holocene relative sea level change and shoreline displacement in the Dornoch Firth area, Scotland. *Proceedings of the Geologists Association,* **103**, 237–257.

Stapleton, C. and Pethick, J.S. 1996. Coastal processes and management of Scottish Estuaries 1: The Dornoch, Cromarty and Beauly/Inverness Firths. *Scottish Natural Heritage Review,* No. 50.

Warrick, R.A. 1993. Climate and sea level change: a synthesis. *In* Warrick, R.A., Barrow, E.M. and Wigley, T.M.L. (eds) *Climate and Sea Level Change: Observations, Projections and Implications.* Cambridge University Press, Cambridge, UK, 3–21.

5 EXPERIENCES AND OPPORTUNITIES OF SHORELINE MANAGEMENT PLANS

R. Leafe and T. Collins

Summary

1. The concept of Shoreline Management Planning is now well established in England and Wales with plans complete or under development for all of the open coast and some of the major estuary systems.
2. Experience gained during the process has reinforced the need for, and potential benefits of, adopting a proactive approach to strategic shoreline management covering coherent lengths of coast.
3. It is clear that the realisation of the full benefits of the process will take some time to accrue. In many cases the Shoreline Management Plan (SMP) represents the first stage in the planning of new approaches to coastal defence.
4. More detailed analysis of often complex coastal functions is required before management decisions can be made with confidence. In many plans it has been found difficult to promote moves away from the *status quo*, which serves to highlight the need for more innovative approaches to shoreline management planning.
5. This chapter reviews some of the experience to date and suggests changes required to realise the full potential of the process and achieve sustainable coastal defences and associated environmental benefits. Given the evidence for relative sea-level rise in Scotland, the English experience is of key relevance to Scotland.

5.1 The development of Shoreline Management Plans in England and Wales

The move towards a strategic approach to coastal defence was outlined in the Ministry of Agriculture, Fisheries and Food's (MAFF) *Strategy for Flood and Coastal Defence in England and Wales*, published in 1993. It provided a positive response to English Nature's 1992 *Campaign for a Living Coast* which highlighted the nature conservation losses resulting from the *ad hoc* and spatially limited planning of past defences (English Nature, 1992). In 1995 guidance on the process of Shoreline Management Planning was published (MAFF, 1995) and targets set for the production of such plans in England and Wales. Plans are now well advanced for all of the English and Welsh open coast and some of the major estuaries. England and Wales are covered by a total of 41 plans, of which 24 are now complete.

The setting and delivery of environmental objectives is an integral part of the adopted SMP process (Swash *et al.*, 1995). English Nature has been developing a methodology for the incorporation of environmental objectives into the SMP process. This has been further refined with the benefit of practical experience from 'live' SMPs undertaken by Mouchel Consulting Ltd, and the results of this work are now available from English Nature, as a research report (English Nature, 1997).

5.2 Experience with the process

Coastal defence groups (composed of operating authorities and English Nature representatives) have been charged with the production of SMPs for their coastal cell. Practicalities of group sizes in terms of operating authorities have resulted in plans prepared, or being prepared, on a sub-cell or combination of sub-cells basis. Although not an ideal situation, as in many cases sub-cells are in no way discrete geomorphological units but inter-connected with adjoining coasts, the management task for preparing a quality plan is large enough. Project groups, with a nominated lead authority providing management and financial control, composed of the operating authorities with responsibilities in the sub-cell, have been established to steer the preparation of a plan. In many cases, English Nature has been represented on project groups, which has proved beneficial in providing an inside track to influence the outcome and quality of the plan and its proposals, provide direct access for the group and its consultants to environmental data, and jointly develop environmental objectives. Although representation of English Nature has by no means been mandatory, experience has shown that close involvement has enabled the more rapid progress of plans, particularly through consultations with other conservation bodies and a better-quality product. Without this direct involvement, considerable time has been expended by both parties at the consultation stage in sorting out errors in environmental data and differences of opinion on content.

A major strength of the approach has been the process itself; setting up a dialogue on long-term strategic coastal defence issues, in some detail, between adjacent coastal defence authorities. The identification of key issues and needs for further understanding on coastal functioning has led to significant changes in direction in some areas (Hutchison and Leafe, 1995).

All groups have employed consultants, or consortia of consultants, to prepare the plans. They have all followed the MAFF guidance on how to prepare a plan with varying degrees of closeness. In English Nature's experience, the quality of the work and the final product has varied from location to location. The key factor in determining these variations appears to be the experience of the consultant team undertaking the work. Second to this is the ability of the project group, and particularly the project manager, who has often been in daily contact with the team throughout the process. The more successful plans have been distinguished by:

- a well-balanced team including engineers, environmentalists and specialist geomorphological input – often from experts in the local area

- a flexible approach to the MAFF guidance document

- a thorough consultation process, including a face to face pre-plan consultation

- regular project group meetings – including an English Nature representative

- a public consultation process

- a political adoption process

- a well-planned and funded implementation process.

The process has benefited from the production by MAFF of its Shoreline Management Planning guidance document. This has achieved a good degree of consistency between plans in terms of process and content. However, with hindsight, in some cases strict adherence to the letter of the guidance may have hindered creativity in approach. The concept of 'management units', the subject of much discussion within the working group charged with preparing the guidance, has in some instances constrained the process, resulting in short-termism and in a plan that maintains the *status quo*.

5.3 Quality of outputs

A strategic approach based on a firm understanding of natural processes is vital in ensuring that future decisions in relation to coastal defence are sustainable. Ultimately this will provide society with a higher standard of defence that is not only functional and cost-effective but also sympathetic to the environment and the needs of nature conservation.

There are, however, a number of limitations to this first generation of SMPs. Some have failed to look at the reality and scale of the geomorphological processes that are operating within coastal cells, for example plans prepared at a sub-cell level have not been effectively linked to others in the same cell. This conceals the important issues that SMPs were designed to address and in consequence they cannot take the strategic overview that is necessary in order to adopt long-term and sustainable solutions. The development of coastal authority groups, whereby councils within coastal cells get together to discuss coastal issues of mutual concern, is helping to resolve this problem. Some local authorities have seen the SMP as a task to be completed before they can qualify for their grant aid on individual coastal defence schemes. Once complete they will have 'jumped' the necessary hurdle and can proceed with business as usual. The importance attached by MAFF, the grant-aiding body, to the SMP process, means that authorities promoting a scheme on the basis of a poor or non-existent SMP will have a harder task in justifying the need for exchequer support.

The question of coastal mobility referred to earlier, is by and large poorly tackled by SMPs: there is a lack of appreciation that environmental assets on the coast are best conserved by allowing them to respond dynamically to natural processes. This lack of understanding has led to the selection of inappropriate defence options. For example, the recently completed North Norfolk SMP suggested 'hold the line' in the medium term at a number of sites, yet little more than a year after its completion the Environment Agency is promoting a realignment scheme on the basis of urgent need.

5.4 Implementation

The execution of completed plans is still at an early stage. In some areas they are leading to worthwhile research that will provide a key component of long-term management; examples include the Southern North Sea Sediment Transport Study in East Anglia and the Essex Sea Wall Management Study undertaken by the Environment Agency. However, there are relatively few examples of an integrated series of coastal defence works based on a clear understanding of physical processes. One potential exception is the Holderness coast in East Yorkshire, where the impossibility of protecting all existing settlements in the long-term has been recognised in the draft plan. This process can be expected to evolve as more SMPs are completed, allowing local authorities and the Environment Agency to plan and execute strategic works. It is supported by the provision of new guidance produced by MAFF (MAFF, 1997) on the strategic planning and appraisal of coastal defence schemes.

Another method of fudging difficult issues is to defer a decision until 'further studies have been completed', but there is sometimes little commitment to pursuing these studies. Almost all plans have been led by local authority engineers, who, while skilled in their own discipline, have not necessarily had the vision to adopt imaginative solutions to problems. At Cuckmere Haven in Sussex a simple and expedient solution to an ongoing beach management problem was to cease manipulating the beach and to allow the river access to its currently constrained flood plain. Yet the proposed solution involved an ongoing commitment to expensive beach management and continued maintenance of long stretches of flood defences.

5.5 Conclusions and recommendations

There is no doubt that the process of strategic shoreline planning embarked upon in England and Wales is a much needed and positive move in the right direction. Indeed the innovative approach developed is certainly a world leader in the planning of coastal defences. Given the high level of investment in existing defences, the degree of urbanisation and development of the coastline, and the high value of the natural coastal environment, commitment to the sound planning of this sector must remain a priority.

The SMP procedure developed to date is sound and robust. If ever there was to be a revolution in the way the coastal defence sector operated, it has happened. The current policy is radically different from that which existed just 10 years ago. What is needed for the future is the progressive evolution of the process combined with greater innovation in implementation.

This chapter has attempted to highlight some of the areas needing attention as the process develops. In summary these are:

- a multi-disciplinary approach to plan preparation and delivery

- a long-term view of changes needed in coastal land use to deliver sustainable defences

- more creativity and innovation to realise sustainability goals

- compliance with the SMP to become a mandatory part of coastal defence scheme financing

- greater incorporation of SMP outcomes into local development plans.

The coastal defence industry, under the leadership of MAFF's Flood and Coastal Defence Division, has embraced concepts and practices of strategic planning. The challenge now lies with the integration of the sector with other users of the coast. To this end the EU Demonstration Programme on Coastal Zone Management will be of value. However, more practical demonstrations of what strategic shoreline planning has to offer other coastal users is required. The work on the implementation of plans in East Anglia, and for habitat compensation as part of existing and proposed port developments in southern England, provide the opportunity to demonstrate what is now practical for shoreline managers.

In particular there is a need to see the strategic understanding that is evolving from the SMP process being incorporated into local authority development plans. This has been done successfully by Waveney District Council in Suffolk who have produced 'red lines' in their plans, parallel to the eroding shoreline, further development being prohibited seaward of this line.

Looking forward to the next generation of plans (they are due to be reviewed every five years) it is possible to envisage a process of positive evolution occurring. With each generation of SMPs demonstrating an improved understanding of processes they are better able to select appropriate and sustainable options.

References

English Nature. 1992. *Campaign for a Living Coast*. English Nature, Peterborough.

English Nature. 1997. Nature conservation objectives in Shoreline Management Plans – a suggested approach. *English Nature Research Reports*, **243**, by Mouchel Consulting Ltd.

Hutchison, J. and Leafe, R.N. 1995. Shoreline management: a view of the way ahead. *Institute of Civil Engineers Coastal Management '95: Putting Policy into Practice, 12–14 November 1995, Bournemouth*. Proceedings. Thomas Telford, London.

MAFF. 1993. *Strategy for Flood and Coastal Defence in England and Wales*. MAFF Publications PB 1471. Ministry of Agriculture, Fisheries and Food.

MAFF. 1995. *Shoreline Management Plans – A Guide for Coastal Defence Authorities.* MAFF Publications PB 2197. Ministry of Agriculture, Fisheries and Food.

MAFF. 1997. *Interim Guidance for the Strategic Planning and Appraisal of Flood and Coastal Defence Schemes.* Ministry of Agriculture, Fisheries and Food.

Swash, A.R.H., Leafe, R.N. and Radley, G.P. 1995. Shoreline Management Plans and environmental considerations. *In* Healy, M.G. and Doody, J.P. (eds), *Directions in European Coastal Management.* Samara Publishing Ltd, Cardigan, Wales, 161–167.

6 THE COASTAL CELLS OF SCOTLAND AND THEIR APPLICATION

A. H. Brampton, R. G. Lees and D. L. Ramsay

Summary

1. This chapter describes work carried out under a research contract funded jointly by Scottish Natural Heritage, Historic Scotland and the Scottish Office (Agriculture, Environment and Fisheries Department).
2. This project:
- identified the major natural divisions of Scotland's coastline, i.e. sections of coastline along which the behaviour of beach sands/gravels or the general geomorphology are different to and evolve independently from the adjacent division(s). These divisions are called coastal cells; and

- identified and catalogued information about both the natural physical environment and the past and present human development and uses of the coastal zone within each cell.

3. Apart from describing the methods used, and the outputs from the contract, this chapter also discusses the practical uses of the coastal cell concept, the defined coastal cells, and the information gathered for each cell, to help in the future sensible management of Scotland's coast.

6.1 Background to research contract

6.1.1 Defining the problem: coastal erosion and defence in Scotland

The Scottish coastline is a dynamic environment. In spite of its predominantly rocky character, features such as raised beaches, drowned peats, magnificent shingle spits and vast dune systems all testify to areas of changing coastline since the end of the last Ice Age (Plates 16, 21). Yet there is also much evidence of change in more recent times: eroding fence-lines, golf courses and historic caves, contrasted to dry-stone dykes, and ancient settlements now buried in sand; former harbours no longer viable because of silting up of channels or progressive separation from the original coastline, and lines of World War II defences, formerly built upon the shoreline but now variously located hundreds of metres inland or submerged beneath today's low-water mark.

Much of the Scottish coastline is exposed to the full force of Atlantic storms, but even on North Sea coasts, fetches typically extend for hundreds of kilometres. Moreover, although the country is composed largely of ancient and durable rock types, these are often overlain at the coast by softer sediments, less resistant to erosion, such as glacial tills, shingle beds, sand dunes and links, or mudflats. The huge quantities of sand and gravel brought to the coast by rivers towards the end of the last glaciation form an important percentage of present-day beaches, added to by shell fragments, erosion of soft cliffs, and in a few cases by modern rivers. In places, the accumulation of sediments in dunes and coastal plains is very substantial. The coincidence of such soft, erodible landforms with such a notoriously windy climate, and the associated waves generated, means the potential for change in these areas is exceptionally high. At Barry Links, for instance, analysis of maps, aerial photographs, and historic records indicates that the southern tip, Buddon Ness, has shifted by at least 200 m since the 16th century (Wright, 1981). Slightly further north at Montrose, routine monitoring of the coastline by Angus Council has revealed up to 9 m retreat of the sand dunes in the space of one recent winter. At Tentsmuir in Fife and Morrich More in Easter Ross on the other hand, shorelines have advanced seaward by up to 400 m in the last 100 years (Ritchie, 1979; Hansom and Leafe, 1990).

Most of Scotland's coastline is remote and undeveloped. Around the central belt and in the east, however, coastal development is widespread in the form of towns, harbours, industry and tourist facilities (Ritchie and McLean, 1988) (Plates 20, 22). Road and rail networks also follow the coastline. Although less commonly developed for housing or industry, even those areas most susceptible to change, such as dunes, links and machair plains may nonetheless support Ministry of Defence establishments, golf courses, caravan parks and other recreational facilities such as promenades and footpaths. Cemeteries and a wealth of historical and archaeological monuments are especially common in coastal areas of the Western and Northern Isles.

Where developments such as these coincide with a shifting coastline there is, understandably, pressure upon local authorities or landowners to protect the land or facilities concerned from the perceived threat of erosion. Typical approaches pursued include the construction of seawalls and rock armour revetments (Plate 18), emplacement of lines of gabion baskets or groynes (e.g. see ASH, 1994). Soft engineering approaches such as beach recharge or dune management are increasingly being considered. Indeed the first major beach nourishment scheme in the UK was carried out at Portobello near Edinburgh in 1972. Even today, however, the tipping of demolition rubble or other debris into dunes or on to the shore is still, sadly, considered by some landowners to be the most convenient practice to pursue. In some areas, too, the extraction of beach sand for agriculture and industry contributes to coastal erosion.

The wider environmental impacts of any type of proposed coastal defence schemes, or their long-term sustainability, have rarely been considered to date in

Scotland. In particular, effects upon coastal sediment supply or evolution are rarely predicted. By analogy with experience in England and Wales (e.g. Bray and Hooke, 1995), where defences are more commonplace, and given the prevalence of longshore drift on many developed coastlines in Scotland (Plate 16), one might anticipate that inappropriate coastal defences in Scotland could have potentially damaging effects upon adjacent unprotected coasts. Links between coast protection, or other shoreline developments, and increased erosion downdrift have only rarely been documented in Scotland, possibly because of a lack of monitoring. However, the potential for defences, and other structures built on the shore, to influence coastal evolution beyond the immediate area of construction clearly exists. For instance, structures such as breakwaters, built normal to the shoreline, frequently display sediment accretion on updrift sides and sediment starvation downdrift. Field inspection of seawalls and similar defences often reveals effects such as terminal scour or, less commonly, beach lowering. Indeed, the repeated extension of defences along the coast in certain locations in itself implies the existence of knock-on effects (ASH, 1994).

6.1.2 *Scottish Natural Heritage and coastal defence*

Scotland's coastline is renowned for its beauty; unspoiled beaches and sensational landscapes abound (Plate 23). Such is the diversity of coastal habitats, landforms and rock sequences that around 400 sites have been designated as Sites of Special Scientific Interest (SSSI) and 40 put forward as candidate Special Areas of Conservation (cSAC) and Special Protection Areas (SPA). The very existence and quality of many such sites depends on the continued operation of natural processes of sediment erosion and accretion. Coastal erosion can benefit the natural environment, for instance through the generation of sediment for maintaining beaches or for habitat creation in estuaries.

By stabilising naturally dynamic systems, such as dunes and saltmarshes, obscuring landforms and rock outcrops and altering previously natural landscapes, coastal defences can cause significant damage to the natural environment (Lees *et al.*, 1998). Such impacts are compounded when the construction of defence causes erosion elsewhere, leading to further intervention where none was formerly required.

One of the primary roles of Scottish Natural Heritage is to help safeguard this valuable natural resource. Scottish Natural Heritage is therefore consulted on all planning applications which might affect designated areas such as SSSIs, and is, moreover, a statutory consultee on all coast protection proposals put forward by local authorities, whether within an area designated on account of its natural heritage importance or not.

If potential effects of proposed defences on coastal evolution are to be predicted at the planning stage it is essential that an understanding is obtained of the coastal processes operating at the site concerned and, in particular, the nature of the littoral drift regime into which they are to be placed (Hansom, Chapter 3).

Unfortunately, compared to England and Wales, information on drift directions and magnitudes in Scotland is sparse and localised.

As a result Scottish Natural Heritage, Historic Scotland, who promote the conservation of Scotland's built heritage, and the Scottish Office's Agriculture, Environment and Fisheries Department, who have departmental responsibility for coast protection in Scotland, jointly commissioned a review of littoral transport around the mainland coastline of Scotland, in order to help fill this knowledge gap and so aid coastal defence planning and impact assessment. Because of the relative abundance of ancient monuments threatened by coastal erosion in the Northern and Western Isles, these areas were also incorporated into the study. The remaining island groups were, however, omitted.

By disseminating such information to authorities involved in defence construction and consent, it was felt that this might encourage wider appreciation and understanding of the changes inherent in the coastline, the inevitability and potential benefits of these and the possible disadvantages of interfering with them. In particular, it was believed that demarcation and description of 'coastal cells'(see below) would enable a more strategic approach to coastal erosion management to be pursued, on appropriate Scottish coastlines, compared with the often piecemeal approaches followed to date.

6.2 The concept of coastal cells and their definition for Scotland

The natural processes that affect and shape a coastline show no respect for administrative boundaries, for example between adjacent counties or regions. Coastal defences installed by one local authority have, at some sites in the UK, contributed to erosion in another authority's area, by interrupting the normal movement of sand or gravel along the coast. From a national viewpoint, it is important to avoid this 'beggar thy neighbour' attitude to coastal management, and to develop a more regional approach. This has led, in England and Wales, to the adoption of 'coastal cells' as a basis for strategic planning of coastal defences (MAFF, 1993).

It is useful to start by defining 'sediment cells', i.e. natural divisions of the shoreline, within which beach sediments (i.e. sand and gravel) are contained. Boundaries between sediment cells occur at points where there is a complete break in the longshore transport of this sediment, e.g. at major headlands or at the mouths of estuaries. Where major unnatural features such as harbours completely interrupt sediment transport, these too become sediment cell boundaries. Interference with the movement of sediment in any one such cell may affect the coastline along the whole length of that cell, but is unlikely to affect the evolution of the shoreline in adjacent sediment cells. Knowledge of these cells, and their boundaries, is therefore helpful when assessing the likely distance of coastline that might be affected by proposed developments, and hence who should be involved in consultations.

The concept of sediment cells is most useful when considering the management of long beaches, as for example in East Anglia. Sand and gravel may travel across many local authority boundaries between its arrival at the shoreline (e.g. from a river or an eroding cliff) and its eventual 'final' resting place (e.g. in an estuary). In deeply embayed and predominantly rocky coastlines (e.g. the Western Highlands), however, each beach may itself be a sediment cell. The demarcation of each such (small) cell, and the calculation of a sediment 'budget' for it (i.e. quantifying the losses and gains of sediment, and its transport rates), is valuable for that sediment cell, although it may add little to a regional strategy for managing the coast.

Care must be taken in defining sediment cells when tidal currents affect shorelines; beaches on opposite sides of some estuaries may experience an interchange of sediments that would not be predicted by consideration of wave-induced longshore drift alone.

It has been found in England and Wales that the concept of sediment cells has produced advantages for managing the coastline over and above the increase in knowledge of the transport of beach sand and gravel. The demarcation of sediment cells provides a 'neutral' framework for planning and management of the coastal zone, independent of administrative boundaries, within which local authorities, national conservation organisations and others can co-operate. This co-operation may involve:

- pooling and sharing information (e.g. on waves, tidal levels, and experience with types of coastal defences)

- creating a forum for identifying and discussing the hopes and fears of the 'stakeholders' for that stretch of coastline

- holding consultations on the needs, priorities and best methods for any future intervention works, and

- jointly funded management action, such as monitoring.

These advantages cannot realistically be achieved for each sediment cell where they are small, and separated by long stretches of rocky coast, for example in north-west Scotland. This leads to the idea of 'coastal cells'. Each coastal cell comprises one or more sediment cells, and is defined taking into account a number of other factors, such as the general orientation and exposure of the coastline. The mainland coast of Scotland can be divided into seven coastal cells (Figure 6.1), and the Northern and Western Isles into a further two each, respectively. The definition and character of these coastal cells are described more fully in HR Wallingford (1997).

From a management or planning viewpoint, however, some of these cells are too large to consider as a whole. As a result, 'sub-cells' (i.e. sub-divisions of coastal cells) have also been defined, themselves comprising one or more sediment cells. The boundaries of these are also indicated in Figure 6.1. The choice of boundaries for these major coastal cells and sub-cells for Scotland reflects the experience gained in England and Wales (see Motyka and Brampton, 1993). For example, the inner parts of estuaries have been identified as single sub-cells, despite including

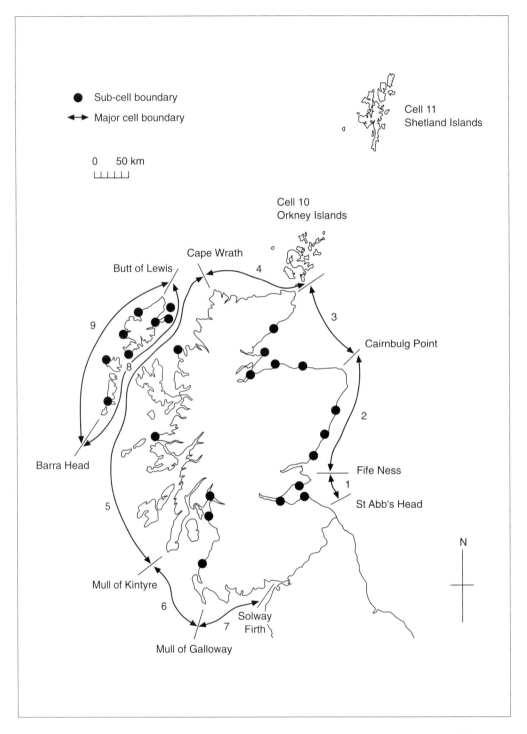

Figure 6.1 Coastal cells and sub-cells on the mainland of Scotland and the Western Isles. Sub-cell boundaries on Orkney and Shetland are not indicated due to scale. Coastal cells are not defined for remaining island coastlines (see text for details). Reproduced from HR Wallingford (1997).

two coastlines and, often, distinct sediment cells. In England and Wales, sub-cells have been used as a basis for strategic planning of coastal defences, known as Shoreline Management Plans (MAFF, 1995).

As a first step in any potential shoreline management strategy, it is important to have a convenient summary of existing knowledge on coastal processes and certain aspects of land use in the coastal cell or sub-cell concerned. Individual reports for each coastal cell in Scotland are therefore being compiled (HR Wallingford, 1998). These use published information from a variety of sources, combined with data derived from specific site visits to sensitive sedimentary coastlines where changes were deemed likely to cause major damage to human development or the natural or cultural heritage.

Each report contains information, for each sub-cell, on:

- Geology. A brief section is provided which gives details of the solid geology, with approximate ages, and the more recent glacial and post-glacial deposits.

- Hydraulic processes, e.g. waves and tides. The hydraulic processes shape the coastline by mobilising and transporting loose sediment deposits, and more gradually by eroding the solid geology on which these sediments lie. A section describes both tides, including information on normal tidal ranges, currents and extreme high water levels, and offshore wave conditions. Where measurements are known to have been made, this is noted.

- Beach evolution. The type of coastline is described using a keyed chart that provides information on the character of the beaches or foreshore, and of the immediate hinterland (e.g. dunes, cliffs and links). This is followed by a description of the various beaches, and their relationship to each other. The directions and approximate rates of sediment transport, and the areas of erosion and accretion (where known), are crucially important for coastal management and planning, and these are also summarised.

- Existing coastal defences. Although not all the defences along the coastline of Scotland have necessarily been listed, where information on the presence, length and type of structures was available (e.g. from the Scottish Office or local councils), this has been included. Where beach monitoring is being carried out as part of a coastal management strategy, then this is also noted.

In addition to these details for the individual sub-cells, summaries are provided, for each coastal cell, on the natural and cultural heritage assets at or near the shoreline. SNH and Historic Scotland respectively have very largely provided the basic information for this section of the report. Finally, the reports discuss the likely effects of future coastline change on natural/cultural heritage sites, and the likely effects of climatic change, including their consequences for methods of future coastal management.

6.3 Future development and applications

In spite of their potential value, these reports cannot be regarded as a 'completed' review and understanding of Scotland's coastline. Unlike the coastal cells study carried out for England and Wales (Motyka and Brampton, 1993), this research was started from the 'top down', i.e. by identifying the major coastal cells and sub-cells first, and then seeking information on each part of the coast. The availability of such detailed information for each sub-cell of the Scottish coast is far from complete and indeed is unlikely ever to be, especially in remoter, undeveloped areas. Instead, the reports should be regarded as an initial attempt at collating and synthesising coastal data pertinent to shoreline management in Scotland. As such, they will require periodic revision if they are to reflect increased knowledge and changes in both the political and natural 'climate' of Scotland.

The data presented in these reports can therefore form an initial input to an overall shoreline management initiative. In many cases, however, the existing information on even the most basic aspects of Scotland's coastline relevant to shoreline management, such as the location, design and age of defences, is very sparse. Moreover, long-term beach monitoring data are exceptionally uncommon in Scotland, even although problems of coastal erosion/flooding do exist and are not likely to simply 'heal' with time.

Identifying these gaps in knowledge will assist in establishing priorities for research and survey; clearly not all the problems can be tackled at once, and a joint effort is needed to discuss and agree where action is needed most urgently.

Dissemination of this research to coast protection authorities in Scotland and other relevant organisations will, it is hoped, raise awareness of the changing nature of the coastline and the existence and location of coastal cells, resulting in greater consideration being given to the potential impacts upon the coast which inappropriate defences may have.

The data will also form a vital input to wider coastal initiatives, especially the many firths' initiatives developing around the country, helping to ensure that the coastal zone management strategies being produced are founded on a sound understanding of the process links which exist along the shorelines of the project areas concerned.

Ultimately it is SNH's hope that the delineation of coastal cells in Scotland may be used to facilitate the adoption of strategic approaches to the management of coastal erosion and defence, where these are warranted, such as the preparation of Shoreline Management Plans (SMPs). The revolution in strategic management of the coastline, which has swept through England and Wales, is gradually gaining momentum in Scotland. An SMP for the Highland Council, covering much of the Inner Moray Firth, has been completed (HR Wallingford, 1996) and a similar study for Fife is presently underway (Posford Duvivier, 1998). Both initiatives have received financial and technical support from SNH.

Commendation from the Scottish Office of the benefits of SMP, in the newly published NPPG on Coastal Planning (Scottish Office, 1997), should maintain this impetus.

Local government reorganisation in 1996 saw the demise of Scotland's only formal discussion group on coastal defence, the Tayside Coastal Group. The Scottish Office has, however, promoted the concept of voluntary coastal fora in recent years (e.g. Scottish Office, 1996) and, with SNH, encouraged the formation of separate fora for each of the major Scottish firths. Most of the firths' fora now in existence have topic groups specifically concerned with coastal processes and defence. The coincidence of the areas embraced by each of the fora (e.g. the Forth, Clyde, Solway, Cromarty and Moray Firths) with coastal cells or sub-cells identified in this study has, in effect, re-established a means for local authorities and other appropriate organisations in these areas to liaise over coast protection proposals of mutual concern and, potentially, to share in the costs and benefits of strategic coastal defence initiatives.

6.4 Conclusions

Although the coastal cells concept is of less relevance to shoreline management on the more remote and indented stretches of Scotland's coastlines, it has considerable relevance elsewhere. Many of the country's more developed coastlines, such as those in Ayrshire, the Lothians, Fife and Tayside, also exhibit the clearest patterns of longshore drift (HR Wallingford, 1997). Consequently, those coasts under greatest development pressure are, by coincidence, those where the natural processes dictate that strategic planning of coastal defences is paramount.

On these coasts in particular, it is the authors' belief that an awareness and understanding of coastal cells should ensure, firstly, that constructions and developments are not undertaken without an appreciation of the potential impacts which these may have on coastal evolution there and elsewhere and, secondly, that future generations will not be tied into maintaining defences or shorelines in ultimately untenable positions.

The coastal cells concept should act as a catalyst that changes the way we think about shoreline management in Scotland. In so doing, it will help safeguard those elements of our coastal natural heritage most at risk from inappropriate and potentially unsustainable coastal defence options.

References

ASH Consulting Group. 1994. *Coastal Erosion and Tourism in Scotland.* Scottish Natural Heritage Review **12**, Scottish Natural Heritage, Edinburgh.

Bray, M.J. and Hooke, J.M. 1995. Strategies for conserving dynamic coastal landforms. *In* Healy, M.G. and Doody, J.P. (eds) *Directions in European Coastal Management.* Samara, Cardigan, Wales, 275–290.

Hansom, J.D. and Leafe, R.N. 1990. *The Geomorphology of Morrich More: Development of a Scientific Database and Management Prescription.* Dept. of Geography, University of Sheffield. Unpublished report to Nature Conservancy Council, Peterborough.

HR Wallingford. 1996. *Shoreline Management Plan: Inverness Firth and part of Moray Firth (Burghead to the Sutors).* Unpublished report to Highland Regional Council. HR Wallingford Report EX 3230.

HR Wallingford. 1997. *Coastal Cells in Scotland.* Scottish Natural Heritage Research, Survey and Monitoring Report **56**. Scottish Natural Heritage, Edinburgh.

HR Wallingford. 1998. *Coastal Cells in Scotland. Cells 1-10.* Unpublished reports to Scottish Natural Heritage, the Scottish Office and Historic Scotland. HR Wallingford Reports EX 3471.

Lees, R.G., Gordon, J.E. and McKirdy, A.P. 1998. Coastal erosion, coastal defences and the earth heritage in Scotland. *In* Hooke, J. (ed.) *Coastal Defence and Earth Science Conservation.* The Geological Society, London, 133–150.

Ministry of Agriculture, Fisheries and Food. 1993. *Strategy for Flood and Coastal Defence in England and Wales.* MAFF Publications PB 1471.

Ministry of Agriculture, Fisheries and Food. 1995. *Shoreline Management Plans: A Guide for Coastal Defence Authorities.* MAFF Publications PB 2197.

Motyka, J.M. and Brampton, A.H. 1993. *Coastal Management. Mapping of Littoral Cells.* HR Wallingford Report SP328.

Posford Duvivier. 1998. *Fife Shoreline Management Plan.* Report to Fife Council. May 1998.

Ritchie, W. 1979. *The Beaches of Fife.* Dept. of Geography, University of Aberdeen. Report to Countryside Commission for Scotland, Battleby.

Ritchie, W. and McLean, L. 1988. UK – Scotland. *In* Walker, H.J. (ed.) *Artificial Structures and Shorelines.* Kluwer Academic Publishers, Dordrecht, 127–135.

Scottish Office. 1996. *Scotland's Coasts. A Discussion Paper.* The Scottish Office, Edinburgh.

Scottish Office. 1997. *National Planning Policy Guideline (NPPG) 13 Coastal Planning.* The Scottish Office (Development Department), Edinburgh.

Wright, R. 1981. *Beaches of Tayside.* Dept. of Geography, University of Aberdeen. Report to Countryside Commission for Scotland, Battleby.

PART THREE

Management of Scotland's Coast

This volume is published at an exciting time of change when new approaches to the management of Scotland's coastline are developing rapidly. The five chapters in this section discuss four major new national-level coastal management initiatives in their trial stages around Scotland's coasts: Focus on Firths and other integrated coastal zone management (ICZM) projects; the implementation of the EC Habitats Directive (Council of the European Communities, 1992) with the development of management for marine Special Areas of Conservation; the early stages of Shoreline Management Plans; and the establishment of the Scottish Coastal Forum.

Focus on Firths was launched in 1993 under the sponsorship of SNH. Stephen Atkins shows how this initiative is demonstrating that the concept of voluntary ICZM can have an important and valuable role in large firth environments. Progress and experience of firths projects are reviewed, pointing out the benefits and limitations of the approach. Many ICZM projects from other countries have failed at the point of implementing the management plan. Ways in which ICZM could support the wider objectives of partner organisations are explored to avoid this danger and a range of tasks and functions with which firths projects could assist are suggested to secure their future in the longer term.

The firths projects in the Solway, Clyde, Forth, Moray and Cromarty Firths have been followed by other ICZM initiatives in Scotland such as the Minch, Skye, Fair Isle, Tay and Loch Ryan projects. Two case studies showing contrasting approaches to ICZM, appropriate for two very different sets of circumstances and issues, are discussed in separate chapters: the Forth Estuary Forum, described by Mark Jennison and David Kay, has developed from small beginnings to a position of receiving funding from the European Union LIFE programme in 1997/8. It now has two full-time staff and 250 members and is contributing to an EU DGXI demonstration project on ICZM in Europe. The Fair Isle Marine Environment and Tourism Initiative reviewed by Anthony Bryant is supported by all the residents of Fair Isle, the Fair Isle Bird Observatory and the National Trust for Scotland, with contributions from many other partner bodies. Its aim includes the sustainable management of the natural marine resources around the island.

Implementation of the Habitats Directive has resulted in the proposal of 14 particularly important areas of Scotland's coastal waters as marine candidate Special Areas of Conservation (marine cSAC) to the European Commission with a number of further possible sites still under consideration. All these sites are already receiving protection as candidate sites. If they are designated as expected, they will form part of the Natura 2000 suite of sites conserving and sustainably managing some of the best examples of the range of habitats and species across Europe. John Baxter and Alistair Davison show how the 14 sites, covering a wide range of different marine habitats, and their simultaneous designation, pose a significant challenge. Separate partnerships are being established for each site and the conditions for working together and building consensus must be developed in each area if the model process for developing management schemes is to be successful. Draft conservation objectives and a draft matrix of management issues for the Sound of Arisaig marine cSAC are used as an example of the process in operation.

The Scottish Coastal Forum (SCF) was proposed in the government discussion paper *Scotland's Coasts* (Scottish Office, 1996) and subsequently set up in March 1997 by the Scottish Office. It has the widespread support of many organisations having an interest or role in coastal management and all key bodies are represented in its membership. As explained by Steve Sankey, the SCF has taken on the ambitious remit of providing a national focus for Scottish coastal issues, encouraging the local forum approach to ICZM and advising government on coastal policy. In addition, the SCF intends to take on a co-ordination role for Scotland in the development and dissemination of guidance on good practice in coastal management.

References

Council of the European Communities. 1992. Council Directive 92/43/EEC of 21 May 1992: on the conservation of natural habitats and of wild fauna and flora. *Official Journal of the European Communities*, L206/7.

Scottish Office. 1996. *Scotland's Coasts: a Discussion Paper*. HMSO, Edinburgh.

7 THE PROGRESS, EXPERIENCE AND POTENTIAL OF INTEGRATED COASTAL MANAGEMENT PROJECTS FOR FIRTHS

S. M. Atkins

Summary

1. This chapter will:
- review the current state of progress of four key firth ICM partnership projects in Scotland (Moray, Cromarty, Forth and Solway Firths)

- draw out common themes relating to initiating and maintaining partnerships, including some national implications

- explore the benefits now being delivered, and suggest other work to which firth projects could contribute

- identify issues to be resolved if these initiatives are to continue.

2. The Forth Estuary Forum, Solway Firth Partnership and Moray Firth Partnership are all aiming to develop integrated management for their areas as targeted in the UK Biodiversity Action Plan. The current position of other projects varies from the Firth of Tay, where an inaugural meeting to start the initiative took place in December 1997, to the Cromarty Firth Liaison Group which has published a management strategy and action plan and is facing the challenge of implementing that plan.

3. The role of firth partnerships as advisory, influencing bodies, and the strengths and weaknesses of voluntary partnerships, which have become well defined, are discussed. The benefits from firth projects which are now being realised include new collaborative groupings of experience and expertise to address issues, cost savings and efficiency gains from partnerships that are working and new levels of community involvement and consultation in the management planning process.

4. Firth projects are now achieving a broader cross-sectoral base of resourcing and thus have a strong level of partnership commitment. They could become more effective and secure by contributing to a wide range of other suggested tasks which partner bodies want to deliver, including Natura 2000, Biodiversity Action Plan and Local Agenda 21. Firth partnerships are starting to plan the implementation of developing management strategies, and the importance of maintaining the partnerships into this phase of work is discussed. Some national implications of firth projects are discussed, including a proposal to extend the approach to the rest of the Scottish coastline.

7.1 Focus on Firths: background and methods

This Scotland-wide initiative was launched in 1993 by SNH with the twin objectives of developing sustainable integrated coastal management (ICM) strategies for firths and raising appreciation and understanding of the vital importance of firth environments and their flora and fauna (Atkins, 1994) (Plates 24–26). Priority sites were the Moray (Plate 27), Forth (Plate 25) and Solway Firths (Plate 24) identified by the range and concentration of environmental, cultural and economic pressures. These sites were named as Biodiversity Action Plan (BAP) targets for ICM (Anon., 1994). The approach, methods and early stages of firths ICM projects have been reported and discussed by Atkins (1996).

By October 1997 plans and work programmes were in place to complete management strategies for the three priority sites. In addition, the Focus on Firths approach is being adopted by management partnerships for the Cromarty Firth, Firth of Clyde and the Firth of Tay.

7.2 Current progress and plans, site by site

7.2.1 *The Moray Firth Partnership*

The Moray Firth Partnership (MFP) was launched only in summer 1996 but with four years prior background of awareness raising, community involvement and seminars, such as the 'Future Firth' events held by Scottish Wildlife Trust, it has made excellent progress.

The 13 topic groups had reported by December 1997. These reports are being used to draft an 'Issues and Opportunities' document and Strategic Management Guidelines. Stages in the process included a series of issue-resolving workshops, a Moray Firth Partnership conference in spring 1998 and drafting of guidelines in the summer. After wide consultation the aim is to publish final agreed strategic management guidelines and an action programme by the end of 1998 (Harding-Hill, 1997).

Two issues needed a good deal of attention in the early stages:

• agreeing common ground as a basis for a partnership

• defining the role and remit of this non-statutory partnership.

The first was addressed by drafting very general initial aims for the partnership:

• to debate management issues and develop management guidelines

• to involve a broad and balanced membership of users and communities

• to develop and sustain effective management of the partnership.

The second issue involved detailed consideration of what the management planning process could do, and just as importantly, what it could not do. A typical management plan with prescriptive detail was not felt to be appropriate or possible for such a geographically large and complex area as the Moray Firth. Therefore, the Moray Firth Partnership has agreed to produce strategic management guidelines which will provide a management framework and mechanism for the resolution of issues. These guidelines will:

- define long- and short-term management needs
- promote understanding of existing management systems and recommend new management measures where appropriate
- provide a framework for members to work together to co-ordinate initiatives, exploit opportunities and resolve conflicts
- establish action priorities to implement the guidelines.

Conversely the guidelines will not:

- solve all management problems at once
- be statutory (but statutory bodies will be encouraged to implement them)
- be locally or site-specific to areas within the firth
- be rigid and inflexible, but adaptable to new issues and circumstances in the area.

7.2.2 The Cromarty Firth Liaison Group

The Cromarty Firth Liaison Group (CFLG) is the longest-running firth partnership. It was originally set up as an industry, local authority, environment discussion forum, pre-dating the Focus on Firths programme. Following the experience of firths projects, the CFLG expanded their membership and remit, adopting full ICM objectives, including the aim of producing a management strategy and action plan.

Following an information audit and issues report in 1996, the CFLG became the first firth project to complete and publish a consultation draft management strategy (Cromarty Firth Liaison Group, 1997) with an action programme for implementation. The aim of the strategy is: *to promote the maintenance and enhancement of the natural, economic and cultural resources of the Cromarty Firth.*

There are four strategic objectives, drafted in very general terms:

- to safeguard and enhance the natural, cultural and economic resources
- to promote sustainable use of all these resources
- to improve understanding of the firth
- to involve all interests in the integrated management process.

Under these four objectives the strategy becomes much more specific, with 30 policies under nine topic headings and over 90 specific actions or projects to be carried out. The strategy also contains a three year agreed action plan and monitoring programme, all of which have been agreed following wide consultation.

The advanced stage that the CFLG has reached highlights an issue which will be faced by other firths soon: that of implementation of the management strategy. European funding for the employment of an implementation officer was obtained and will provide the co-ordination required for effective implementation of the strategy.

7.2.3 *The Forth Estuary Forum*

The Forth Estuary Forum (FEF) is discussed in detail elsewhere in this volume (Jennison and Kay, Chapter 8); however, three general points are relevant to this paper:

(i) *The effectiveness of 'pump priming'* The SNH funding from 1993 to the present has resulted in significant further contributions from the public and private sector, including Edinburgh City Council, where the project is now based, Scottish Environment Protection Agency, Forth Ports and Crown Estate Commissioners. It has also provided the collateral for successful applications to the European LIFE fund and to Objective 2 for the Forth Economic Audit.

(ii) *The increased scale of the project* The EU 'LIFE' funding of FEF has provided the opportunity to monitor the progress of a project with very significantly increased resources. There are now three staff and budgets for the economic audit, information systems, education and communication projects. Effectively, FEF is able to start implementation of agreed action programmes before the overall strategy is completed.

(iii) *The importance of networking* FEF has laid emphasis on building networks and linkages in its early years. It has successfully created a very high level of commitment to the work programme from a wide range of organisations and individuals. For example, there is a marketing specialist leading the education and awareness work, an industrialist leading the economic audit (supported by 'in kind' donations of staff time from another agency) and Information Systems (IS) expertise providing advice on Geographic Information Systems (GIS) and the web site. 'Hands on' involvement of other partners, assisting with the work programme with financial and 'in kind' contributions, has enabled the project to expand far beyond the capacity of the project staff alone. This support is a measure of the success of the initiative and the high importance that is attached to it by forum members. It is widely recognised as contributing to not just nature conservation objectives but also (for example) to the economic development objectives and environmental quality objectives of key partners.

7.2.4 *The Solway Firth Partnership*

The Solway Firth Partnership (SFP) has concentrated on testing a range of approaches to community participation and consultation during the management planning process. Along with ten topic groups which consulted widely before reporting in 1996, the partnership held participatory seminars in 1994, early in the life of the project, regional issues workshops in 1996, and a major strategy seminar in 1997. The partnership has also published leaflets, a touring exhibition, a regular newsletter and co-ordinated environmental education events and training workshops.

Plans leading up to the publication of the Solway Firth Strategy (Cameron, 1997) follow a similar pattern, including specialist working groups considering aspects of the proposed strategy, followed by community level participatory workshops covering the whole firth. There will be a full public consultation on the draft strategy and action programme before it is published.

Like the Moray Firth proposed 'strategic guidelines', the Solway Firth Partnership propose an overview management strategy rather than a prescriptive management plan. The action programme to be published with the strategy will have a more targeted local focus based on the proposals from six community participatory workshops to be held in the larger towns around the Solway. The approach of developing more local action programmes seems appropriate for a large firth and may be an appropriate model for other projects to adopt. The Solway Firth Strategy will:

- discuss strategic options for sustainable management

- provide a framework to promote sustainability in decision-making

- discuss issues within the remit of partnership members

- discuss plans, policies and programmes of partners and show how they inter-relate

- provide agreed guidance for managers, planners and users

- influence partnership members to implement the strategy

- involve local users in the planning process

- acknowledge that existing authorities and responsibilities are not changed.

The Solway Firth Partnership and its strategy make it clear that they will not directly manage any aspect of the Solway Firth resources, but will act by influence on bodies with management responsibility (Cameron, 1997).

7.3 Experience from Focus on Firths

7.3.1 *The meaning of 'integrated' and the basis for partnership*

Focus on Firths interprets ICM to mean the use of a voluntary cross-sectoral partnership (forum) to develop coastal management which has the support of all stakeholders. In order to obtain the consensus required from the earliest stages of a project, partnerships must be based on principles formulated at the lowest common denominator to which all parties can agree. There is then a process set in motion of deriving a management strategy from these first principles using two mechanisms to maintain the consensus.

Firstly, existing data and information from all sectors are collated and analysed, for example by topic groups. From this analysis, actual and potential conflicts of interest (issues which require management solutions) are identified. As far as possible, the issues should be identified without *a priori* views and conclusions which could prejudge the outcome of the analysis. It is essential that partners come to the table willing to put up their own remit or interests for discussion; if positions are not negotiable the partnership will not function. Genuine integration depends on the willingness of all parties to compromise in the light of agreed data and information, together with the views of other interests.

This requirement to develop management from first principles is the reason why it is difficult for a firth partnership to take a view on controversial issues before the management planning process is completed. For example, early agreement within the Forth Estuary Forum about future port developments in the Forth would be difficult, as would agreement on dolphin management to the Moray Firth Partnership. No single partner or interest group in the forum should be seen to prejudge the management solution to a particular issue. However, by the time the management strategy is published, the approach to solving difficult issues such as these should be clear.

The second key mechanism in the development of the management strategy from first principles, is liaison. During the first meetings of a forum there is a steady process of increasing awareness between delegates of the role and remit of each organisation. Networking relationships between interest groups are further developed in the work of topic groups which are also cross-sectoral in their representation.

The increase in understanding which results from the dynamics of firth partnerships is the basis for mutual respect, trust and consensus building which facilitates the compromises required for agreement in the management planning process. Progress in the early stages may be slow and the time required to generate an effective partnership should not be underestimated. Comments from partners have confirmed that networking and liaison are highly effective and often the most important factors which draw members into the partnerships.

7.3.2 Role and remit of firth partnerships

The non-statutory nature of firth projects has been raised as their weakness, because of the lack of actual authority to implement policies and recommendations. They have also been dismissed as environmental lobby groups. However, the voluntary approach to ICM gives a strength resulting from the comprehensive representation of all interests on the partnerships. The cross-sectoral structure of the partnerships gives their views and recommendations a strong credibility, and influences the policies and programmes of the statutory bodies, which effect change in the firth. These statutory bodies are in any case represented on partnerships and fully involved in the process of management strategy development. Cross-sectoral representation also prevents firth partnerships becoming sidetracked towards a narrow agenda or single issue such as the environment. They can only publish management recommendations which have broad agreement of all members. They will not be respected and will not retain wide representation if this consensus cannot be obtained or if the partnership attempts to lobby on issues which do not have broad agreement. The role of firth partnerships is that of advisory and influencing organisations promoting all aspects of sustainable management. They are not new administrative bodies looking to take over management of the coastal zone.

7.4 Benefits of firths projects

7.4.1 Networking and liaison

Cross-sectoral partnerships are able to develop innovative solutions to management problems by bringing together new groups of experts who have not worked together in the past. The topic groups are examples of such groups and their reports contain wide ranging recommendations which reflect the diversity of the contributions. The economic audit of the Forth is one example of a joint project which has widespread support because it will answer questions posed by many partners on the forum.

Partnerships also generate increased ownership of the management proposals by members. Proposals are not imposed top down, they are the priorities as identified by the people who live and work around the firths. The draft strategy for the Cromarty Firth has not generated serious controversy because many interests have contributed to its production.

7.4.2 Efficiency and cost effectiveness

Firth partnerships offer the potential for all members to deliver agreed objectives more cheaply and efficiently by acting in partnership. For example, they will assist with the delivery of management of EC Habitats Directive sites, BAP and Local Agenda 21 objectives and could be used for many other purposes as indicated in section 7.5 below. Any projects that require the integration of the remits of a group of partners or which contribute to the objectives of a number of partners could potentially be done more efficiently and effectively through a partnership than through acting alone.

7.4.3 Consultation and community involvement

The projects (the Solway in particular) are demonstrating new approaches to involve communities in decision-making as they try to bring organisational and community views together. They are also achieving higher levels of consultation among all interests as projects strive to achieve genuine integration.

7.4.4 Education and awareness

Materials published and events held include: newsletters, leaflets, posters, slide pack, site directory, exhibitions, contact directories, internet site, information reviews, topic reports, issues reports, participatory seminars and workshops.

7.5 What else could firths projects deliver?

In order to be secure and effective, firth projects must deliver products and services that satisfy the objectives of a wide range of partners. This section lists some ideas of other work which could be undertaken by or supported by firth partnerships.

- Contributions to Agenda 21 and Biodiversity Action Plan objectives, including supply of information for habitat and species action plans, co-ordinating local biodiversity action plans for coastal areas, or working with local record centres to manage data as part of the National Biodiversity Network initiative.

- Access to funding opportunities and delivery mechanisms. Many current mechanisms in the UK, and more so in Europe, are linked to partnership working, community involvement and rural development, particularly in relation to Agenda 21 and BAP objectives.

- Management of European designated sites such as Natura 2000. The Solway and Moray Firth Partnerships are contributing to emerging Special Area of Conservation management and all projects could similarly support Special Protection Areas if required.

- Education, interpretation and guidance projects and production of appropriate materials. All partners can make use of the newsletters and other communication networks for publicity and to raise awareness of their role in the firth.

- An internet-based information management service, including directory of contacts (Forth and Solway already published), directory of data and information holdings and map-based information derived from partners' GIS. This is a logical extension from the audits, directories and GIS work already published.

- Promotion of the region for tourism and sustainable development. Firth partnerships could work with tourist boards and enterprise companies. The backing of such a broad-based partnership would give strong support and credence to these sectors.

- A neutral forum for discussion and debate of controversial issues such as development proposals. This could be a key service that partnerships provide to enable a matter to be explored between partners before it reaches the stage of legal challenge.

- Shoreline management plans and managed retreat opportunities. This developing area of work in Scotland requires the integration of the functions of a number of different organisations. Firth projects could co-ordinate these plans and in many cases much background work has been done through coastal defence topic groups.

7.6 Some conclusions from the progress made by Focus on Firths

7.6.1 *Starting point and remit of a firth partnership*

The firths' approach, which involves the development of an acceptable management framework from a basis of agreed data and close liaison, is proving to be effective in generating cross-sectoral commitment to the results. The most successful projects are those which have committed resources to:

• defining a common base of agreement to start from

• defining a role and remit for the partnership

• establishing a genuine partnership based on mutual understanding and respect.

7.6.2 *National implications of firth projects*

This section discusses three issues that could usefully be considered by a national coastal body such as the recently formed Scottish Coastal Forum.

• The large proportion of Scotland's coastline covered by ICM partnerships is shown in Figure 7.1. A planned Tay project is expected to include much of the rest of the east coast of Scotland, and three further projects for Shetland, Orkney and the north of Scotland and the west coast would provide partnerships for almost the entire Scottish coastline. This level of coverage is an implied objective in the terms of reference of the Scottish Coastal Forum (Scottish Coastal Forum, 1997).

• Common local proposals may lead to general principles for the Scottish coast. Parallel thinking between firth partnerships in policy and action proposals suggest that there may be benefit in looking at the extent to which these proposals can or should be generalised around the coast of Scotland. Since they have been identified and agreed by a broad base of partners at a local level, it is likely that there would be a similar level of support for incorporation of them into national policies. There may be a role here for the Scottish Coastal Forum to review policy and action proposals to identify general principles.

• A common approach to community consultation and involvement. Community involvement is resource-intensive and only a few demonstration exercises have been possible in firth projects so far. Where local people have been consulted, the participation exercises have been very well received. They do, however, create the expectation that the outputs will influence management and that future consultation will take place. Community involvement has not been co-ordinated between firth projects in any way and has been resourced from within existing firth project budgets and staff time. A national review would be valuable to indicate the scale of community consultation which is required in the development of integrated management, the best approaches to be adopted to undertake the consultation and how the consultation should be resourced. A national review could

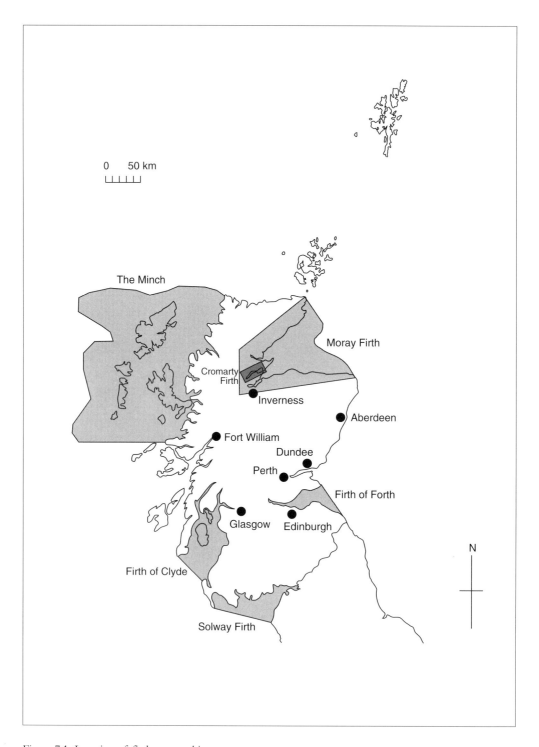

Figure 7.1 Location of firth partnerships.

also examine how firth management consultation could be incorporated into consultations on other planning processes to gain efficiency benefits.

7.6.3 Raised expectations regarding the effectiveness of ICM and the need to continue partnerships into implementation

At both the organisational level and the local community involvement level many partners have been persuaded to try ICM. A large amount of goodwill would be lost if the projects fail to deliver because they are not resourced into an implementation phase. Such a scenario would severely set back the cause of coastal management. Other experience suggests that it will not be sufficient to expect that the recommendations and action programme of management strategies will be carried out by responsible bodies, without continued partnership co-ordination.

UK and overseas experience of estuary management implementation is not good. A global track record is emerging of generating a plan but losing the commitment of participating bodies to deliver the action programme. Posford Duvivier Environment (1997), reviewing overseas experience, concluded that estuary management programmes in Spain and the USA have recognised the need to adopt more formal mechanisms to encourage organisations to honour their commitment to management actions. In America they seem to be going down the route of legislation and formal agreements to provide funding, while in Spain they are trying economic incentives.

In England, many of the estuary projects have reached the stage of publishing management plans but there appears to be much reduced resources for implementation. Loss of the project officer, dissolution of the partnership and, at best, long delays are occurring following publication of the plan before any action takes place.

If this is to be avoided for firth projects, an implementation plan must be part of the management strategy. Posford Duvivier Environment (1997) demonstrates that implementation does not happen if the partnership fails to continue functioning. Partnerships must recognise the need for the project officer and back up resources to service the partnership and co-ordinate implementation projects, many of which will be funded by groups of partner organisations.

References

Anon. 1994. *Biodiversity Action Plan*. HMSO, London.

Atkins, S.M. 1994. Focus on Firths Project Plan. SNH Unpublished report, 2 Anderson Place, Edinburgh EH6 5NP.

Atkins, S.M. 1996. Experience from firth partnerships in Scotland: the process and benefits of management strategy development. *In* Taussik, J. and Mitchell, J. (eds) *Partnership in Coastal Zone Management*, Samara Publishing, Cardigan, Wales.

Cameron, R. 1997. Unpublished report to the Solway Firth Partnership, September 1997. c/o Scottish Natural Heritage, Carmont House, The Crichton, Bankend Road, Dumfries DG1 4ZF.

Cromarty Firth Liaison Group. 1997. *The Cromarty Firth Management Strategy and Action Plan Public Consultation Draft*. Cromarty Firth Liaison Group, c/o Cromarty Firth Port Authority, Port Office, Invergordon IV18 0HP.

Harding-Hill, R. 1997. *Developing Management Guidelines for the Moray Firth*. Moray Firth Partnership Information Bulletin, September 1997. c/o Scottish Natural Heritage, 27 Ardconnel Terrace, Inverness IV2 3AE.

Posford Duvivier Environment. 1997. Estuary management – a review of overseas experience. Report to: English Nature, Northminster House, Peterborough PE1 1UA.

Scottish Coastal Forum. 1997. Report of the second meeting in: Wavelength Issue 1. *Newsletter of the National Coastal Fora in the UK*. Department of the Environment, Transport and Regions, Tollgate House, Houlton Street, Bristol BS2 9DJ.

8 ESTUARINE MANAGEMENT BY PARTNERSHIP: ITS POTENTIAL AND IMPLICATIONS

M. Jennison and D. Kay

Summary

1. The Forth Estuary Forum (FEF) is reaching a crucial point in its development. In November 1997 its ten topic groups completed the lengthy and detailed issue review and analysis stage in the process of producing its integrated management strategy for the estuary and Firth of Forth. This now opens the way for the next and most important stage, that of integration and the development of key areas of work, which the strategy, published as a draft for consultation, will need to address.

2. In parallel with, and complementary to its strategic work, the FEF is running a two-year EU LIFE Environment funded project, which aims to demonstrate the ability of a voluntary partnership (which FEF is) in achieving integrated coastal zone management in an urban estuarine environment. In addition, the LIFE project enters FEF as one of 35 European projects in a three-year European Commission led Integrated Coastal Zone Management (ICZM) demonstration programme.

3. FEF has also taken its first step towards greater self-reliance, having recently been incorporated as a limited liability company under the Companies Act, and is currently initiating a recruitment programme intended to build upon and strengthen its current membership base.

4. This chapter provides an update on FEF progress in all these areas and considers the work lying ahead up to and beyond the target strategy completion date of May 1999. The chapter considers potential opportunities on offer from such a voluntary non-statutory partnership but adds a note of caution by highlighting possible implications of realising this potential. The chapter concludes with some lessons learnt from the current work of FEF and other similar partnerships worldwide, presenting some suggestions for assisting the work of such partnerships now and in the future.

8.1 Forth Estuary Forum

8.1.1 Background and progress

The Forth Estuary Forum (FEF) is a voluntary non-statutory partnership comprising approximately 250 different organisations, individuals, agencies and authorities. It was launched in November 1993, with the aim of promoting the wise and sustainable use of the tidal waters of the Forth. FEF was established as part of the SNH Focus on Firths initiative which has the twin objectives of developing sustainable Integrated Coastal Management (ICM) strategies for the Forth, Moray and Solway Firths, and raising appreciation and understanding of the vital importance of firth environments (Atkins, 1994).

FEF produced a draft integrated management strategy for the Forth in late 1998, thereby meeting the target set by the UK's Biodiversity Action Plan (Anon., 1994). The production of the strategy is based upon a participatory, consensus-building approach, with the intention of generating a wide sense of ownership. FEF is a non-statutory partnership that can only deliver recommendations by influence and persuasion, but wide ownership will encourage co-operation when the implementation phase is reached.

Up to 1996, the work programme focused on setting up the FEF with topic groups and sub-groups, completing topic papers and establishing communication across a wide network through newsletters and other publications (Forth Estuary Forum, 1995). The approach, methods, structures and progress of the forum towards this target has been well documented and reported in FEF Progress Reports Numbers 1–8.

An application to the European Union 1996 LIFE Environment Programme to fund a project demonstrating FEF's ability to achieve ICM was successful. Thus, a new two-year work programme began in March 1997 which adopted the original strategy development work into a much larger and comprehensive package (Forth Estuary Forum, 1997a) described in section 8.2.

8.1.2 Incorporation

At the 1996 annual general meeting (AGM), FEF approved working towards a change in legal status to that of an incorporated company limited by guarantee. Early in 1997, a set of Articles of Association and Memorandum of Understanding for Forth Estuary Forum Limited were approved, and in May 1997 FEF was incorporated as a Companies Act company (Forth Estuary Forum, 1997b). Charitable status for the company is currently being pursued with the Inland Revenue.

Although there is no requirement by law for a voluntary group to have such a legal structure, the advantages are considerable: it states clearly the aims of the group and creates a body which outside agencies can recognise and easily relate to (simplifying funding applications, etc.), and the establishment of a limited company provides protection from liability.

In the long-term FEF aims to become more self-sufficient. To that end an annual membership subscription is proposed to help cover administrative costs and the dissemination of progress reports. The Articles of Association allow for three levels of membership: corporate, ordinary and affiliate. The membership scheme developed reflects these different types, with associated annual membership subscriptions. Membership is open to everyone, and the range of options has been created to meet different needs and interests. A membership leaflet outlining the benefits offered for each membership type has been produced, and the membership scheme was agreed at the 1997 AGM.

The changeover to subscription membership will be a test of the commitment of partners to continued involvement, and it will draw in new members from an ever-increasing audience. A successful transition will help FEF to operate more efficiently and effectively in the future.

8.2 EU LIFE environment funded project – the Forth Estuary Forum: a demonstration of effective integrated coastal zone management

The object of this project is to prepare an integrated management strategy for the estuary and Firth of Forth, which will demonstrate the effectiveness of a non-statutory management partnership approach in achieving ICM of a large estuarine area. The Forth contains a wide range of environmental pressures and natural resources (Plates 28–31), and is typical of large European estuaries. The outcomes and experience gained during the project will have wide applicability throughout Europe. The project includes five main tasks (Forth Estuary Forum, 1997b).

8.2.1 Task 1 – Project management

This task will ensure that the project is managed in a co-ordinated manner allowing all participants to participate fully and contribute their own experience and lessons learnt.

8.2.2 Task 2 – Integrated management strategy development

The development of the strategy is at a crucial stage. The comprehensive review work being undertaken by FEF's ten topic groups is complete, and the task of integrating the various issues and recommendations that each paper provides has begun. The main stages in this process are:

- integrating the work of the topic groups to develop cross-topic themes and goals

- developing the topic group recommendations into a series of guiding principles and actions

- developing a draft strategy for consultation

- running a comprehensive consultation programme with all key interests, organisations and communities.

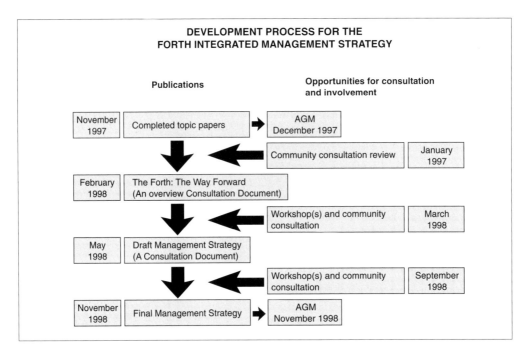

Figure 8.1 An illustrative overview of the intended development process for the Forth Estuary Forum's integrated management strategy.

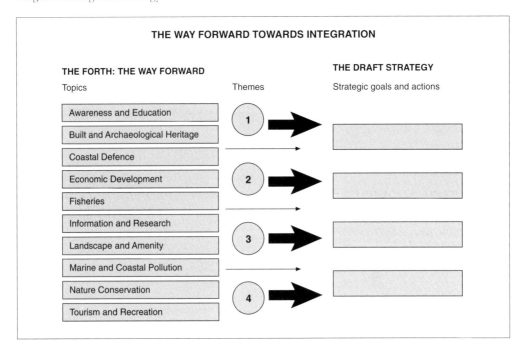

Figure 8.2 Representation of the thinking behind the process of integration, showing the link between the work of the topic groups and that of integrated themes, goals and actions.

The intended process for development of the strategy is illustrated in Figure 8.1, and the thinking behind the process of integration, showing links between topic group reports and integrated themes and goals, is illustrated in Figure 8.2. The first step will be the publication of an overview document in 1998 entitled *The Forth: The Way Forward*, summarising the topic group reports, developing integrated themes and proposing a possible way forward for development of the draft strategy. In parallel with the strategy development will be the development of a work and funding programme for longer-term implementation.

The difficulty and importance of effectively involving local communities in the process of producing the management strategy is under consideration by FEF. There are advantages in holding community consultation workshops at the initial stages, for example to tease out issues that are important to communities. However, this is resource-intensive and many community consultation exercises have and are already taking place throughout the area, e.g. Structure, Local Plan and Local Agenda 21 community meetings, conferences, and research studies.

Therefore, the forum proposes that the well-informed topic group reports are used with the results from current and past community consultation initiatives to confirm that issues of concern locally are being addressed. Later consultation will be undertaken widely, to inform all relevant parties about FEF and provide opportunities to contribute.

8.2.3 Task 3 – Implementation

FEF will not be successful unless it can provide visible demonstration of its intent and capacity to affect real change or action towards wise and sustainable use of the Forth. In addition to setting policy objectives and guiding principles, it needs to demonstrate Forth-wide and site-specific successes through the development of projects and innovative products, that will build momentum and support for its aims and its strategy. This task involves taking priority actions identified by the topic groups, developing them into tangible products and partnership projects, and enabling their implementation. Four 'Demonstration Flagship Projects' are currently proposed:

Demonstration Project 1 – Forth Estuary Modelling Seminar (FEMS)

Although the Forth has been studied by scientists for many years, these studies cannot easily be combined. It is therefore difficult to predict how changes in one area might affect other parts of the system. In an effort to remedy this situation, the FEF Nature Conservation Topic Group has drawn up proposals to develop an interactive model of the Forth ecosystem and its sustainable management.

The model was created during a week-long workshop in February 1998, at which experts from various ecological and related disciplines will work, together with computer modelling specialists, to create the database. Where such models have been created elsewhere in the world, they have proved a useful way of transferring scientific knowledge from academic researchers to coastal managers.

Demonstration Project 2 – At Home with the Forth

This project will encompass a range of products and activities intended to increase public awareness of the Forth. One component exploits an opportunity to develop a number of cross-topic messages through a project focused on marine litter. The project could be generated by FEF in consultation with the statutory, voluntary and community sector members. It would demonstrate the added value of generating a co-operative, participatory approach to minimising litter, and the essential role of a partnership in tackling litter pollution problems in an environment such as the Forth.

Demonstration Project 3 – Forth Information System (FIS)

This project involves the development of a shared information network to support good decision-making on the Forth by putting effective information at the fingertips of its planners and managers. Using the Internet, geographical information systems (GIS) and other more conventional technologies, the system will be established on a demonstration basis. It is intended that specific applications will be run by the system, for example support for oil spill contingency plans, to demonstrate its use at a Forth-wide scale.

Demonstration Project 4 – The Future Forth Conference

This project proposes a conference in spring 1999 at the end of the LIFE project, to look at its success and consider the future development and work programme for FEF. It will also present an up-to-date picture of our current understanding and knowledge of the Forth and will identify any gaps for future research.

These demonstration flagship projects are all intended to be Forth-wide and run on a partnership basis with cross-sectoral support and funding.

8.2.4 Task 4 – Assessment

Worldwide there is a lack of evaluation of the outcomes of ICZM programmes and only a small proportion of the knowledge that can be gained from the 31 year history and rich experience of ICZM is being learned.

An inherent characteristic of project evaluation is the strong tendency to assess the inputs such as plans, strategies, and the numbers of public participation exercises because these are relatively easy to measure. However, the inputs do not always result in useful project outcomes which may be much more difficult to assess. To what extent have plans, strategies, meetings, publications and all such input served to deliver ICZM outcomes, such as projects, goals and objectives achieved? Does ICZM make a difference (Sorensen, 1997)? FEF thinks it does, but we need to prove it.

We need to know what works, and what doesn't work, and why, but first we need to agree what questions to ask. How will we know, in the future, whether coastal management has succeeded or failed if we don't start evaluating now, or establish some kind of benchmark (Kay and Lester, 1997)? This task aims to assess the success of FEF in achieving ICZM by developing an appraisal system containing a series of indicators to monitor the quality, performance, products, input and outcomes of FEF up to and beyond the completion of the strategy.

8.2.5 Task 5 – Dissemination

The process undertaken, the results obtained and the lessons learnt from the project will be disseminated to a wide audience, from a local to a European level, as an integral part of the process. This task will include the production of an annual newsletter and bi-annual progress reports, and the running of the AGM and conference.

8.3 Better management of coastal resources: a European programme for ICZM

FEF's LIFE Project has won recognition in a European-wide demonstration programme of ICZM. Effective management and planning of the coastal zones requires concerted action at all levels. The European Parliament have acknowledged that the EU must assume some responsibility, and have developed a demonstration programme with three key aims:

- to identify the conditions that must be met to achieve sustainable management in coastal zones

- to stimulate debate by the main parties involved in the development of the coastal zone

- to lead to European Commission proposals for a coherent programme of actions and measures at community level.

The programme is based on a series of 35 demonstration projects located in a variety of natural, socio-economic and cultural settings around the EU. Each project shows an innovative approach to addressing complex issues of coastal management. FEF has been chosen to demonstrate the effectiveness of a voluntary partnership approach on a large urbanised estuarine area.

The experiences of these demonstration projects will test hypotheses about the factors necessary for sustainable coastal management. They focus particularly on multi-sectoral co-ordination and wide participation in decision-making. The projects will help to identify the practical steps and solutions that can contribute to preventing continued degradation, unsustainable pressures and increasing landuse conflicts in European coastal zones (European Commission, 1996).

LIFE funding has presented FEF with a good opportunity to demonstrate effective ICZM through a partnership mechanism. The project has the potential to demonstrate methods that could be replicated elsewhere, and influence the future direction of coastal policy on a UK and European scale.

8.4 The potential, opportunities and implications facing a voluntary non-statutory partnership

While partnerships have an inherent potential to be far more successful than a conventional sectoral approach to coastal management the considerable demands that it brings must not be underestimated or ignored. The forum approach is relatively new in the UK and has not yet matured to the extent that its success, in respect of measurable outcomes, can be properly evaluated. Unfortunately there is no blueprint for us to follow, and we are well aware of the potential to make mistakes.

8.4.1 The issue of funding

Successful fora are resource-intensive. Operational and administrative needs are significant and implementation costs require further funding. Furthermore, fora do not deliver overnight, and their future funding and membership must be considered in the medium to long term. Experience has shown that most fora have similar needs and problems at some time or another. Funding is required for both essential administration and for implementation. How funding is achieved can have far-reaching implications upon the potential for success of a project. A forum must maintain a positive image and facilitate the equal participation of all partners. At present, the burden of core-funding tends to be unevenly spread between partners (Tarmey, 1997) causing problems in the smooth running and decision-making of the group.

A well-balanced forum comprises members of the statutory, economic, voluntary and community sectors. If core funding is provided by a single organisation, they are likely to be looked upon as having more influence than others in decision-making. For example, if funding was provided by a conservation body or was obtained through a mechanism that required Environmental Trust status, then the industrial sector may shy away from membership through fear of an environmental bias to the management strategy.

Conversely, if the major source of funding was from a body with a strong development-orientated image, then the partnership could be perceived by other potential members as being too pro-development. Securing funding is essential to a partnership's development and its level of success, but the appropriateness of the source of funding must be considered.

8.4.2 Does size matter?

The partnership approach provides the potential to develop a broadly based forum comprising essential users concerned about the future care of an area. This suggests that all interests can be brought together on a voluntary basis and a single planning document be prepared that addresses decision-making and consensus building at the local level. But is this realistic?

The scale of a partnership is important, both in terms of the spatial area encompassed and the number of partners and project staff employed. The speed at which a forum develops is a concern: if it is allowed to grow too big too rapidly, it may become a victim of its own success, where staff can become overwhelmed by administration.

A forum will only function effectively if members actively participate, take responsibility and make use of project staff strategically. Sectoral attitudes have to give way to co-operation between all players, with a genuine commitment to compromise on difficult issues.

Project staff need to be resourceful, technologically aware and able to devise the most appropriate mechanisms for co-ordination, communication, information exchange and dissemination. Effective communication is important to maintain impetus and involvement. Communication at board level is generally good and well-focused; problems tend to arise in communication with the wider partnership. Personal contact is undoubtedly best, but is not always possible due to time constraints. E-mail and the World Wide Web make information cheap and rapid to exchange, but are not yet universally accessible, and hence cannot be used alone.

These are some experiences to indicate the type of issues that may be faced and the questions that need to be answered when striving to maximise a forum's potential. They introduce some of the conditions needed for a voluntary partnership to succeed, working with finite resources, where the interests of members need to be maintained and the needs of a diverse range of organisations continuously managed.

8.5 Lessons we can learn from the work of the Forth Estuary Forum and other estuary management partnerships

(i)   The first and most important lesson is that *estuary partnerships do work*. There are many examples worldwide to demonstrate that their approach can be successful in progressing sustainable ICZM aims and objectives.

(ii) *They must be given enough time to work.* Because of the way the partnerships operate, involving many different bodies in decision-making, the work may take longer. However, they are successful because they have greater commitment to the end result. A partnership-led ICZM initiative is not a short-term solution, it should be seen as a long-term investment in the management of an estuary, with many benefits which can only be achieved in the medium to long term.

Since the ultimate goal of ICZM is sustainability, it is essential to recognise the time that it takes to achieve this goal. Mature ICZM projects show that it takes a sustained effort spanning decades to achieve tangible expressions of this goal on significant scales (Olsen, 1997). This timescale is beyond the funding currently available to projects in Scotland and underscores the importance of identifying a sequence of intermediate outcomes which will maintain commitment in both political and financial terms.

From the outset, an ICZM project must deliver tangible products, that build credibility and attract support and commitment from partners.

However, actions in the short term usually only set the stage and begin to build the body of experience for making a sustained and effective thrust towards the end goal. Clearly differentiating between the ultimate goal and intermediate project objectives is critical for future success. The most successful and sustainable projects make good judgements of what they can reasonably hope to achieve in any particular period of time with the resources available.

(iii) *The production of a partnership-led estuary management strategy is proving a successful way of bringing people together.* The process of preparing an estuary management strategy is as important as the final strategy itself. Many of the actions within estuary management strategies can only be achieved by the organisations and individuals involved altering the way they operate. This may not be costly in financial terms but requires a high level of continuing commitment.

(iv) *The production of a paper-based strategy is the 'easy' stage.* Implementation is fundamental if ICZM strategies are to be used to improve coastal management. There is experience of implementing ICZM around the world, in differing political contexts, which provide examples of turning paper-based strategies into action on the ground. This experience shows that the participatory approach to strategy development works but the hardest and most demanding period is required when these strategies reach the implementation stage.

(v) *Implementation needs to be considered at a very early stage in the process.* Implementation of estuary strategies has to overcome many uncertainties, not least of which is the problem of finding sufficient resources to ensure that the actions proposed can be carried out. This is an area which must be considered as early as possible, preferably being developed and considered in parallel with the strategy's own development.

(vi) *The importance of monitoring and evaluation needs to be recognised.* Wide and effective use of rigorous monitoring, evaluation, reporting and feedback is vital if we are to measure and document successes, failures, and lessons learnt. This is crucial to demonstrate the effective use of resources and gain future support.

(vii) *An estuarine management partnership needs to demonstrate its worth by undertaking cost-effectively a series of activities which provide added value to the current planning and management system.* To become really effective partnerships must become less orientated towards fund-raising, and move away from a 'hand to mouth' existence that is subject to annual funding cuts in non-priority budgets. They must secure long-term funding to allow a greater focus on the work they do best, namely education, local consensus building and action on the ground. They need to demonstrate their worth not only as targeted discussion groups but also by demonstrating their ability to reduce the operating costs of the organisations with which they are involved.

(viii) *We need to learn from others.* There are many lessons we can learn from three decades of ICZM around the world. It should be part of our work to obtain and share this information, to acquire new ideas and prevent repetition of old mistakes. Better links between academic ICZM development, and those involved at the practical implementation level are required, and an appropriate mechanism for the dissemination and feedback of this information to practitioners in Scotland needs to be developed.

The challenge now for everyone involved in estuary management in Scotland is to ensure that the strong partnerships which have been formed over the past four years are long-lasting and continue to receive the commitment they deserve, yielding results well into the future.

References

Anon. 1994. *Biodiversity Action* Plan. HMSO, London.

Atkins, S.M. 1994. *Focus on Firths Project Plan*. SNH Unpublished report. 2 Anderson Place, Edinburgh EH6 5NP.

European Commission. 1996. *Demonstration Programme on Integrated Management of Coastal Zones*. Information Document. European Commission Services, Brussels.

Forth Estuary Forum. 1995. *A Forward Plan to guide the Forth Estuary Forum in the development of a Forth Estuary Management Strategy*. Unpublished Report. FEF, 1, Cockburn Street, Edinburgh EH1 1BJ.

Forth Estuary Forum. 1997a. *The Forth Estuary Forum: A Demonstration of Effective Integrated Coastal Zone Management*. Unpublished Report. FEF, 1, Cockburn Street, Edinburgh EH1 1BJ.

Forth Estuary Forum. 1997b. *Memorandum and Articles of Association of Forth Estuary Forum*. FEF, 1, Cockburn Street, Edinburgh EH1 1BJ.

Kay, R. and Lester, C. 1997. *Possible Future Directions for Coastal Zone Management in Australia*. Coastal Zone '97, Boston, MA.

Olsen, S.B. 1997. *The Temporal Management Context of ICM Program Assessment*. Coastal Zone '97, Boston, MA.

Sorensen, J. 1997. *National and International Efforts at Integrated Coastal Management: Definitions, Achievements, and Lessons*. Coastal Zone '97, Boston, MA.

Tarmey, J. 1997. Green Partnerships – A Panacea for Environmental Conflict in the 1990s ? *Undergraduate Dissertation*. University of Dundee.

9 THE FAIR ISLE MARINE ENVIRONMENT AND TOURISM INITIATIVE

A. B. Bryant

Summary

1. The common perception of the sea as powerful, vast and frightening is beginning to change. Television provides immediate and persuasive images of the sea's vulnerability to the effects of oil spills. Fishing disputes demonstrate competition for scarce stocks, and beautifully filmed programmes of attractive animals such as dolphins have given the public a taste for marine life that has encouraged voluntary bodies and local communities to want to play their own part in its conservation.

2. Small island communities need no persuading of the need to protect the seas that so intimately affect their lives. However, not so easy for these communities or voluntary bodies is to find a practical way to make a contribution. They require just the same understanding of the resource, the measures that would protect it and the mechanisms that would secure those measures, but do not enjoy the financial resources or authority of government. The Fair Isle Marine Environment and Tourism Initiative (FIMETI) is an illustration of what a community and voluntary bodies, working together, can do in practice.

9.1 Introduction to Fair Isle

Fair Isle (Plate 32) is half-way between Sumburgh Head on Shetland and North Ronaldsay in Orkney. It is approximately 3 miles by 1 mile in size, has a thriving population of about 70 people, and fits Schumacher's dictum that 'small is beautiful'. It has a shop, makes electricity by aerogenerator, and has an economy founded on crofting (Plate 33), although professions (for example, teacher, meteorologist and nurse) and craft industry provide most of the income to individual households. Fair Isle knitwear is well known but boats, fiddles, stained glass, spinning wheels and straw-backed chairs are also made on the island to a high standard. All these activities are directly or indirectly dependent on tourism for most of their customers. However, travel to the isle is expensive and time-consuming, so the tourist incentive must be strong and the value of Fair Isle to supplier and customer alike must be as great as possible if visitors are to be attracted in sufficient numbers.

The incentive to visit Fair Isle is that the island is recognised as one of the premier ornithological sites in Britain, indeed Europe. Many of the birds, especially those that breed on the isle, are seabirds dependent on the sea for food, and many live at sea for much of the year. There are other marine interests too, such as archaeology, and history: for example, the distinctive Fair Isle yole (Plate 35), an open boat which owes its origin to the Vikings; and fishing line tubs demonstrate dependence on the sea. In short there is a close and direct link between healthy seas and island economics. The bird interest particularly has led to the application of nearly every available designation on the isle, yet there is no protection for its surrounding seas.

9.2 How can Fair Isle be protected without equal care being taken of its seas?

It was, not unnaturally, the islanders who first raised this issue, spurred on by illogically restrictive designations on Fair Isle to protect birds, when these same birds were at just as great a risk at sea, principally through lack of food.

The isle has many advantages for practical marine conservation. The Fair Isle Bird Observatory Trust was established in 1948, and has researched and recorded bird populations ever since. The National Trust for Scotland (NTS) accepted the isle in 1954 and declared it inalienable. Fair Isle has the accolades of a European Diploma, first granted in 1984, and the Crofting Township of the Year Award of 1996. Above all, it has a population which regards marine conservation as important and has in its midst three ecologists, a meteorologist, and talents in several other relevant fields.

Three basic threats to the health of the seas around the island have been identified: fishing, shipping, and oil and gas exploration. The danger from shipping, and oil and gas exploration are readily apparent. The *MV Braer*, which went aground on Fitful Head on Shetland only 28 miles away, spilling almost 85 000 tonnes of crude oil into the sea, is a potent reminder of what could happen on Fair Isle. Exploratory drilling for hydrocarbon reserves has occurred within 25 miles of Fair Isle.

9.3 The issue of fish stocks

Important though the above issues are, this paper concentrates on the problem of fish stocks. The lack of sand eels was the first specific problem identified in the late 1980s. Sand eels are important food for many seabirds and larger fish, so the noticeable breeding and fledging failures were graphic illustrations of a lack of these prey. But it was the 'crash' in commercial sand eel catches that led to the ban on fishing for the species, and pressure from the industry has led to its partial lifting since.

On Fair Isle, however, the issue came to a head from a different direction. Council of Europe Diplomas carry conditions which, if not met, can lead to withdrawal of the Diploma. In Fair Isle's case, at each renewal the condition concerning the health of the sea has been tightened, starting with the encouragement to tackle the sand eel question and now covering all aspects of marine management.

Bird breeding problems were not the only evidence of the need for protection. Islanders' experiences of past catches are fascinating (Plate 34). Alec Stout of Barkland told this story:

> When the summer came, the yoles were made ready. The boys would plead with their fathers until it was agreed they could go out fishing with the three men normally acting as crew. On a good day we could get two or three halibut of at least a hundredweight and a half. They were really exciting to catch. Once they were on the line, they had to be played for quite a long period before we could get them in the boat. Each time they neared the surface and saw the light, they seemed to gather new strength and would plunge back to the bottom of the sea. Eventually we were able to get the fish alongside the boat and flip it in. You had to be very careful for the fish were both strong and heavy and could easily capsize the yole. They were great days for us boys. Now there are no halibut, and the haddock are the size of herring.

In spite of this ornithological and fish stocks evidence, it became clear from consultation with the Scottish Office, Agriculture, Environment and Fisheries Department that, whilst research into fishing methods and dynamics for the industry was being undertaken, none of their research was directed at obtaining evidence of the effect of fishing on features of conservation importance. Fair Isle was challenged to prove that fishing affects anything but the industry itself.

Overfishing is universally blamed for any problem with fish stocks. Within and outside the industry there are many views on, for example, whether too many fish are taken, or if merely the wrong fish are caught, and whether fish stock problems arise from fishing or other factors. Information on species, age classes and biological interactions, natural changes or even straightforward numbers are difficult to assess when the main count is of fish that, by definition, are no longer there. They have already been caught.

9.4 Developing management

Clearly there will be no solution for Fair Isle without the wholehearted support of fishermen. If there is to be a management regime, fishermen must be persuaded that it is in their interests to support it. No voluntary body nor community has the authority to dictate what should be done.

Consultation with the Shetland Fishermen's Association showed them to be sympathetic, especially as Shetland has similar problems on a larger scale. Discussion revealed the main problems to be practical. What management arrangement would be effective? Who is to fish and who is to be constrained? If boat sizes and fishing methods are controlled, how are they defined? How are the results monitored?

For Fair Isle, it was concluded that a scheme was needed to gather the basic evidence, to demonstrate the management requirement, and enlist support to work out a tentative management plan.

9.5 The Fair Isle Marine Environment and Tourism Initiative (FIMETI)

FIMETI is a project led by the Fair Isle Committee (a committee of all households on the isle, the Fair Isle Bird Observatory Trust and the National Trust for Scotland). Its agreed mission statement is:

> To establish the long-term protection and sustainable management of the natural marine resources around Fair Isle to the mutual benefit of the community of Fair Isle, the users of the marine area and for the education and enjoyment of visitors.

Table 9.1 shows just how many organisations are involved in one way or another and the elements that make up the work itself: data collection, the provision of information, the management arrangements and generating recognition and respect of those outside the immediate circle involved in the scheme.

The data and information elements are being provided almost entirely by islanders with the help of a Rural Challenge Fund Grant. This financial backing is vital, and in many ways barely adequate for the size of the job. The Royal Society for the Protection of Birds (RSPB) have sponsored a report under the banner of FIMETI (Riddiford and Thompson, 1997), similar to one that has been produced for the Firth of Forth (RSPB, 1997) as part of a national campaign. The report suggests how a voluntary management plan for the seas around Fair Isle might work. A committee of all interests would be set up, including the fishing industry and Scottish Natural Heritage. That committee would aim to shape the ideas outlined in the report into a workable management regime and to do so in a way that ensured that all the interests could give it their wholehearted support and agreement on a voluntary basis. In outline, the report proposes a simple zoning technique. In each zone activities are defined and delineated, the objectives are set out, policies recommended and potential hazards are identified and evaluated, and measures to meet them suggested. A second report, addressing the non-ornithological marine issues, is planned and when taken together the two should ensure that the island, its life and its sea area is considered as a single, inextricably linked entity.

9.6 Discussion

Early days though it may be, the advantages and disadvantages of a 'private sector' initiative of this sort are emerging. The fishing industry (and other marine interests) are more comfortable and perhaps feel less threatened by this approach.

Fair Isle is not the only example of a voluntary partnership approach to marine conservation, and a study of other work is valuable. In Scotland the St Abbs and Eyemouth Voluntary Marine Reserve is an excellent example of what can be done on a voluntary basis, and the NTS and Scottish Wildlife Trust are both involved, along with 15 other organisations. It is dependent on agreement, as is the Fair Isle Initiative, in this case largely between fishermen and divers, who were previously in dispute. St Abbs' success demonstrates the great importance of having someone on site to keep all parties together and respectful of each other's interests, in

Table 9.1 Fair Isle Marine Environment and Tourism Initiative. The purpose of this initiative is to establish the long-term protection and suitable management of the natural marine resources around Fair Isle, to the mutual benefit of the community of Fair Isle, users of the marine area and for the education and enjoyment of visitors.

Who is involved?		Data	Information	Management	Recognition
		The requirements			
Partners	The Fair Isle community The National Trust for Scotland The Fair Isle Bird Observatory Trust	To demonstrate the need, monitor the results and support management	To provide information, interpret results, focus attention, heighten public perception and awareness, demonstrate value of initiative, provide a model for the future	There being no ownership of the sea, management by agreement is essential with those who use or control maritime resources	Universal recognition of the importance of the resource is vital to gain and keep support
Users Fishing	Fishing interests including the Shetland Fishermen's Association				
Oil	DTI				
Recreation	International maritime organisations Yachting interests, Cruise liner companies, divers	*Action needed* Historical and current data to be gathered	A newsletter Internet pages CD-ROM for general and educational use	Develop management proposals	Obtain an appropriate designation to add to SPA
Conservation interests Statutory	Scottish Natural Heritage				
NGO	RSPB Marine Conservation Society				
		Reports to give shape to ideas as they emerge		Obtain agreement	CE Diploma and other symbols of recognition on the Isle
Grant agencies	Highlands and Islands Partnership Programme (ERDF) Rural Challenge Fund Others	Liaison with other research bodies and other marine protected areas	Liaison, conferences, papers	Liaison with statutory, national and international bodies	
Indirectly Nationally	Shetland Enterprise Company Shetland Islands Council SOAEFD North Atlantic Fisheries College Crown Estate Commissioners	*Structure needed* Steering group/management committee A manager Contracts for specific work			
Other	Council of Europe EU KIMO Other maritime reserves	Financial contribution to be sought from (a) Grant agencies (b) Partner contribution (c) Contributions from other bodies involved (d) Sponsorship or other private sources			

this case a full-time ranger. The Wildlife and Countryside Act of 1981 provides for statutory marine nature reserves (MNR). Theoretically the provision for regulating bylaws looks sound and comprehensive; but with only three MNRs established in the UK in 16 years, it has a limited track record.

Lundy was the first MNR. The island is in the Bristol Channel, and slightly smaller than Fair Isle. It has no indigenous population and although it has only beach landings, it can have around 400 visitors at any one time. Lundy is owned by the National Trust and run by the Landmark Trust whose core purpose is the restoration of small unusual buildings for holiday lets. English Nature leads on the marine front and although this management structure is complex, it appears reasonably secure.

In spite of Lundy's name (Norse for Puffin Isle), its bird life is minimal compared to Fair Isle, but its marine animal and plant communities are exceptionally fine. It too is at risk from the adjacent shipping lane, but the main threat is physical damage: potting (creels), diving and anchoring are the main problems. The management and prescriptions are based on a fully zoned management plan, agreed by all, which designates what may or may not happen in each zone (Laffoley, 1995).

The lesson, however, is the same as St Abbs. Not even legislation can work without co-operation and agreement, especially of the fishermen. The Devon Fisheries Board, a statutory body with no direct Scottish equivalent, represents commercial fishing, ensuring collective agreement, but the Lundy experience suggests there are still mavericks and sports fishermen, whose co-operation is hard to obtain.

If public authorities cannot progress protected sites in marine areas without voluntary agreement, then they are in no better position than local communities or voluntary bodies to undertake marine protection measures. In other parts of the world, marine reserve legislation is more akin to our Site of Special Scientific Interest (SSSI) and National Nature Reserve land designations. Some go further, resembling ownership of the sea by the reserve authority.

The Cabrera Marine and Terrestrial National Park covers a 10 000 ha sea area within which there are 18 uninhabited islands lying off the south-eastern tip of Mallorca, Spain. As the whole area had been reserved for military purposes, mainly for exercises, since 1914, it has a marine resource which has been largely undisturbed for 75 years, which is especially unusual in the Mediterranean. The park was set up through a single national law, with one park authority covering both land and water, and encompassing everything within the park, for example, historic buildings, museum, woodland, marine ecology, tourism, yachting, diving, and even the relict of military activity. The park authority is a local and national government partnership, with full legal powers to control all activities as if it is an owner. Its management plan sets zones for various activities or prohibited areas which are fully backed up by law and operated through a strict licensing system.

In New Zealand they go further still, enacting 'no take' reserves that simply ban everything (Ballantine, 1991).

It is interesting to compare the strength and simplicity of these arrangements with the plethora of designations (for land only) on Fair Isle. As ownership is so much a key mechanism for land management, should the same principle apply at sea? Nations, throughout history, have claimed ownership of the sea. The United Nations and European Union have adopted rules to regulate it and parcel up its resources, but ownership in the sense we understand it on land, has been limited to crown interest in the sea bed. Private ownership appears never to have been considered. In modern jargon, authorities are to encourage local 'ownership' of ideas and places, because to own means to take stewardship, care and responsibility for them.

There is a view in fishing circles that the further a boat is from its home port, the less it cares about the conservation of fish stocks, and that if sea areas were 'owned' by specific ports, then the conservation of fish stocks within them becomes both desirable and practicable. On the one hand this philosophy could be said to be behind shellfish Several Orders, but on the other it is not a universally accepted view, not least within the Common Fisheries Policy. But why not try it on a small scale as an experiment in conservation to encourage new attitudes and mechanisms to emerge?

How exactly ownership of the sea could be arranged and what legal twists might be involved needs further consideration. Perhaps the National Trust for Scotland should lobby for government legislation to enable the exercise of its purposes for 'the benefit of the nation' at sea as well as on land. If that is presumptuous, then let the ownership be by a local community or other appropriate body.

If some form of ownership would encourage the practical protection of this important resource, then the obstacles are surely worth overcoming. One thing is certain. If there is no enthusiasm for new initiatives, then little protection will be achieved.

References

Ballantine, W.J. 1991. *Marine Reserves for New Zealand*. Bulletin No. 25. University of Auckland, Leigh Marine Laboratory, Warkworth, New Zealand.

Laffoley, D. 1995. Techniques for managing marine protected areas: zoning. *In* Gubbay, S. (ed.) *Marine Protected Areas – Principles and Techniques for Management*. Chapman and Hall, London, 103–118.

Riddiford, N.J. and Thompson, G. 1997. *Managing the Sea for Birds – Fair Isle and Adjacent Waters*.

RSPB. 1997. *Managing the Sea for Birds – the Outer Firth of Forth. An Illustrative Management Plan for the Outer Firth of Forth and Adjacent Offshore Waters*. RSPB, Sandy, Bedfordshire.

10 MANAGEMENT OF SCOTLAND'S MARINE AND COASTAL SPECIAL AREAS OF CONSERVATION

J. M. Baxter and A. Davison

Summary

1. This chapter reviews the range of marine and coastal habitats for which there are candidate Special Areas of Conservation (SAC).
2. The use of the Sites of Special Scientific Interest management process to protect the coastal SAC interests is briefly discussed, and the desire for greater involvement by local people is highlighted.
3. The significant challenge presented by the simultaneous designation of at least 14 marine SACs is considered. The importance of establishing clear lines of communication, providing unambiguous information and advice to relevant authorities, user groups and the general public is identified.
4. The importance of generating ownership and a co-operative spirit is highlighted, and the process of developing both Scottish Natural Heritage's statutory advice on conservation objectives and operations, which may cause deterioration or disturbance, and the overall management scheme, is outlined.

10.1 Introduction

In many of the initiatives promoting wider integrated management of coastal resources, conservation is part of but not necessarily the primary driving force. The implementation of Council Directive 92/43/EEC on the conservation of natural habitats and of wild fauna and flora (commonly referred to as the Habitats Directive) in the marine environment and the resultant designation of marine Special Areas of Conservation (SACs) is a process driven primarily by conservation. In order to fulfil the requirements of the Directive, the UK government with advice from the statutory nature conservation agencies has, for the first time, had to consider the selection and subsequent management of a coherent network of SACs in the marine and coastal environment.

This has resulted in a significant step forward in statutory site-based marine conservation in Scotland (Plate 36). Prior to the implementation of the Habitats

Directive there were no statutory marine protected areas. To date 14 marine SACs in Scotland have been proposed to the European Commission (these are known as marine candidate SACs) and these already receive a degree of statutory protection as a result of the government policy to regard candidate sites as if they were designated, and a further number of sites referred to as marine possible SACs are still under consideration.

Increasingly, local communities and individuals are beginning to demonstrate the high value that they place on their local environment, especially the coastal and marine environment. Scotland's coastal and marine landscape, environment and biodiversity are all considered important factors by local communities and tourists alike. The coastal strip which is the boundary between the marine and terrestrial environments, spans the gap between two very different legislative systems. On land there is a formalised system of ownership and permissions whereas in the marine environment the legislative structure is based on common ownership and a system of overlapping rights and responsibilities. More and more the local communities and individuals want to have a say in how the coastal and marine environments are to be managed, and this is especially true of the special areas identified as SACs under the Habitats Directive.

To this end, many initiatives have been progressed which provide useful models to engage local community involvement in SAC management. SNH has most notably contributed through its promotion of the Firths Project. This project has successfully developed a much wider feeling of ownership and consensus between a large variety of interest groups to promote a more integrated management regime in the firths. It is hoped that through more integrated management, marine and coastal conservation can receive wider consideration and implementation.

Table 10.1 Habitats Directive Annex 1 marine and coastal habitat types.

Marine	Coastal
Estuaries	Atlantic salt meadows (*Glauco – Puccinellietalia*)
Large shallow inlets and bays	Decalcified fixed dunes with *Empetrum nigrum*
Lagoons	Dune juniper thickets (*Juniperus* spp.)
Mudflats and sandflats not covered by seawater at low tide	Dunes with *Salix arenaria*
	Embryonic shifting dunes
Reefs	Eu-atlantic decalcified dunes (*Calluno – Ulicetea*)
Sand banks which are slightly covered by seawater at all times	Fixed dunes with herbaceous vegetation (grey dunes)
	Humid dune slacks
Submerged or partly submerged sea caves	Machair
	Perennial vegetation of stony banks
	Salicornia and other annuals colonising mud and sand
	Shifting dunes along the shoreline with *Ammophila arenaria* (white dunes)
	Vegetated sea cliffs of the Atlantic and Baltic coasts

The government has already signalled its wish for a more co-operative and integrated system of management of Scotland's coast and inshore marine areas in the recent papers, *Scotland's Coasts: a discussion paper* (The Scottish Office, 1996), and the NPPG No. 13 (The Scottish Office, 1997) on coastal planning issues.

10.2 The Habitats Directive

The 'Council Directive 92/43/EEC on the conservation of natural habitats and of wild fauna and flora' (Council of the European Communities, 1992) was adopted in 1992. The Habitats Directive complements Council Directive 79/409/EEC on the conservation of wild birds (Council of the European Communities, 1979) (referred to as the 1979 Birds Directive). The resultant network of designated sites comprise Natura 2000. The requirements of the Habitats Directive were transposed into UK law by the Conservation (Natural Habitats, etc.) Regulations 1994 (Anon., 1994) (referred to as the Regulations). The Habitats Directive requires sites to be designated as SACs where they support typical, rare or vulnerable natural habitats and species of plants or animals as set out in Annex I and Annex II respectively of the Directive. Table 10.1 lists the various marine and coastal habitats listed in Annex I of the Habitats Directive.

Site selection involved an iterative process of internal peer review. This resulted in a list of sites (referred to as possible SACs) which satisfied the main selection criteria of representation and the conservation of structure and function as defined in Brown *et al.* (1997). Public consultation on the list of possible SACs was an important part in the confirmation of the candidate SACs proposed to the European Commission. Where SACs have an intertidal or marine component then they are known as European marine sites. The UK government, in drafting the Regulations, recognised the novel nature of statutory conservation designation in the marine environment and made a number of special provisions, set out in paragraphs 33–36 of the Regulations, to facilitate the effective management of European marine sites.

10.3 Marine and coastal SACs in Scotland

Figure 10.1 shows the distribution of marine and coastal candidate and possible SACs in Scotland. Thus far, 17 coastal candidate SACs have been proposed to the EC covering a range of habitats, including examples of the rich and varied saltmarshes of the Solway Firth, and the vegetated sea cliffs of St Kilda and the Stromness heaths and coast in Orkney. There are also sites for vegetated shingle at Spey Bay on the southern coast of the Moray Firth and for a variety of sand dune habitats such as Sands of Forvie, Morrich More and Barry Links, a habitat for which Scotland holds a significant proportion of the EU resource. A number of sites, including the Monach Islands, Tiree and Oldshoremore and Sandwood, have also been identified for their machair interest. This habitat has a very restricted range, being found only on the west of Ireland and the west of Scotland.

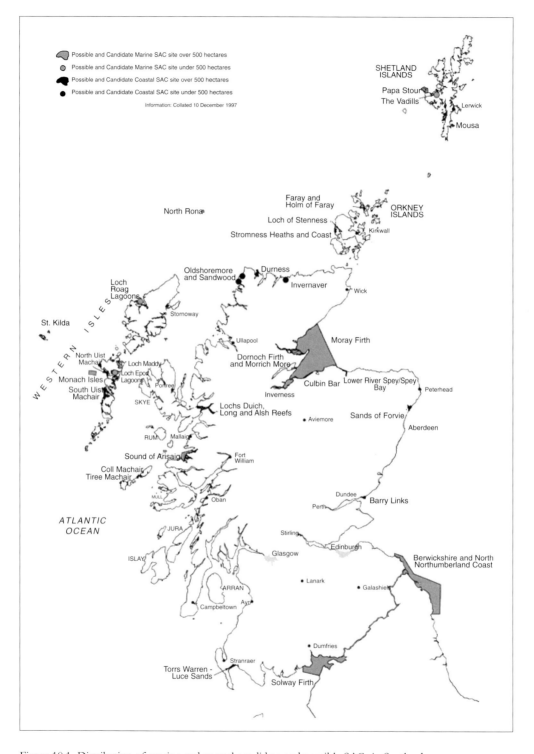

Figure 10.1 Distribution of marine and coastal candidate and possible SACs in Scotland.

The 14 marine candidate SACs cover a diverse range of habitat types from large physiographic features such as estuaries, lagoons and large shallow inlets and bays, to more specific habitats such as sea caves, reefs and intertidal sand- and mudflats. The marine candidate SACs vary greatly in size and complexity, ranging from some of the small, discrete, saline lagoon sites of the Western Isles, such as Loch Roag lagoons at 0.43 km^2, to extensive areas such as the Sound of Arisaig at 55 km^2 and the Moray Firth which covers 1513 km^2.

Within these broad habitat types there is considerable variety which must be embraced if the Natura 2000 network is to be truly representative of the Scottish and UK resource. Reefs are a good example. The selection of the sites has need-ed to embrace a great diversity of flora and fauna influenced by a wide variety of environmental conditions, such as wave exposure, depth, temperature and current speed. The wave-exposed, shallow, open-coast reefs of Papa Stour marine cSAC in Shetland have a very different biota to the very unusual communities found on some of Scotland's deepest and most sheltered vertical bed rock reefs that are found in Lochs Duich, Long and Alsh marine possible SAC. Even within the Loch Duich, Long and Alsh marine possible SAC, these deep low-energy reefs are con-trasted vividly by the current-swept communities of Kyle Rhea. St Kilda, with its superb water clarity and extreme wave exposure (Plate 37), supports communities which complement and contrast with those found on the vertical reef faces in the more turbid North Sea waters around St Abbs in the Berwickshire and north Northumberland coast marine cSAC. This diversity of habitats and community types is reflected in the variety of management issues which need to be addressed at these different sites.

10.4 Management of coastal SACs

There is an established process and history of management of Sites of Special Scientific Interest (SSSIs) in the UK. It is this tried and tested mechanism that is at the core of the management process of all terrestrial and coastal SACs.

All the sites on land, including intertidal areas of marine sites, must be desig-nated as SSSI. SSSIs allow for management agreements of various sorts to be drawn up with the owners and occupiers of the site. These can include financial incentives or take the form of advice and assistance in land management tech-niques. In many cases, however, maintaining the quality of the interest of the SSSI requires no intervention.

The management agreements for SSSIs are restricted to owners and occupiers. Many coastal areas, however, are important for recreation and other activities and there are sometimes difficulties in controlling the aspirations and expectations of these third parties which often present the greatest threat to the site. In extreme cases, for example, dune systems can be badly affected by inappropriate recre-ation, such as all-terrain motor bikes, or intertidal mud- and sandflats can be adversely affected by intensive bait digging. In practice the majority of third-party activities and issues are resolved through voluntary agreement and bylaws. Some third-party activities, however, are very difficult to control through voluntary agreements, and regulation may be necessary through Nature Conservation Orders or the implementation of other legislation such as bylaws.

Increasingly, local communities and the general public are beginning to value the coastal and marine environment, and there is an increasing desire from them to have a say in the management of these special areas. Management initiatives addressing the integration of multiple demands of private, public and community interests have been taken forward for a number of years in relation to coastal SSSI and are now being considered in response to SAC designations. To address these issues SNH is formulating site management systems to promote working in partnership with interested groups and local communities to develop more flexible management systems.

10.5 Management of marine Special Areas of Conservation

The successful delivery of effective management on a large number of marine SACs all at once represents not only a very large step forward in statutory marine site-based conservation in the UK, but also a large challenge in Scotland to SNH, the various relevant authorities, as defined in paragraph 5 of the Regulations, and the local communities involved. The real challenge is to develop and achieve effective, targeted and unburdensome management of the sites, which delivers the necessary level of protection for the features for which the site is designated, whilst taking on board the legitimate views and aspirations of local communities and interests. In order to achieve this, there needs to be clear, unambiguous communication between all parties which will enable differences to be resolved, suspicions to be allayed and bridges to be built. There is a common goal, and what is important is that a climate is created where all parties can recognise this and work towards achieving conservation-led integrated management of the site in a co-operative manner.

Recognising the need to work in consensus and co-operation with all interested parties, the Regulations make two fundamental provisions that relate specifically to European marine sites. Firstly, they require SNH to develop certain statutory advice. This advice has two parts: advice on 'conservation objectives', and advice on 'operations likely to cause damage or disturbance to the conservation features of the site', referred to as 'operations'. Secondly, the Regulations make provision for a single management scheme to be developed, when one is seen to be necessary in order to deliver the conservation objectives through co-operation between the relevant authorities, with one relevant authority taking the lead. It is intended that the management scheme will deliver the conservation objectives through a combination of voluntary measures and, where necessary, the respective relevant authorities using their existing powers of control to limit or prevent certain activities. The development and implementation of the management scheme will rely heavily on the advice and co-operation of the site users and other interested groups.

A model process for developing a management scheme for marine SACs is shown in Figure 10.2 (Scottish Natural Heritage *et al.*, 1997). The management of the marine SACs will involve those relevant authorities with statutory responsibilities for managing different aspects of the site. The Regulations place a requirement on the relevant authorities to undertake their duties to ensure the maintenance of the conservation features of the site, although it will be for SNH to advise if this is the case.

When considering the management of marine SACs it must be borne in mind that there is no precedent of statutory marine protected areas and management in Scotland. Voluntary initiatives such as the Focus on Firths Project, the Minch Project and other voluntary marine conservation areas do provide many useful lessons on the development of management schemes for European marine sites, but novel principles and practices are still required.

Whereas the legislative structure in the coastal and terrestrial environment is based on a well-established system of ownership where responsibilities and regulations are clearly defined, the legislative system in the marine environment is very different. It is based on a system of overlapping public rights and responsibilities. The basic concept of site-based conservation in the marine environment has been shown to be fraught with difficulties, as evidenced by the lack of any marine nature reserves in Scotland. The real challenge for the future of the European marine sites is the establishment of effective management schemes, which will ensure the conservation and protection of the features of interest of the sites as a priority, and will also include, and wherever possible, facilitate, sustainable local use and development within the SACs.

10.6 Formulating conservation objectives

The conservation objectives are the starting point for the development of a management scheme for the site. They should be viewed as a public statement of the conservation goals for the site, and as such the style and content of their presentation is vital if the development of management schemes through wide-ranging co-operation is to succeed.

The approach to the formulation and presentation of conservation objectives which is being developed by SNH is based on six simple steps resulting in a package of advice and supporting information. Whilst there is a clear order to the final package, its development involves a much more integrated process with much of the material and thinking being developed in parallel. The approach first takes stock of all aspects of the site, including details of the conservation features of that site and assesses the current activities known to be taking place on the site. Using this information a suite of simple conservation objectives is prepared. Supporting information, interpreting the conservation objectives in more detail

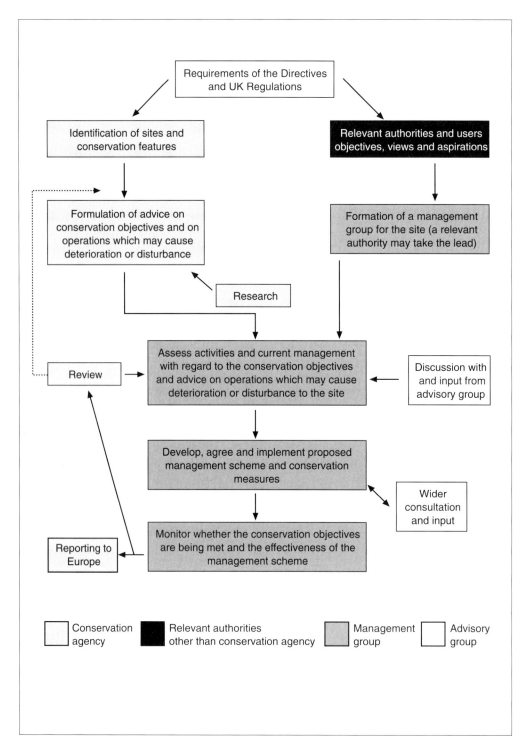

Figure 10.2 Model process for developing a management scheme.

and suggesting the key management issues to be addressed by the management group, is produced. To further assist the management group an assessment of the sensitivity of the features to human activities and their likely vulnerability to such activities must be made. Some fundamental questions about sensitivity and vulnerability of certain features remain as yet unanswered but will be addressed, as necessary, as the development of the various management schemes proceed.

In order to assist the debate and discussions of the management group an initial appraisal of the possible management measures is produced. The novelty of the situation and the scepticism of some of those involved means that it is vitally important that there is a comprehensive package of information which provides a clear explanation of the conservation objectives and that can inform and guide the early stages of the development of a management scheme for a site.

This approach acknowledges that the conservation objectives must be a public statement of the conservation goals for management of the site. They need to be unambiguous and as such it is essential that as full an explanation as possible is provided of the process.

10.6.1 *The identification of conservation features*

There should be a clear statement of the conservation importance of the site. All the marine SACs in Scotland support features of the highest quality and scientific interest. For each site, all relevant details of the conservation features of the sites must be made clear in non-technical terms. Wherever possible, the distribution of the conservation features within the site should be identified and mapped in detail (Plate 38) and then summarised if necessary for the sake of clarity (Plate 39). In some circumstances it may be possible to introduce the idea that the conservation features can be divided into different zones within the site, based either on their sensitivity to certain activities or on the distribution of specific features (Plate 40).

10.6.2 *An outline assessment of the current and likely activities on the site*

The conservation objectives for a site will, of necessity, need to seek to avoid any detrimental change due to human activities; changes due to natural events or processes should be regarded as acceptable. In order to formulate specific, targeted conservation objectives, it is important to assess the potential impact of current and likely activities taking place on the site. Ideally this information can be location-specific and may be confined to different zones defined by either feature distribution or by sensitivity/vulnerability considerations. The SNH statutory advice on operations likely to cause deterioration or disturbance to the conservation features will be based on the above assessment and should comprise a short list of relevant activities.

10.6.3 *Draft conservation objectives*

The conservation objectives should be simple 'stand alone' statements which explain the conservation goals for the features of the site. The conservation objectives will comprise a number of parts:

- a goal or action such as 'maintain', 'ensure no net loss', 'restore to …'

- the attribute, e.g. 'area', 'community richness', ' population size', 'diversity of communities and habitats'

- the feature, e.g. 'estuary', 'intertidal sediment habitats', 'mussel community', 'the communities within zone 1'.

The conservation objectives can be set at a number of levels. Broad, overarching objectives can be set for the whole site. More targeted objectives can be set for individual conservation features or specific zones. It is essential that the language used is simple, clear and unambiguous.

10.6.4 *Supporting advice to relevant authorities in relation to the SAC*

The management group of relevant authorities are expected to develop the management scheme and implement the necessary management measures to deliver the conservation objectives. The conservation objectives should be supported by a more considered and detailed interpretation of the conservation objectives and should highlight the issues which relevant authorities should consider. It will identify possible areas where the relevant authorities could consider reviewing their management policy in the light of the requirements of the conservation objectives.

10.6.5 *Sensitivity and vulnerability matrices*

The production of a matrix of conservation features expressed against current or likely activities will assist in the identification of management issues. This matrix will highlight those features which are *sensitive* to current or likely activities within the site. A *vulnerability* matrix can then be produced which identifies the likely vulnerability of the features at a site to detrimental change as a result of these activities.

Examples of draft conservation objectives for Sound of Arisaig marine candidate SAC

- To ensure that there is no net loss of area or change to the structure, biodiversity or distribution pattern of the highly sensitive maerl communities (Plate 41) that occur within the candidate SAC sensitivity zone 4 areas (Plate 40), whilst taking account of the natural variability within these communities.

- To ensure that there is no net loss of area or significant change to the structure of the shallow sublittoral sediment communities found within the candidate SAC sensitivity zone 2 area (Plate 40), whilst taking account of the natural variability within these communities.

This exercise is important in identifying where management measures may be required. Just as importantly it will demonstrate that in many cases there are few, if any, contentious management issues on a site. This clear expression of the likely impact of the designation is an important step in the consensus-building process, which is vital to the success of these designations in protecting the natural heritage features of the site.

10.6.6 Possible management measures to be considered

The development of the management scheme is the statutory responsibility of the relevant authorities, but just as importantly it must include local people, user groups and other interested bodies. The development process will involve considerable discussion and consultation through the management group and, in order to initiate this debate, a set of proposals are useful. The draft management matrix produced for the Sound of Arisaig is presented in Table 10.2.

This 'up front' approach was required for the Sound of Arisaig and was widely welcomed. It stimulated useful debate and crucially showed how few management measures may be required on the site. Where measures were a possibility, the structure of the document meant that the reasons for this were very apparent and identified some areas where the SAC can offer opportunities of more local management of some resources.

10.7 Conclusion

The implementation of the Habitats Directive provides a real opportunity to further the protection and conservation of much of Scotland's priceless natural

Table 10.2 Extract from draft management matrix for Sound of Arisaig marine candidate SAC.

Activity	Sensitivity Zone 1	Sensitivity Zone 2	Sensitivity Zone 3	Sensitivity Zone 4
Suction dredging	Limited 1[a]	Limited 1[a]	No	No
Scallop dredging	Yes	Yes	Limited 2[a]	No
Nephrops/demersal trawling	Yes	Yes	Yes	N/A
Pelagic trawling	Yes	Yes	Yes	N/A
Creeling	Yes	Yes	Yes	Yes
Scallop diving	Yes	Yes	Yes	Yes
Aggregate extraction	N/A	No	No	No
Fin fish farming	Yes	Yes	Yes	Limited 3[a]
Shell fish farming	Yes	Yes	Yes	Limited 4[a]
Anchoring	Yes	Yes	Yes	Limited 5[a]
Boating	Yes	Yes	Yes	Yes
Water sports	Yes	Yes	Yes	Yes

[a]These refer to specific caveats attached to the particular management proposals.

heritage in the marine environment. In particular it presents both SNH and others with a number of new challenges. SNH has been charged with the introduction of the concept of marine protected areas to a whole new audience which in many quarters is already feeling very beleaguered. Winning the hearts and minds of the local communities and their support is important. However, the real challenge for the future is the delivery of effective management of these sites. The real measure of success of any marine SAC designation will be how effective the management scheme is in achieving the conservation of the features of the site whilst enabling legitimate sustainable exploitation to continue. The management of the Natura 2000 network of sites presents many challenges and new opportunities for integrated management of marine and coastal areas, to enable the conservation of important features to be achieved, whilst facilitating the continued sustainable use of the area.

References

Anon. 1994. *The Conservation (Natural Habitats, etc.) Regulations.* Statutory Instrument No. 2716.

Brown, A.E., Burn, A.J., Hopkins, J.J. and Way, S.F. 1997. *The Habitats Directive: Selection of Special Areas of Conservation in the UK.* JNCC Report No. 270.

Council of the European Communities. 1979. Council Directive 79/409/EEC of 2 April 1979: on the conservation of wild birds.

Council of the European Communities. 1992. Council Directive 92/43/EEC of 21 May 1992: on the conservation of natural habitats and of wild fauna and flora. *Official Journal of the European Communities*, L206/7.

Scottish Natural Heritage, EN, EH(DOE(NI)), CCW and JNCC. 1997. *Natura 2000: European marine sites: an introduction to management.* Scottish Natural Heritage, Perth.

The Scottish Office. 1996. *Scotland's coasts: a discussion paper.* HMSO, Edinburgh.

The Scottish Office, Development Department. 1997. *Coastal planning.* NPPG13. HMSO, Edinburgh.

11 THE SCOTTISH COASTAL FORUM: AN INDEPENDENT ADVISORY BODY TO GOVERNMENT*

S. Sankey

Summary

1. The background to the inauguration of the Scottish Coastal Forum (SCF) in 1996 is outlined against a series of government and voluntary sector initiatives in recent years. The remit and membership of the SCF is summarised. Its independent role is emphasised.
2. The future role of the SCF is amplified, especially with respect to its relationship with estuary fora; the production of guidance and best-practice papers; and the assistance to government in the development of holistic and integrated coastal and marine policies for Scotland.
3. Sustainable resource management and planning is proposed as a key approach for the future.

11.1 Introduction

The Scottish Coastal Forum (SCF) was established in March 1997, and held its third meeting in Inverness in October 1997. The forum brings together 16 representatives of industry, sport and tourism, development and the environment. After two meetings, the SCF determined the following terms of reference. The SCF should:

- encourage a voluntary, sustainable and holistic approach to the management of Scotland's coasts through the formation of local fora

- act as the national focus for coastal issues and co-ordinate the dissemination of advice on best practice

- reflect the views and aspirations of local fora for the coast of Scotland and guide a national policy framework within which local initiatives can operate

- advise government in the development of coastal policies for Scotland.

Despite the differences in emphasis in coastal policy in the four countries of the

---

*This chapter represents the SCF from the perspective of the author who is a member of the forum. It does not necessarily reflect the views of the whole forum.

UK, the establishment of the SCF paralleled the situation in England, where a National Coastal Forum had been established a few months earlier. For comparison, the SCF's southern counterpart has as its remit:

- to promote the understanding of coastal zone initiatives

- to build on existing liaison arrangements at regional and local level

- to assist the evaluation of action to implement coastal zone initiatives and monitor the preparation of a guide to good practice

- to complement – but not overlap – the work of other bodies with interests in coastal issues

- to liaise with other relevant initiatives elsewhere in the UK.

Coastal fora with similar remits have also been set up recently for Wales and Northern Ireland. Such similarity of remit is surprising, since Scottish Office civil servants have traditionally emphasised the differences between the English and Welsh and Scottish coastal contexts. Indeed, the House of Commons' deliberations into coastal policy and matters (Anon., 1992) were given a lukewarm reception in Scotland because of these perceived differences. Government corridors echoed to the familiar mantra: Scottish solutions were needed for Scottish problems.

11.2 Membership of the Scottish Coastal Forum

Members of the SCF are therefore looking forward to addressing particular challenges. The arrival of the Scottish Parliament in the year 1999 gives an added incentive to advise the present government, and the future Scottish Executive on improvements to the Scottish coastal policy. Present SCF membership is outlined in Table 11.1. Happily there is overlap between the various experiences of these members, both on a local and national context, and several members are actively involved in Scottish estuary fora at office-bearer level. This overlap may yet prove to be a vital component of the SCF's success.

One important aspect of the composition of the SCF is its independent chair, which is free, in theory, from the constraints of government departments or agencies. It is felt that a truly independent chair is an important point of principle. Government advisers, after all, should be free to counsel ministers from a position of genuine independence. Environmental non-governmental organisations (NGOs) in Scotland are currently lobbying to extend this principle to the Scottish Parliament: let the Scottish Parliament and its ministers determine policy, but with the benefit of transparent and independent advice from its advisory agencies.

11.3 The history of Scottish coastal policy

Interest in Scottish coastal issues has been expanding in the 1990s. It is worth reiterating that in the 1980s Scotland had seen a decade of industrial fish farm expansion on the west coast and Northern Isles; two decades of a Common

Table 11.1   Membership of the SCF (October 1997).

Chairman, Captain Tony Wilks
Association of Scottish Shellfish Growers
British Ports Association
CoastNET
Confederation of British Industries Scotland
Convention of Scottish Local Authorities
The Crown Estate
Highlands and Islands Enterprise
Scottish Enterprise
Scottish Environment Protection Agency
Scottish Fishermens' Federation
Scottish Natural Heritage
Scottish Salmon Growers Association
Scottish Sports Council
Scottish Wildlife and Countryside Link
Scottish Tourist Board
The Scottish Office

Fisheries Policy, with its attendant booms and busts; and nearly three decades of oil and gas development. In recent years, Scotland has suffered the wreck of the *Braer* and the embarrassment of the Brent Spar. Where Scotland had led the way with the publication of the pioneering *North Sea Oil and Gas, Coastal Planning Guidelines* (Anon., 1974), 25 years later we are witnessing a strategic policy vacuum of considerable size. No one could deny that the time is right for a radical over-haul of Scottish coastal policy.

In the 1980s and 1990s in England and Wales, a series of initiatives were under-way, designed to address coastal conflicts and policy. Sea fisheries committees enabled local interests to manage their own resources; estuary fora were set up at major sites in England and Wales; shoreline management plans were inaugurated to help plan positively for coastal erosion and sea-level rise. Some of these mod-els would not be appropriate to Scotland, if transferred direct, but many Scottish environmentalists were frustrated in the last decade by an apparent unwillingness by the Scottish Office to provide guidance and leadership over coastal matters.

A series of marine and coastal campaigns by environmental NGOs such as the Royal Society for Protection of Birds' *Turning the Tide, Save our Shorebirds* and marine life campaigns (Rothwell and Housden, 1990; RSPB, 1993; Gubbay, 1994) helped to raise awareness in Scotland of coastal issues. A storm of voluntary activity was crashing over Scotland's coastline, very much after the spirit of the Earth Summit in Rio in 1992, and its call for local environmental action based on the concept of sustainability (Anon., 1994a), and the popular appeal to think globally and act locally. It was a logical extension of this campaigning by environmental NGOs that encouraged local authorities and others to collaborate with Scottish Natural Heritage (SNH) to establish the various estuary fora of recent years through the provision of funding by means of project officers in their Firths Initiative (see Table 11.2).

In the early years these fora struggled to persuade the Scottish Office to collaborate, although there appears now to be a welcome change in the willingness of central government to co-ordinate and guide future progress. Prior to the establishment of the SCF, the Scottish Office had commissioned a review of Scottish coastal issues and policy (Burbridge and Burbridge, 1994), which led, in turn, to the release of *Scotland's Coasts – A Discussion Paper* (Anon., 1996a). In addition, we have recently seen the publication of National Planning Policy Guideline 13 on *Coast Planning* (Anon., 1997a), which contains some innovative ideas. At last the tide seems to have turned, and the SCF has the opportunity to be an integral part of this change.

Table 11.2 Date of establishment of estuary fora in Scotland.

Cromarty Firth Liaison Group	1992
Forth Estuary Forum	1993
Minch Project[a]	1993
SNH Firths Initiative	1993
Solway Partnership	1994
Minch Forum[a]	1994
Clyde Estuary Forum	1995
Moray Firth Partnership	1996
Tay Forum (inaugural meeting)	1997

[a] Subject to review at present.

Coastal conflicts also helped to persuade the key players that there had to be a better way. Examples of these conflicts included the Parklea Business Park proposal on the Clyde; a tidal barrage feasibility proposal and second Forth Road Bridge on the Forth; and the Longman Bay access road and coup on the Moray Firth. There may yet be future conflicts over refuse disposal in Dundee and perhaps Inverness. These conflicts are set against the spirit of Rio, when at the Earth Summit in 1992, world governments agreed, among other things, that development must become more sustainable; and that local communities must become more involved in the priority setting and management of resources. This should also be the spirit of the SCF, following on from the cultures inspired by the local estuary fora, working through consensus and partnership towards integrated management strategies for some of Scotland's most sensitive and vulnerable areas.

11.4 Challenges for the SCF

There will inevitably be tough challenges ahead of the SCF. Some are process- or culture-related challenges, and others refer to real issues.

11.4.1 *Overcoming sectoralism*

Overcoming the natural sectoralism of government and its institutions is perhaps the first and most formidable challenge ahead. Every recent review of UK coastal and marine policy describes a need to break down the barriers of sectoralism and work towards a more holistic approach (Anon., 1992; Burbridge and Burbridge, 1994; Rothwell and Housden, 1990; RSPB, 1993). No doubt the true sustainable development solutions lie along this holistic route, and the SCF must discover these.

11.4.2 *Building consensus*

Arriving at the consensus that such an holistic approach requires is not easy, and the techniques that facilitate this may not be readily available or accepted in Scotland. There may, therefore, be a lack of experience at consensus-building in Scotland. Scottish Parliamentarians are going to have to arrive at consensus, shortly, however, with the arrival of proportional representation, and the forecasted four-way split of Scottish politics in the new millennium. At present there is a lack of government guidance in consensus-building techniques despite government rhetoric regarding the need to build consensus through the use of partnerships. The various Scottish estuary fora have shown remarkable creativity in building consensus, but support and guidance on consensus-building techniques is still urgently needed.

11.4.3 *Environmental sustainability indicators*

There is a pressing need to extend and implement the thinking about environmental sustainability indicators to a coastal and marine context (Anon., 1996b). RSPB and others, including government, have emphasised that biodiversity is a key test of sustainability (Gubbay, 1994; Anon., 1996c), and that we need to ensure that future generations experience at least our present variety of coastal and marine habitats and wildlife, if true sustainability is to be achieved. Water quality is another obvious environmental indicator in a coastal context. The UK government is committed to a new way of prioritising biodiversity planning through the relevant habitat action plans (e.g. saline lagoons) and species action plans (e.g. harbour porpoise and otter) (Anon., 1995a,b). We need to ensure that the objectives, targets and actions identified in these plans are implemented by all relevant government departments, agencies and organisations.

11.4.4 *Difficult issues for consensus*

There are examples of sensitive issues in a marine and coastal context that may prove difficult subjects for consensus or solutions. For example, there is the oil and gas dilemma, of how to continue sanctioning the development of fossil fuels whilst meeting tough air-pollution emission targets at the same time (Greenpeace UK, 1997). Perhaps the resolution of this issue is outside the scope of the SCF, but it does not lie outside UK governmental responsibility, and the SCF is tasked with advising the Scottish Office. Even the development of green energy alternatives to oil and gas, such as wind turbines and wave energy schemes, may have serious coastal implications.

11.4.5 *Fisheries-related issues*

The deficiencies of the Common Fisheries Policy are well known. 'Too many boats chasing too few fish' is a succinct generalisation of the situation. Whilst the SCF may be limited in its ability to offer solutions or indeed influence at the pan-European level required of this debate, there are sensible fisheries-related issues which the SCF should and must influence, such as the local control of inshore fisheries, and the regulation of the sand eel and other so-called industrial fisheries off our shores.

11.4.6 *Legislative improvements*

There is the perennial question of whether to revise our Town and Country Planning legislation, in order to accommodate coastal and marine matters. Ironically it has just been rationalised (Anon., 1997b) but there was no opportunity to include coastal zone management within this exercise. Similarly, the development planning system is also being reviewed in Scotland at present, although once again there is little hope of coastal zone management being accommodated in the present deliberations. Nor has the SCF included this issue in its programme at present, although it has just commenced an analysis of the present gaps in strategic guidance relating to Scottish coastal issues. It will not be long before the inevitable conclusion that the present mechanisms for dealing with coastal issues are as wanting as some of the gaps that exist in guidance. The arrival of the Scottish Parliament will give unparalleled legislative time and opportunities, and some of it will be devoted to improvements in Scottish coastal and marine planning.

11.4.7 *Designating special sites*

A sensitive issue is the process of marine designations, marine nature reserves and Natura 2000 sites. At present there are no marine designations in Scotland except for the voluntary St Abb's reserve in Berwickshire, although the government has proposed 14 marine Special Areas of Conservation to the European Commission, and there is much work ahead for all competent and relevant authorities, as defined by the Conservation (Natural Habitats, etc.) Regulations 1994 (Anon., 1994b) which transpose the requirements of the Birds Directive (Council of the European Communities, 1979) and the Habitats Directive (Council of the European Communities, 1992) into UK law.

11.4.8 *Resourcing and implementation of solutions*

Lastly, resourcing is an issue that the SCF must address. Already the estuary fora have made it clear that the long-term projects that they have embarked upon will outlast the pump-priming resources of SNH's Focus on Firths Initiative. European Union structural funds, as deployed at present by the Forth Estuary

Forum for example, will also expire shortly. The prioritising of marine and coastal issues and the subsequent resourcing and implementation of solutions is a critical challenge ahead. We should question how many incidents such as the *Braer* and the *Sea Empress* are required before the full implementation of the Donaldson Inquiry recommendations (Anon., 1994c) is achieved? In October 1997 the tanker *Yusup K* floundered helplessly off the Caithness coast carrying a dangerous cargo of naphtha, and had to await a tug from Stornoway to clear her from danger.

11.5 The terms of reference in detail

To conclude this chapter the terms of reference for the SCF will be revisited and expanded in detail:

(a) To encourage a voluntary, sustainable and holistic approach to the management of Scotland's coasts through the formation of local fora.

This first term of reference is in some ways the most interesting one! The key word is voluntary, for it generates a whole series of further questions. Is the deployment of the voluntary principle for the management of our coasts and seas correct? Is the use of the voluntary principle not the baggage of the old administration, which was thrown out of power by the people on 1 May 1997? Do we not want to see our priceless maritime assets put on to the same legal platform as the terrestrial equivalents (i.e. Planning Acts and control delivered on a statutory base)? On the other hand, the spirit of Rio encourages consultation and participation, which are essentially voluntary values; and the present estuary fora have succeeded in implementing the voluntary principle. In addition, consensus usually works best with the threat of regulation on the horizon! So far, therefore, so good with respect to the voluntary principle – but the estuary fora must still implement the difficult bits of their strategies.

SNH also wish to build consensus in the management of marine Special Areas of Conservation and Special Protection Areas rather than have the various relevant authorities use their statutory powers from the outset. At this stage, therefore, the continuation of the voluntary ethos by the SCF is perhaps correct, but it should watch carefully to see that sustainability actually materialises. If it does not, government will need to be ready to regulate should the need arise. To achieve sustainability in our marine environment will require a massive effort by innumerable government departments and agencies, organisations and individuals, and will require the holistic approach that this term of reference demands.

(b) To act as the national focus for coastal issues and co-ordinate the dissemination of advice on best practice.

This is a clear vacuum to fill, since strategic guidance on a variety of issues has been lacking in recent years in Scotland. The essential question is whether government itself should fill the void, or request the SCF to do so. The RSPB recommended that the Scottish Office set up a Scottish Coastal Unit after the model of the new Sustainable Development Unit in the Scottish Office, except with more resourcing and influence (RSPB, 1996). It wishes to see coastal issues pervade all government departments, agencies and policies. In some ways there is such an embryonic unit, in the form of the SCF, which, if it is successful, will succeed in gaining acceptance of sustainable policies for marine issues across all government departments.

(c) To reflect the views and aspirations of local fora for the coast of Scotland and guide a national policy framework within which local initiatives can operate.

It is essential that the SCF strikes the right relationship and tone with the existing estuary fora. The evolution of consensus began at the sharp end, and it would be a grave error of judgement for the SCF to be too authoritarian in its approach. That is not to say that a framework and support are not needed – they are – but the SCF must take care to develop its relationship with local fora and get it right. Already the local fora have given an indication that the SCF could give support over the following issues:

- assistance with the balance of membership
- production of guidance on how to deal with funding issues
- adding value to contributions from local fora to government consultation exercises
- identification of gaps in strategic planning
- production of guidance on the structure of local fora and advice on the methods of dealing with wider issues
- provision of briefings for government departments and agencies on coastal issues
- endorsement of individual initiatives
- endorsement of fora in areas outside the Firths Initiative
- assessment of the need for further coastal fora.

It has been agreed that the SCF will conduct a review of issues that affect local fora, and this work is underway at present, in association with the various fora throughout Scotland.

(d) To advise government in the development of coastal policies for Scotland.

Here is where it starts to hurt! Is the SCF up to the job? Even if it is, will government listen? This is a trickier question, especially with a new administration and a Scottish Parliament on the horizon. Both these developments may be to the advantage of better coastal and marine policies for Scotland. Already the SCF has prepared an action plan to take forward the work of the forum. It has also agreed to look at issues surrounding the extension of planning controls around the coast; and it is analysing the issues for which strategic guidance is not currently available.

11.6 Conclusion

In a statement that he made before the general election of 1 May 1997, Michael Meacher, the current Minister for the Environment, said:

> Labour will draw up a coastal zone policy for the whole coastline, in consultation with local and regional government, conservation groups and the fishing industry. This will identify areas that require special protection, those which could be designated as marine nature reserves, and those identified for pollution clean-up, leisure development, or commercial fishing (Marine Conservation Society, 1997).

The challenge for the SCF is to hold Michael Meacher to his word, with, of course, Scottish solutions for Scottish problems.

References

Anon. 1974. Scottish Development Department, *North Sea Oil and Gas, Coastal Planning Guidelines*. HMSO, Edinburgh.

Anon. 1992. *House of Commons Environment Committee Second Report, Coastal Zone Protection and Planning*. HMSO, London.

Anon. 1994a. *Sustainable Development, the UK Strategy* (Command 2426). HMSO, London.

Anon. 1994b. *The Conservation (Natural Habitats, etc) Regulations 1994*. HMSO, London.

Anon. 1994c. *Safer Ships, Cleaner Seas, Report of Lord Donaldson's inquiry into the prevention of pollution from Merchant Shipping* (Command 2560). HMSO, London.

Anon. 1995a. *Biodiversity: The UK Steering Group Report, Volume 1: Meeting the Rio Challenge*. HMSO, London.

Anon. 1995b. *Biodiversity: The UK Steering Group Report, Volume 2: Action Plans*. HMSO, London.

Anon. 1996a. Scottish Office, Agriculture, Environment and Fisheries Department, *Scotland's Coasts – A Discussion Paper*. HMSO, Edinburgh.

Anon. 1996b. Government Statistical Service, *Indicators of Sustainable Development for the United Kingdom*. HMSO, London.

Anon. 1996c. *Government Response to the UK Steering Group Report on Biodiversity* (Command 3260). HMSO, London.

Anon. 1997a. Scottish Office Development Department, National Planning Policy Guideline 13, *Coastal Planning*. HMSO, Edinburgh.

Anon. 1997b. *The Town and Country Planning (Scotland) Act 1997*. HMSO, London.

Burbridge, P.R. and Burbridge, V. 1994. *Review of Scottish Coastal Issues. A Consultant's Report to the Scottish Office*. Scottish Office Central Research Unit, Edinburgh.

Council of the European Communities. 1979. Council Directive 79/409/EEC of 2 April 1979 on the conservation of wild birds.

Council of the European Communities. 1992. Council Directive 92/43/EEC of 21 May 1992: on the conservation of natural habitats and of wild fauna and flora. *Official Journal of the European Community* L206/7.

Greenpeace UK. 1997. *Putting the lid on fossil fuels: why the Atlantic should be a frontier against oil exploration*. Greenpeace UK, Canonbury Villas, London.

Gubbay, S. 1994. *Seas: the Opportunity*, RSPB Marine Life Campaign. RSPB, Sandy, Bedfordshire.

Marine Conservation Society. 1997. Marine Conservation. Volume 3, Number 10, *Party Pieces – Election Special*, Marine Conservation Society.

RSPB. 1993. *Save our Shorebirds Campaign, A Shore Future*. RSPB, Sandy, Bedfordshire.

RSPB. 1996. *Response to Scotland's Coasts – A Discussion Paper*. RSPB, Edinburgh.

Rothwell, P.I. and Housden, S.D. 1990. *Turning the Tide, a Future for Estuaries*. RSPB, Sandy, Bedfordshire.

Plate 1.   Loch Eport, North Uist.
Plate 2.   Scarista Beach, Harris.
Plate 3.   The Bar, Culbin.

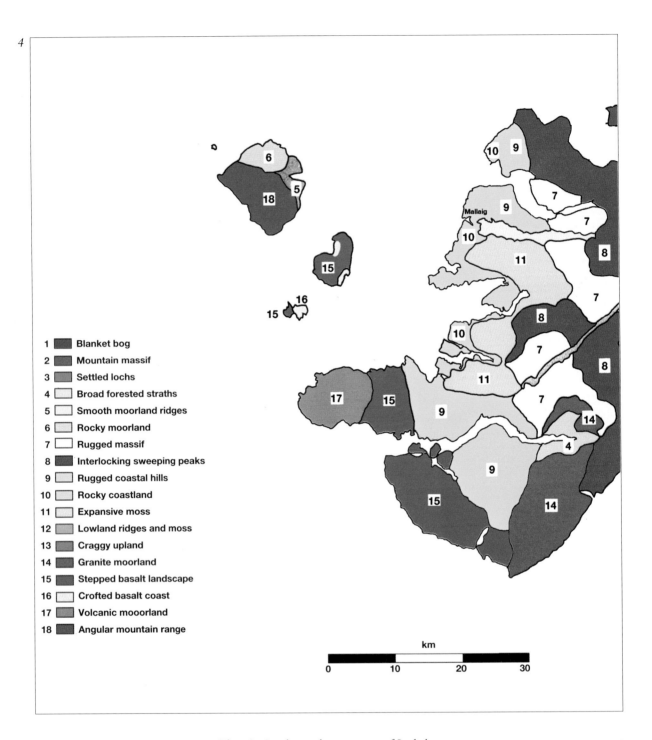

1 Blanket bog
2 Mountain massif
3 Settled lochs
4 Broad forested straths
5 Smooth moorland ridges
6 Rocky moorland
7 Rugged massif
8 Interlocking sweeping peaks
9 Rugged coastal hills
10 Rocky coastland
11 Expansive moss
12 Lowland ridges and moss
13 Craggy upland
14 Granite moorland
15 Stepped basalt landscape
16 Crofted basalt coast
17 Volcanic mooorland
18 Angular mountain range

Plate 4. Landscape character types of Lochaber.

Plate 5. *Stepped basalt landscape, west of Mull.*
Plate 6. *West coast of Mull: Ulva Ferry to Ben More.*
Plate 7. *Gully, Ben More, Mull.*

8

Plate 8. Gully vegetation, Ben More, Mull.
Plate 9. Inner Solway.
Plate 10. Knoydart (Ladhair Bheinn and Loch Hourn).

9

10

Plate 11. Lingerabay, Harris, 1996.
Plate 12. Lingerabay, Harris – simulation of proposed superquarry operation.

13

14

Plate 13. Black Cuillins and Strathaird, Skye.

Plate 14. Sandwood Bay.

15

Plate 15. Yesnaby Castle and cliffs, Orkney.

Plate 16. Shingle spits, Spey Bay, Moray. Large-scale depositional features are common on the east coast of Scotland due to the prevalence of long-shore drift.

Plate 17. Baleshare dunes, Benbecula, Western Isles. Eroded frontal edge of a mature dune system is a common sight where the classic sequence of developing dunes is restricted to areas where sediment is locally plentiful.

16

17

Plate 18. Buddon Ness/Barry Links SSSI, Angus, flanked to the north and south by encroachment of shore protection structures.

Plate 19. Alloa Inch and the inner Forth estuary. Much of the former mudflat and saltmarsh has been claimed for farmland and development. Such areas will be particularly vulnerable to flooding as a result of sea-level rise.

Plate 20. Cockenzie power station and Port Seton. Coastal defences may be inevitable if industrial developments are threatened by flooding and erosion.

Plate 21. West coast of Jura, Argyll. Raised platforms, cliff-line and shingle ridges are the result of glacial activity and isostatic uplift.

Plate 22. South Links, Montrose. These coastal defences have been repeatedly extended and re-designed to combat persistent erosion.

Plate 23. Scarista Beach, Harris. Remote and unspoilt beaches abound in north-west Scotland.

Plate 24. Saltmarsh at Caelaverock, Solway Firth.
Plate 25. River Carron mudflats, Grangemouth, Firth of Forth.
Plate 26. Common sea lavender – Limonium vulgare.

27

28

Plate 27. Inner Moray Firth looking east over Chanonry Point and Fort George.
Plate 28. Pittenweem fishing village on the east coast of Fife.

29

30

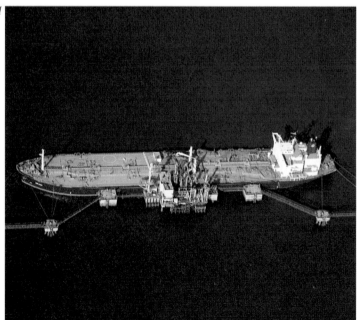

31

Plate 29. Port Edgar Marina and Forth Road Bridge.
Plate 30. North Queensferry, Firth of Forth.
Plate 31. Hound Point oil terminal, Firth of Forth.

Plate 32. Fair Isle.
Plate 33. Traditional crofting landscape on Fair Isle.

34

Plate 34. Halibut.
Plate 35. Traditional Fair Isle yole.

35

36

Plate 36. From Soay looking north-east to Boreray,
St Kilda.
Plate 37. Stac Lee, Boreray, St Kilda.

Coast (HWM)
Loch Ailort Lifeforms
Algal turf on gravel and stones
Algal turf on sand
Deep mud with burrowing megafauna
Dense maerl with algal turf
Faunal crusts on circalittoral grazed ro
Faunal turf on silty circalittoral stone
Gravel with sparse infauna
Kelp forest on rock/boulders
Kelp park on rock/boulders
Maerl patches and sediment
Rippled maerl and gravel
Sand with burrowing infauna
Shallow mud with mounds and burrows
Silty sand with stones
Tideswept kelp/algal turf on stones

Plate 38. Distribution of lifeforms in Loch Ailort, part of the Sound of Arisaig candidate Special Area of Conservation.

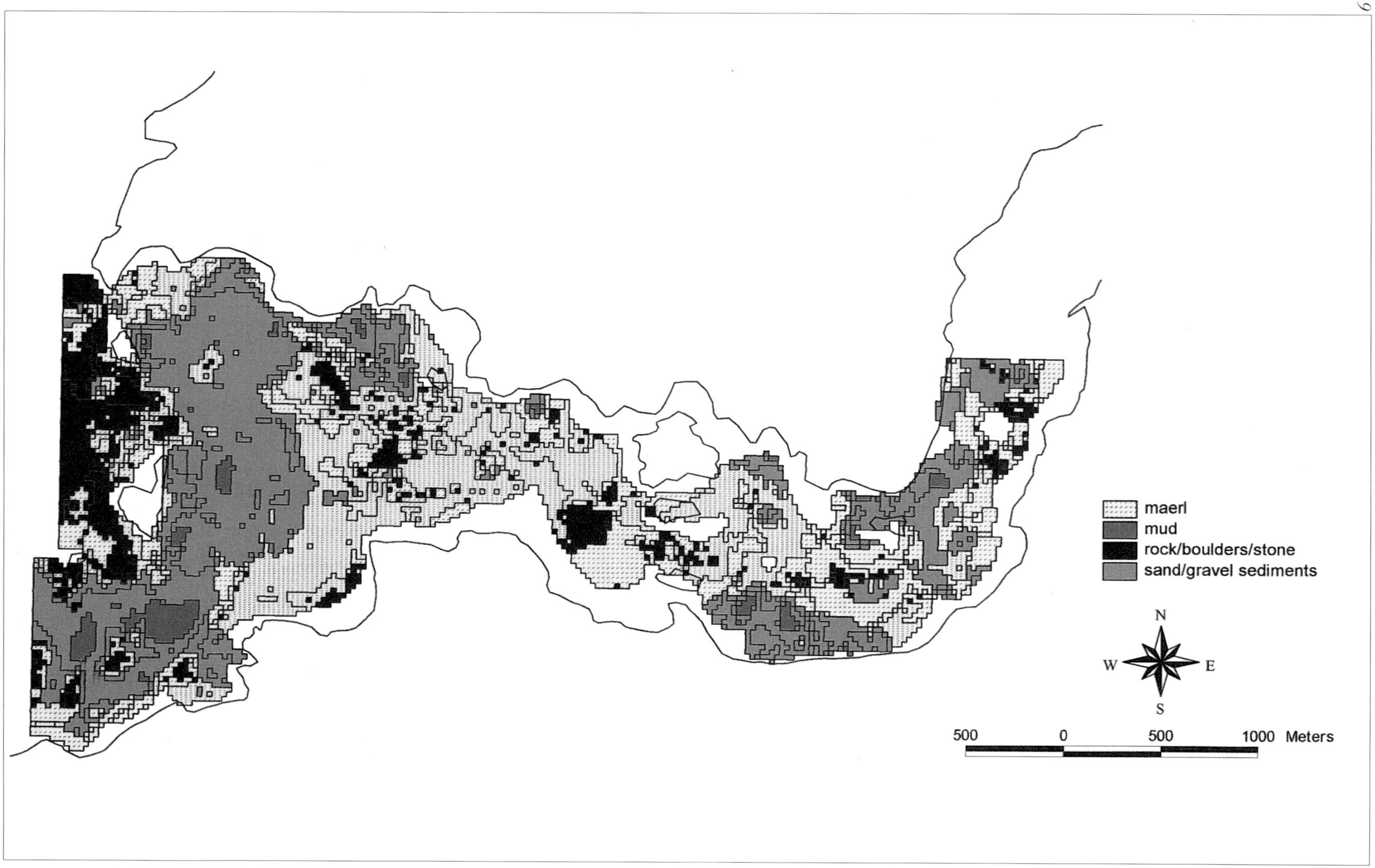

maerl
mud
rock/boulders/stone
sand/gravel sediments

N
W E
S

500 0 500 1000 Meters

Plate 39. Habitat types in Loch Ailort, part of the Sound of Arisaig candidate Special Area of Conservation.

Plate 40. Draft sensitivity zoning scheme for the Sound of Arisaig candidate Special Area of Conservation.

Plate 41. Maerl.

42

43

Plate 42. Traigh Lar, Hougharry, North Uist. Mobile dunes with marram grass.
Plate 43. Machair, near Loch Mor, Barvas, Lewis. Machair is characterised by a rich diversity of wildflowers in summer.

Plate 44. The Houb, Fora Ness, Shetland. A silled saline lagoon.
Plate 45. Loch Obe, Barra. Sea squirts and sponges on a vertical rock face.
Plate 46. Tassleweed – Ruppia cirrhosa.

47

48

49

Plate 47. *Thrift* – Armeria maritima maritima.
Plate 48. *Oysterplant* – Mertensia maritima.
Plate 49. *Scot's lovage* – Ligusticum scoticum.

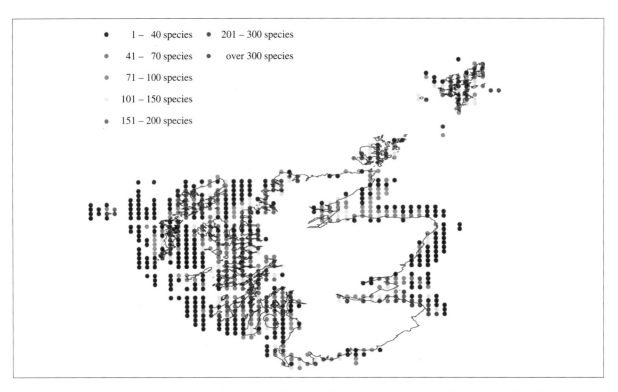

Plate 50. The species richness of coastal cells around Scotland. The data shown are derived from a number of datasets as detailed in the text, but they show where the survey effort in Scottish coastal waters has been focused.

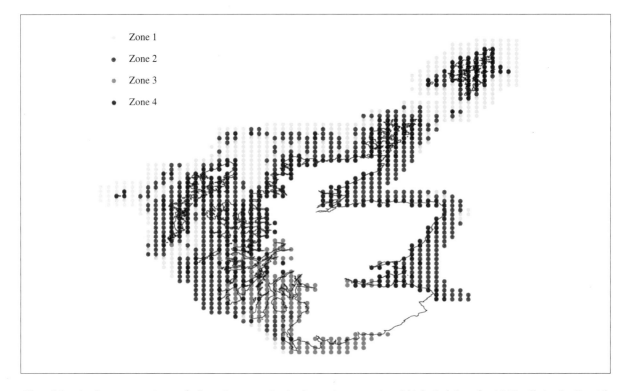

Plate 51. Analyses attempting to find contiguous zones in the environmental and biological data for 1347 cells in the Scottish coastal environment. Here the analysis was stopped at the four-zone stage, when four zones were distinct.

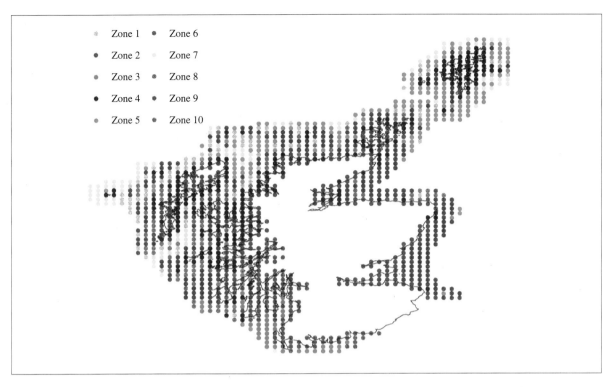

Plate 52. *When ten zones are analysed, there is a mosaic of colour indicating that the subdivision of the data have been continued too far.*

Plate 53. *Loch Duich.* Ascophyllum nodosum *ecad* mackaii *bed, a habitat largely confined to western Scotland and Ireland.*

Plate 54. Euphrasia campbelliae.
Plate 56. Euphrasia rotundifolia.

Plate 55. Euphrasia heslop–harrisonii.
Plate 57. Ord, Skye. Eelgrass (Zostera marina) *bed in maerl gravel with the seven-armed starfish* (Luidia ciliaris).

PART FOUR

SAFEGUARDING COASTAL BIODIVERSITY

Article 2 of the United Nations Convention on Biological Diversity described bio-diversity as being 'the variability among living organisms from all sources including, among other things, terrestrial, marine and other aquatic ecosystems and the ecological complexes of which they are part; this includes diversity with-in species, between species and of ecosystems' (Anon., 1994). Put more simply, biodiversity is therefore the total variety of all living things. Of relevance to this volume is the question 'How significant is coastal biodiversity to the overall bio-diversity within Scotland and does it therefore need to be safeguarded?'

The coastline of Scotland is approximately 11 800 km in length and embraces a great variety of landforms and associated habitats, influenced by climate, geology, geomorphology and active coastal processes. Long sandy beaches front the flat coastal machair plains in the Western Isles; rocky coasts with deeply indented, sheltered sea lochs make up much of the west coast; the predominantly low-lying east coast is broken only by the intrusions of the major firths; and hard, exposed sea cliffs dominate the north and north-west coasts. In addition, there are the three major archipelagos of Shetland, Orkney and the Western Isles, as well as numerous other islands and skerries around the west coast.

The coastline forms the zone where the sea meets the land; where marine organisms meet with terrestrial. Habitat and species diversity in the coastal zone is therefore high, consisting of elements from both environments. However, because the lifeform, physiology and behaviour of organisms found in these two environments are so different, there is very little overlap in their distribution, and the high-water mark forms a relatively distinct boundary between the two. Above this point are found species that, although essentially terrestrial, are strongly influenced by the marine environment and highly adapted to survive the stresses this brings. The effect of tidal flooding, salt spray and a mobile substrate, results in very specialised plant and animal communities fringing the shore. The seaward extent of these essentially terrestrial species is restricted to the limit of high water – only a very few flowering plants, such as *Zostera* and *Ruppia*, are able to survive regular flooding by sea water and these can be found co-existing with marine algae in the intertidal and sub-tidal regions. Below the high-water mark the marine algae and marine fauna are found. In the intertidal region are those species able to tolerate periodic exposure to air and the associated stresses; below the low-water mark are the truly marine species. Seabirds and seals are some of the few groups of animals able to cross the land–sea boundary, needing both environments to feed and live in at different times of the year.

The coastal zone is therefore a highly specialised environment with a high biodiversity – rich in habitats and species. It is made up of highly specialised plants and animals that have adapted to living in a stressful and very dynamic environment. As a result of this specialisation, many coastal species are limited to the coastal zone and are rarely found elsewhere. Others are more widespread in their distribution, found further inland or found out at sea. In addition, the geographical position of Scotland and the influence of the warm Gulf Stream and cold Arctic waters results in there being a number of species at the edge of their geographic range. Many southern species, such as the saltmarsh plants, sea lavender and sea purslane, reach their northern limit in the Solway, resulting in Scotland having a somewhat impoverished coastal flora compared with further south. However, there are also a number of northern species, such as the oyster plant and Scot's lovage which are at the extreme southern extent of their range on the northern shores of Scotland and do not extend any further south. In fact, one of the best known coastal plants is the Scottish primrose – a species found on dunes and cliffs on the very north coast, endemic to Scotland and found nowhere else.

To safeguard coastal biodiversity, an essential first step is to obtain an understanding of what is there. Chapters 12, 13 and 14 describe important inventory work that has been carried out over the last few years in the coastal zone. All three show the value of a comprehensive inventory to our knowledge of coastal habitats and their scientific interest. Tom Dargie and Kathy Duncan describe the extent and distribution of sand dunes and their associated communities. The survey has shown how figures relating to the extent of coastal blown sand in Scotland have been vastly underestimated in the past, and that Scotland has a much greater proportion of the UK resource than previously thought. In addition, as a result of visiting previously unsurveyed sites, it has revealed potentially new vegetation types, unrecognised by the National Vegetation Classification, but typical of many of Scotland's coastal systems.

Roger Covey examines saline lagoons, a priority habitat under the EC Directive on the Conservation of Natural Habitats and of Wild Fauna and Flora (the 'Habitats Directive') (Council of the European Communities, 1992), but about which remarkably little was known until recently. Essential information relating to the type of saline lagoons found in Scotland, their extent and distribution, and their species composition has now been compiled. This chapter shows the need for a national survey, in order to provide the basis for conservation of this fragile habitat and therefore to fulfil obligations under the Habitats Directive.

Stewart Angus describes machair, outlining some of the difficulties in providing a comprehensive definition of this complex habitat. Using the best available knowledge, he describes the extent and distribution of machair in Scotland. As Scotland contains a large proportion of the machair resource world-wide, it has a responsibility to safeguard this habitat by ensuring appropriate land-use management.

In his chapter, Michael Usher seeks to understand some of the principle questions underlying biodiversity in the coastal zone: 'What is it and how can it be measured?' 'How does it vary over time?' These essential questions must be answered in order to safeguard biodiversity in the coastal zone. Lastly, Michael Scott discusses the more practical aspects of safeguarding biodiversity. The preparation and implementation of Biodiversity Action Plans for species and habitats provides the focus for future action. Within the habitats and species listed, there are several of particular relevance to the coastal zone and for which, in some cases, Scotland has a high proportion of the total UK resource. However, there will still be a considerable challenge to achieve the often ambitious targets set within each plan.

References

Anon. 1994. *Biodiversity, the UK Action Plan*. HMSO, London.

Council of the European Communities. 1992. Council Directive 92/43/EEC of 21 May 1992: on the conservation of natural habitats and of wild fauna and flora. *Official Journal of the European Community*, L206/7.

12 THE SAND DUNE VEGETATION SURVEY OF SCOTLAND

T. C. D. Dargie and K. Duncan

Summary

1. A study of almost all dune and machair environments in Scotland is nearing completion, based on the National Vegetation Classification (NVC).
2. Results suggest that there are many potentially new NVC vegetation types associated with strand, semi-fixed dune, calcareous fixed dune, acidic fixed dune, heath, mire, swamp and scrub conditions.
3. Geographical Information System (GIS) data capture provides an inventory of the extent of different vegetation types and allows an aggregation of NVC types into maps of dune habitats. This enables an overview of site character.
4. NVC data allow the distribution and extent of important vegetation types to be recorded and assessments made of the condition of the dune resource on site-, region- and all-Scotland scales.
5. Survey results make an important contribution to the statutory duties of Scottish Natural Heritage (SNH) covering sand dune and machair environments, as well as providing baseline information for surveillance monitoring of site condition and change.

12.1 Introduction

Scottish Natural Heritage commissioned a vegetation survey of dunes in Scotland in August 1994. The project broadly follows the approach adopted by the Sand Dune Vegetation Survey of Great Britain which used the National Vegetation Classification (NVC) (Malloch, 1989; Rodwell, 1991 *et seq.*) as the basis for mapping areas with vegetated windblown sand. That field survey of all the dunes in England, covering 11 897 ha (Radley, 1994), and Wales, covering 6406 ha (Dargie, 1995), took six years between inception in 1987 and completion of survey work in 1992. A partial survey of the larger Scottish dunes (9641 ha in 34 sites) was also achieved in this period, covering 30% of the estimated vegetated sand area (31 436 ha; Ritchie and Mather, 1984) but perhaps only 5% of the total number of dune sites (Dargie, 1993). A report consisting of a site description and NVC map was produced for each site surveyed. The main aim of the current Sand Dune Vegetation Survey of Scotland is to complete work for the remaining dune areas in Scotland which lack NVC surveys.

The principal objectives of this project are:

- to locate all significant areas of vegetated windblown sand around the coast of Scotland

- to map and describe the vegetation of unsurveyed areas in the field using the NVC system

- to harmonise results with existing NVC surveys of other sand dune sites carried out prior to this survey, providing a consistent inventory of the total vegetated dune resource

- to present results in a series of reports covering different geographical regions of the Scottish coast

- to synthesise results from different coastal regions as a national report covering all of Scotland.

This chapter discusses the methods used in data treatment and presents information on potentially new NVC types, major results and uses of data by SNH.

12.2 Data capture, analysis and reporting

12.2.1 Field methods

Surveyed areas extend from the Mean High Water Spring Tide (MHWS) line on OS maps inland, to where windblown sand ceases to be the dominant medium in the plant-rooting zone. This covers a very wide range of ecological conditions from open beach to swamp and fen, and includes arable land, improved pasture, plantation forestry and land taken for tracks, pits, buildings, etc. Large open-water areas upon windblown sand, notably machair lochs, were excluded from the survey, since they represent aquatic rather than terrestrial habitats and are therefore subject to different survey methods to those used for sand dunes and to a non-NVC classification not covered in this chapter. Raised beaches made up of sand were also excluded from the survey unless they had a veneer of sand from adjacent modern dunes or had evidence of reworking of parent sand material by wind.

Field surveys followed a combination of techniques used in the original UK survey and those recommended for NVC survey (Rodwell, 1995). This involved a reconnaissance of the survey area, followed by mapping areas of visually homogeneous vegetation or mosaics at a scale of 1:10 000, and associated recording of quadrats and target notes. On completion the field survey will have mapped about 45 000 polygons (representing different vegetation types) and recorded several thousand quadrats and target notes.

12.2.2 Geographical Information System (GIS) data capture and analysis

Early in the project a decision was taken to use a GIS to hold mapped boundaries, to supply area data for calculating the extent of vegetation and other land-cover extents, and to produce several types of map for inclusion in reports. The major steps used for GIS analysis included digitising and checking field sheet boundaries; insertion of polygon attributes; allocation of a code to each polygon representing its predominant habitat (beach and strand; mobile dune; semi-fixed dune; fixed calcareous dune; fixed acidic dune; dry dune heath; wet dune heath; dune slack and wet grassland; mire, swamp or flush; arable and fallow; improved grassland; other habitats – track, road, sand pit, rubbish tip, tree plantation, houses, gardens, industrial land, car parks, etc.); creation of point layers for quadrat and target-note locations; labelling of layers for annotating NVC maps; and exporting polygon attributes (area, NVC/other land-cover code, dune habitat code) to spreadsheets for calculating areas of each NVC or other land-cover type per site and coastal region.

This approach has also been used to capture existing NVC data from dune sites mapped as part of the original UK survey and selected other dune sites which have been surveyed using the NVC between 1992 and the start of this project. For these cases, quadrat and target-note positions have been ignored. In some cases (mainly 1987 surveys carried out as part of the UK survey) polygon codes had to be carefully harmonised because a 1987 preliminary NVC sand dune conspectus was replaced by the University of Lancaster with the current NVC classification in late 1988. Harmonisation has required a further field visit to all sites surveyed in 1987 to ensure that 1987 codes are replaced by their closest post-1988 equivalents.

12.2.3 Reporting

Results are being presented in a series of eight coastal regions covering all of Scotland (Western Isles, Orkney, Shetland, Inner Hebrides, South-west Mainland, North-west Mainland, Moray Firth, East Mainland). Each region is covered by three volumes. Volume 1 includes survey aims, methods, detailed accounts of NVC and land-cover types, and maps of their distribution in the region. Many NVC communities and sub-communities are described using summary floristic tables giving Domin score ranges (as a measure of abundance) and constancy scores. Volume 2 presents a site-by-site description of dune habitats and dune NVC vegetation types, and other conditions based on target-note information (e.g. coastal edge erosion, blowouts, grazing impacts). The site description includes a map of dune habitats at 1:25 000 (e.g. Figure 12.1). These are derived from the NVC data to provide a more effective overview of results than labelled NVC maps (e.g. Figure 12.2). The relationship between dune habitats and NVC communities is shown in Table 12.1. Spreadsheets giving the areas of each dune habitat and NVC/other land-cover type are included as tables within the report. Information on the conservation status (whether, for example, it is a Site of

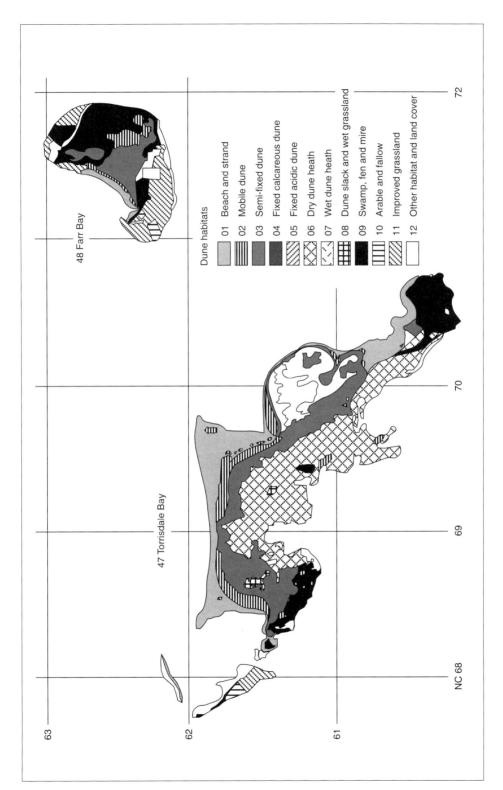

Figure 12.1 Dune habitats of Torrisdale Bay and Farr Bay, Sutherland.

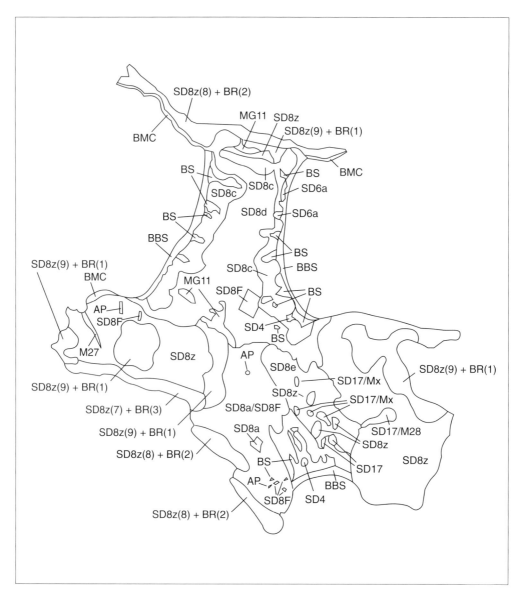

Figure 12.2 NVC map format (South Vatersay, Western Isles).

Special Scientific Interest (SSSI) or within a National Scenic Area) and dune management is also included. Annexes contain floristic tables derived from quadrats, maps of quadrat distribution, target notes and maps of target-note locations. Volume 3 contains the NVC vegetation maps. Loose sets of the original 1:10 000 maps, the scale used to map communities in the field, were produced for archiving and use in local SNH offices. For the purposes of the report, the maps were reduced in size to 1:15 000. Once all coastal regions are complete, an all-Scotland synthesis will be produced.

Table 12.1 Dune habitat categories and their main NVC vegetation types.

Dune habitats	NVC communities
Beach and strand	**Beach above MHWS, strand and embryo dune.** Includes: SD2 *Honkenya peploides–Cakile maritima* strandline SD3 *Matricaria maritima–Galium aparine* strandline SD4 *Elymus farctus* foredune SDx, SDy, SDz provisional new strandline communities
Mobile dune	**Mobile dunes dominated by dune building grasses.** Includes: SD5 *Leymus arenarius* mobile dune SD6 *Ammophila arenaria* mobile dune SD8c *Festuca rubra–Galium verum* fixed dune grassland, *Tortula ruralis* ssp. *ruraliformis* sub-community.
Semi-fixed dune	**Part-stabilised dunes.** Includes: SD7 *Ammophila arenaria–Festuca rubra* semi-fixed dune
Fixed dry calcareous dune grassland	**Calcicolous dune grassland.** Includes: SD8 *Festuca rubra–Galium verum* fixed dune grassland (excluding SD8c and SD8e) SD9 *Ammophila arenaria–Arrhenatherum elatius* dune grassland CG10 *Festuca ovina–Agrostis capillaris–Thymus praecox* grassland CG13 *Dryas octopetala–Carex flacca* heath
Fixed dry acidic dune grassland	**Calcifugous dune grassland.** Includes: SD10b *Carex arenaria* dune, *Festuca ovina* sub-community SD12 *Carex arenaria–Festuca ovina–Agrostis capillaris* grassland
Dry dune heath	**Dune heath on acidic sands.** Includes: SD11 *Carex arenaria–Cornicularia aculeata* lichen heath H11 *Calluna vulgaris–Carex arenaria* dune heath
Wet dune heath	**Vegetation of damp ground on acidic sands.** Includes: M15 *Scirpus cespitosus–Erica tetralix* wet heath M16 *Erica tetralix–Sphagnum compactum* wet heath
Slacks and wet grassland	**Vegetation of damp ground, often inundated in winter.** Includes: SD15 *Salix repens–Calliergon cuspidatum* dune slack SD16 *Salix repens–Holcus lanatus* dune slack SD17 *Potentilla anserina–Carex nigra* dune slack SD8e *Festuca rubra–Galium verum* fixed dune grassland MG10 *Holcus lanatus–Juncus effusus* rush pasture MG11 *Festuca rubra–Agrostis stolonifera–Potentilla anserina* inundation grassland MG13 *Agrostis stolonifera–Alopecurus geniculatus* inundation grassland
Swamp, fen and mire	**Vegetation of very wet ground covering all swamp, tall herb fens and mire-flush vegetation.** Includes: S10 *Equisetum fluviatile* swamp S19 *Eleocharis palustris* swamp M10 *Carex dioica–Pinguicula vulgaris* mire M28 *Iris pseudacorus–Filipendula ulmaria* mire
Arable and fallow	**Cultivated ground and associated fallows.** Includes: SD8F *Festuca rubra–Galium verum* fixed dune grassland–Fallow MG11F *Festuca rubra–Agrostis stolonifera–Potentilla anserina* inundation grassland–Fallow
Improved grassland	**Grassland dominated by species typical of improved pastures.** Includes: MG6 *Lolium perenne–Cynosurus cristatus* pasture MG7 *Lolium perenne* leys
Other habitats	**All other mapped ground.** Includes: buildings, gardens, roads, cemeteries, saltmarsh, open water, maritime cliff grassland, ruderal vegetation

12.3 NVC results

Full data for all of Scotland are not yet available but selected important findings can be reported now.

- There is a great diversity in the range of vegetation types present, covering the full habitat spectrum of the NVC. In total 80 different NVC communities have been mapped on Scottish dunes, excluding aquatic types. These include 2 calcicolous grassland, 3 heath, 14 mire, 3 maritime cliff, 9 mesotrophic grassland, 15 swamp, 17 sand dune, 7 saltmarsh, 3 calcifugous grassland, 7 woodland and scrub communities.

- A large number of potentially new NVC communities and sub-communities, not previously recognised, is present in Scotland (see Table 12.2). These greatly extend the range of variation in strand, semi-fixed dune, calcareous fixed dune, acidic fixed dune, dune slack, dune scrub, mire and swamp conditions compared with earlier descriptions using the NVC system (Malloch, 1989).

- Certain NVC types form five distinct biogeographical distributions with affinities for the bioclimatic zones reported by Birse (1971): a western and northern machair set on strongly calcareous sands (hyperoceanic boreal); a north-western mainland set on calcareous sands (hyperoceanic boreal / hemiArctic); a Moray Firth set on sands of varied base status (hemioceanic boreal); an eastern set on sands of varied base status (euoceanic boreal); and a south-western and south-eastern set on sands of varied base status (euoceanic northern temperate).

- Widespread cliff development can be seen on the foredune edge, with limited areas of mobile dune vegetation. There is little evidence of major accretion in western Scotland, suggesting poor sand supply from the beach zone and a slow retreat of the dune edge.

- There is a more complex mix of eroding, accreting and stable dune coastlines in eastern Scotland with no clear trend compared with west-coast conditions (Plate 42).

- Relatively poor development of dune slack NVC types, which are typical of dunes in England and Wales, is compensated for by the large number and extent of wet mesotrophic grassland, mire, fen, flush and swamp types that come to dominate dune wetlands in the cooler and generally wetter Scottish climate.

- Very large areas of fixed dune grassland in western and northern Scotland have been produced by widespread extensive stock grazing (Plate 43).

- Large areas of weedy fallow vegetation, associated with non-intensive tillage on crofted land, are mostly located in the Western Isles and Tiree.

- Large areas of semi-improved and improved grassland reflect more intensive stock grazing, especially in Orkney and south-west Scotland.

- Displacement of agriculture by forestry, golf courses and other forms of recreation as the major land uses has occurred on dunes of the south-western and eastern Scottish mainland. This is evidenced by clear changes in the type and balance of NVC vegetation types present compared with grazed sites.

These findings broadly agree with results found in the sample set of Scottish sites used in the original survey (Dargie, 1993). However, the full resource survey is required to give an accurate picture of biogeographical variation and also reveals the full extent of dune habitat degradation at the site, regional and national scale. In these areas, sand dune NVC types have been converted to other common, less diverse types. An example of the scale of conversion is given in a comparison of the dune resources of Orkney and the Western Isles (see Figure 12.3). A large proportion of vegetated windblown sand in Orkney (42.6%) has been converted to improved grassland. Most of this is the MG7 perennial rye grass *Lolium perenne* community, probably converted within the last 50 years at the expense of semi-fixed dune, calcareous fixed dune, wet neutral grassland and dune slack. Some conversion on a much smaller scale has also occurred in the Western Isles (6.8%) but this is mainly to the MG6 *Lolium perenne–Cynosurus cristatus* pasture community which often has remnants of SD8 *Festuca rubra–Galium verum* dune grassland present. The extent of fallow and arable land is large in the Western Isles but almost all cases represent traditional non-intensive tillage for oats and rye as winter fodder for stock, with distinctive seral vegetation (Crawford, 1989). Conversion here (mostly from slack and damp SD8 grassland) is much older but retains much nature conservation and economic interest. Arable and fallow ground, together with a large area of wet neutral grassland, provide excellent habitat for corncrake (*Crex crex*) and underpin much of the crofting economy located on dunes in South Uist, Benbecula, North Uist and Berneray (Sound of Harris).

Total dune area was anticipated as 31 436 ha, based on data from Ritchie and Mather (1984) for the average size of dune and machair/links surfaces in Scotland excluding the beach zone. The total extent is in fact much larger and will probably exceed 48 000 ha once surveying is complete, perhaps approximating the combined areas of the Fraserburgh (26 500 ha) and Links (21 900 ha) soil associations, which cover windblown sand as a parent material (Macaulay Institute for Soil Research, 1984). This major difference in figures for total extent appears to be due to large areas of dune wetland (mire and swamp) and climbing dune (sand blown over adjacent hillslopes, sometimes to considerable altitude), which were considered as transitional by Ritchie and Mather (1984) and thus excluded from their totals.

Table 12.2 Potential new NVC communities and sub-communities on dunes in Scotland.

Code	Provisional NVC name and status	Detail
Strand		
SDx	*Potentilla anserina* strandline community	Damp strandline
SDy	*Atriplex glabriuscula–A. prostrata* strandline community	Thin sand over shingle, dry conditions
SDz	*Catabrosa aquatica* strandline community	Wet strandline, mainly Inner Hebrides
SDxx	*Leymus arenarius–Elymus repens* strandline	Common, sheltered strandlines in Moray Firth and Orkney
Semi-fixed dunes		
SD7x	*Ammophila arenaria–Festuca rubra* semi-fixed dune *Galium verum* sub-community	Very extensive in western and northern Scotland, dominant semi-fixed dune type
SD7y	*Hylocomium splendens–Rhytidiadelphus triquetrus* sub-community	Extensive in Moray Firth
Fixed dune grassland		
SD8x	*Festuca rubra–Galium verum* fixed dune grassland *Centaurea nigra–Daucus carota* sub-community	Frequent on undergrazed pastures, western and northern Scotland
SD8y	*Hylocomium splendens–Rhytidiadelphus triquetrus* sub-community	Occasional, Moray Firth
SD8z	*Thymus praecox* sub-community	Very extensive in western and northern Scotland, especially on climbing dunes
SD9x	*Ammophila arenaria–Arrhenatherum elatius* dune grassland *Hylocomium splendens* sub-community	Occasional in Moray Firth
SD11x	*Carex arenaria–Cornicularia aculeata* dune lichen heath *Polytrichum piliferum–Cladonia zopfii* sub-community	Very rare, thin sand over shingle, Moray Firth
SD12x	*Carex arenaria–Festuca ovina–Agrostis capillaris* dune grassland *Hylocomium splendens* sub-community	Occasional, Moray Firth
SD12y	*Carex arenaria* sub-community	Shaded plantation rides, ground disturbed by rabbits, Moray Firth and eastern Scotland
SD12z	*Ammophila arenaria* sub-community	Acidic form of semi-fixed dune, eastern and south-western Scotland
SD12xx	*Racomitrium canescens* sub-community	Acidic dune equivalent of SD8c, occasional in Moray Firth and south-western Scotland
SD12xy	*Deschampsia flexuosa* sub-community	Rare, acidic dunes, Moray Firth
SD12xz	*Corynephorus canescens* sub-community	Very rare, acidic remobilised dunes in western Scotland

Table 12.2 continued

Code	Provisional NVC name and status	Detail
SD12yy	*Cladonia rangiformis–C. portentosa* sub-community	Occasional, acidic sand, eastern and south-western Scotland
CG10x	*Festuca ovina–Agrostis capillaris–Thymus praecox* grassland, *Saxifraga aizoides–S. oppositifolia* fellfield sub-community	Very rare, confined to Invernaver (North Scotland) (see Averis, 1997)
Heath		
Hx	*Juniperus communis–Empetrum nigrum– Arctostaphylos uva-ursi* heath	Rare, Inner Hebrides and Invernaver (North Scotland) (see Averis, 1997)
Dune slacks		
SD16x	*Salix repens–Calliergon cuspidatum* dune slack *Erica tetralix–Juniperus communis nana* sub-community	Very rare, confined to Morrich More (Moray Firth)
SD17x	*Potentilla anserina–Carex nigra* dune slack *Agrostis stolonifera* protoslack sub-community	Occasional, early stages of slack development in blowout floors
Swamp, fen and mire		
M16x	*Erica tetralix–Sphagnum compactum* wet heath Species-poor wet dune heath sub-community	Locally extensive on acidic sands in south-western and eastern Scotland, rare in Orkney
M28x	*Iris pseudacorus–Filipendula ulmaria* mire *Poa trivialis* sub-community	Common in western and northern Scotland, indicates heavy grazing which removes *Filipendula vulgaris*
Mxbd	Mx *Carex nigra* rich fen *Prunella vulgaris–Molinia caerulea* sub-community	Extensive, drier and more acidic areas of machair fens, slacks and flushes
MxCd	*Carex diandra* sub-community	Rare, wetter machair fens in Western Isles
MxMt	*Menyanthes trifoliata* sub-community	Rare, wetter machair fens in Inner Hebrides
MxPp	*Potentilla palustris* sub-community	Occasional, base-poor fens on edge of wind-blown sand, western Scotland
MxTm	*Triglochin maritima* sub-community	Extensive, most typical type of machair fen especially in Western Isles
SHv	*Hippuris vulgaris* swamp	Occasional in wetter swamps of Western Isles, rare elsewhere
SxTHF	*Phragmites australis–Calliergon cordifolium* tall-herb fen	Occasional in Western Isles, rare elsewhere
Scrub		
W23x	*Ulex europaeus–Rubus fruticosus* agg scrub *Cytisus scoparius* sub-community	Occasional in Moray Firth
Wx	*Juniperus communis communis* dune scrub	Rare, Moray Firth

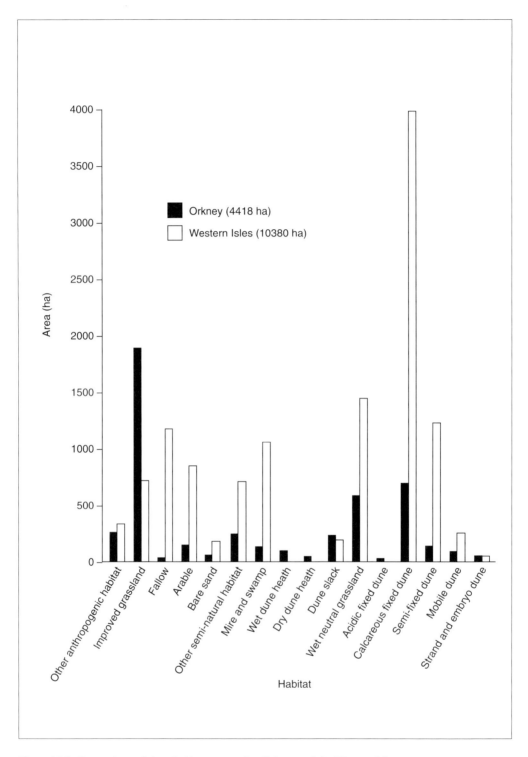

Figure 12.3 Comparison of dune habitat extents for Orkney and the Western Isles.

12.4 SNH uses of survey data

Survey results form a detailed baseline which provides important information for work supporting the statutory duties of SNH. The principal areas of use are as follows.

- Implementation of the Habitats and Birds Directives, most notably providing information to support six Special Areas of Conservation (SACs) for Annex 1 sand dune habitats and six SACs for machair habitat. NVC maps are being used to identify and map the extent of Annex 1 habitats and will inform management. In addition the NVC maps can be used to identify Annex 1 habitats in non-SAC locations as and when required.

- Survey results will aid proposals for monitoring in order to maintain the conservation interest of Annex 1 habitats. As an example of surveillance monitoring, repeat surveying in 1996 of sites on Coll (Inner Hebrides), surveyed using the NVC in 1992 and 1993, shows large amounts of change which are probably due to a major increase in the rabbit population at the same time as stock grazing pressure has been reduced under management agreements (Dargie, 1996). Repeat mapping at Crossapol, Coll (see Figure 12.4) shows large areas of the SD7 *Ammophila arenaria–Festuca rubra* semi-fixed dune community converted to SD8 *Festuca rubra–Galium verum* fixed dune, together with large extents of sub-community change to more open and less stable types in which sand-adapted mosses are prominent (SD7x provisional *Galium verum* to SD7d *Tortula ruralis* ssp. *ruraliformis* sub-community; SD8d *Ranunculus acris–Bellis perennis* to SD8c *Tortula ruralis* ssp. *ruraliformis* sub-community).

- Implementation of the UK Biodiversity Action Plan, providing essential background information to support costed habitat action plans which are being developed for machair and sand dune habitats.

- Provision of information for locations worthy of SSSI status. Data collected have already confirmed the nature conservation importance of existing dune and machair SSSIs and allow each site to be assessed in terms of its regional, national and UK context. Results have also provided information for the possible revision of some existing SSSI boundaries and, in a small number of cases, identified sites that are currently unprotected and worthy of SSSI recognition.

- Provision of information to assist the advisory role of SNH on the natural heritage of Scotland. This work includes providing responses to the potential effects of development proposals, agricultural practices, recreation and other activities, as well as advising on future management to maintain or enhance the nature conservation interest.

References

Averis, A.B.G. 1997. *The Vegetation of Druim Chuibe, Invernaver, Sutherland.* Unpublished report to Scottish Natural Heritage (Contract Number JE 00825). Scottish Natural Heritage, Edinburgh.

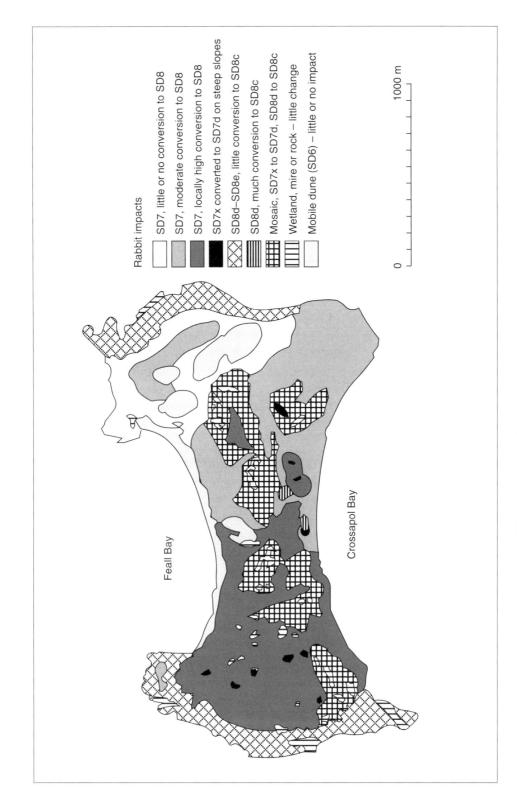

Figure 12.4 Rabbit-induced changes to vegetation (1992–6) at Crossapol, Coll.

Birse, E.L. 1971. *Assessment of Climatic Conditions in Scotland. 3: Bioclimatic Sub-regions.* Macaulay Institute for Soil Research, Aberdeen.

Crawford, I. 1989. Agriculture, weeds, and the Western Isles machair. *Transactions of the Botanical Society of Edinburgh*, **45**, 483–492.

Dargie, T.C.D. 1993. *Sand Dune Vegetation Survey of Great Britain. Part 2 – Scotland.* Joint Nature Conservation Committee, Peterborough.

Dargie, T.C.D. 1995. *Sand Dune Vegetation Survey of Great Britain. Part 3 – Wales.* Joint Nature Conservation Committee, Peterborough.

Dargie, T.C.D. 1996. *Survey of condition of sand dune communities on Crossapol & Gunna SSSI and Totamore Dunes SSSI, Isle of Coll.* Unpublished report to Scottish Natural Heritage (Contract Number 95/J3F). Scottish Natural Heritage, Edinburgh.

Macaulay Institute for Soil Research. 1984. *Organization and Methods of the 1:250 000 Soil Survey of Scotland.* Macaulay Institute for Soil Research. Aberdeen.

Malloch, A.J.C. 1989. Plant communities of the British sand dunes. *Proceedings of the Royal Society of Edinburgh*, **96B**, 53–74.

Radley, G.P. 1994. *Sand Dune Vegetation Survey of Great Britain. Part 1 – England.* Joint Nature Conservation Committee, Peterborough.

Ritchie, W. and Mather, A.S. 1984. *The Beaches of Scotland.* Countryside Commission for Scotland, Perth.

Rodwell, J.S. 1991 *et seq. British Plant Communities. Volumes 1–5.* Cambridge University Press, Cambridge.

Rodwell, J.S. 1995. *Handbook for Using the National Vegetation Classification: A Technique for Vegetation Survey.* Joint Nature Conservation Committee, Peterborough.

13   THE SALINE LAGOON SURVEY OF SCOTLAND

R. Covey

Summary

1. In response to the listing of saline lagoons as a priority habitat under the European Community Directive on the Conservation of Natural Habitats and of Wild Fauna and Flora (the 'Habitats Directive') (Council of the European Communities, 1992), surveys of the resource in Scotland were initiated.
2. For the purposes of the survey lagoons were identified as 'areas of shallow coastal saltwater of varying salinity separated from the sea by sandbanks or shingle or, less frequently, by rocks'.
3. Between 1993 and 1995, 139 lagoons were surveyed using standard Marine Nature Conservation Review (MNCR) survey methodology. The majority of the lagoons occurred in the Outer Hebrides, associated with rocky basins at the head of fjardic sea lochs. Elsewhere, lagoons were distributed from Shetland and Orkney to the mainland coastline of Scotland, and were associated with hard and soft coasts.
4. The data collected were analysed, along with existing published information, to produce descriptions of the 41 biotopes that were present. These ranged from typical lagoonal habitats of soft sediments with *Ruppia* spp., to rocky entrance channels with rich communities of sponges and seas quirts.
5. The data were also used to provide a natural heritage importance assessment of each site using a standard MNCR natural heritage importance assessment protocol. These data will support the conservation of important lagoon sites by Scottish Natural Heritage (SNH).

13.1   Introduction

The inclusion of lagoons (Plate 44) as a priority habitat in the European Community Directive on the Conservation of Natural Habitats and of Wild Fauna and Flora (the 'Habitats Directive') (Commission of the European Communities, 1992; Council of the European Communities, 1992), provided impetus for surveys to describe the resource. Adequate information was available for lagoons in England and Wales, but no comprehensive survey of the lagoons of Scotland had been carried out.

The initial question facing any prospective lagoon surveyor is 'What is a lagoon?' Various workers have used varying definitions which limit or expand the scope of the resource. Barnes (1980) provides a definition of a lagoon as 'an area of salt or brackish water separated from the adjacent sea by a low-lying sand or shingle barrier'. This definition depends on the presence of geomorphological features such as sand or shingle spits or bars, and to a certain extent overlooks the biological features that separate lagoons from other maritime and marine habitats. Ardizzone *et al.* (1988) provide the definition 'bodies of saltwater (from brackish to hypersaline) partially separated from the sea by barriers'. This definition recognises the element of separation from the sea which is of key importance in creating lagoonal conditions, whilst ignoring the nature of the barrier, which may or may not affect the nature of the biological community in the lagoon.

On the basis of the definition provided by Ardizzone *et al.* (1988), an interpretation for the implementation of the Habitats Directive was agreed by the UK Joint Nature Conservation Committee (JNCC) as 'areas of shallow coastal saltwater of varying salinity separated from the sea by sandbanks or shingle, or less frequently by rocks' (Joint Nature Conservation Committee, 1995). The inclusion of coastal saltwater separated by rocky barriers encompasses many of the most important brackish water basins at the head of fjardic inlets in the Hebrides.

Since the main impetus for this survey programme was the collection of data to support the implementation of the Habitats Directive by Scottish Natural Heritage on behalf of the Scottish Office, the JNCC definition formed the basis for initial site selection. The main criterion used to define a lagoon for the purpose of this survey was the restricted exchange of water with the open sea. This restricted water exchange may be due to a rock, shingle or sediment barrier, or may be due to a narrow connecting channel which limits tidal movement within the lagoon but which presents less of a barrier to species recruitment.

13.2 Methodology

Potential survey sites were initially identified by examination of existing literature, and more importantly, by examination of 1:50 000 scale Ordnance Survey maps. Potential sites were identified as areas shown as marine, but appearing to have no intertidal zone (i.e. restricted tidal range) or restricted connection with the sea; or areas which were shown as freshwater but believed to be brackish by virtue of their proximity to the sea or indication of a connecting channel. The initial list of sites was then circulated to local SNH staff who were able to discount some sites as freshwater, and suggest others which had been omitted. The sites included in the final list for survey thus ranged from fully saline sheltered marine inlets with a limited tidal range and water exchange, to extremely low-salinity pools with no tidal fluctuation and which received saltwater only at high water of spring tides.

In order to ensure compatibility with data collected from other marine surveys, methodology was largely that developed by the MNCR (Hiscock, 1996). An initial on-site examination discounted some sites because they were freshwater, or fully marine inlets with a normal tidal exchange. Sites which met the criteria of reduced

Lagoon	Physiographic type	No. of biotopes
14.14 Loch nan Clachan	Sluiced lagoon	1
14.15 Oban Trumisgarry	Sluiced lagoon	4
14.16 Oban nan Struthan	Sluiced lagoon	2
14.17 Loch an Sticir	Sluiced lagoon	2
14.18 Pool east of Loch Iosal an Duin	Silled lagoon	1
14.19 Loch Iosal an Duin	Silled lagoon	4
14.20 Oban Honary	Lagoon inlet	3
14.21 Inlet south of Aird nan Laogh	Silled lagoon	3
14.22 Pool between Loch na Caiginn and Loch Portain	Isolated lagoon	1
14.23 Greaneclett pool	Silled lagoon	6
14.24 Loch Yeor	Lagoon inlet	12
14.25 Loch an Duin	Silled lagoon	9
14.26 Alioter Loch	Sluiced lagoon	4
14.27 Bac-a-Stoc	Silled lagoon	6
14.28 Pool west of Loch Minish	Silled lagoon	2
14.29 Loch an Strumore	Sluiced lagoon	10
14.30 Loch Houram	Lagoon inlet	9
14.31 Pool south-east of Loch Maddy	Sluiced lagoon	5
14.32 Oban nan Stearnan	Silled lagoon	7
14.33 Loch na Ciste and Loch Stromban	Silled lagoon	11
14.34 Leiravay Bay	Lagoon inlet	4
14.35 Oban Sponish	Silled lagoon	5
14.36 North arm of Orasay Bay	Silled lagoon	4
14.37 Oban a Chlachain	Sluiced lagoon	7
14.38 Oban Irpeig	Lagoon inlet	3
14.39 Loch Leodosay	Silled lagoon	4
14.40 Ardheisker pool	Sluiced lagoon	2
14.41 Oban na Curra	Sluiced lagoon	4
14.42 Oban nam Fiadh	Sluiced lagoon	7
14.43 Locheport pool	Silled lagoon	3
14.44 Loch Obisary	Silled lagoon	11
14.45 Oban nam Muca-mara	Lagoon inlet	2
14.46 Oban an Innseanaich	Lagoon inlet	2
14.47 East arm of Scotvein Bay	Silled lagoon	4
14.48 Oban Uaine North	Lagoon inlet	2
14.49 Head of Neavag Bay	Silled lagoon	7
14.50 Pool south-west of Oban Haka	Silled lagoon	2
14.51 Loch ba Alasdair	Silled lagoon	4
14.52 Pool south of Loch Meanervagh	Silled lagoon	2
14.53 Craigastrome pool	Sluiced lagoon	3
14.54 Ob Saile	Sluiced lagoon	5
14.55 Liniclate ponds west	Sluiced lagoon	2
14.56 Liniclate ponds east	Sluiced lagoon	1
14.57 Loch Bee and head of Loch Skipport	Sluiced lagoon	6
14.58 Ardmore pool	Silled lagoon	3
14.59 Pool north-west of Gashernish	Sluiced lagoon	3
14.60 Pool north of East Gerinish	Percolation lagoon	2
14.61 Loch Roag and Howmore pool	Sluiced lagoon	3
	Silled lagoon	
14.62 Loch Ceann a Bhaigh	Silled lagoon	3
14.63 North Locheynort	Sluiced lagoon	7
14.64 Loch a Bharp and Auratote	Lagoon inlet	5
14.65 North Lochboisdale lagoon	Sluiced lagoon	1
14.66 Channel south-west of Aird Buidhe	Sluiced lagoon	2
14.67 East Kilbride	Sluiced lagoon	3
14.68 Bun Sruth	Silled lagoon	3
14.69 North-west of An Acairseid	Lagoon inlet	4
14.70 Loch Obe	Lagoon inlet	4
14.71 Bagh Huilavagh	Lagoon inlet	8
14.72 Bagh Beag	Lagoon inlet	8

Figure 13.1 Sites surveyed in the Uists, Western Isles, as part of the Scottish saline lagoon survey.

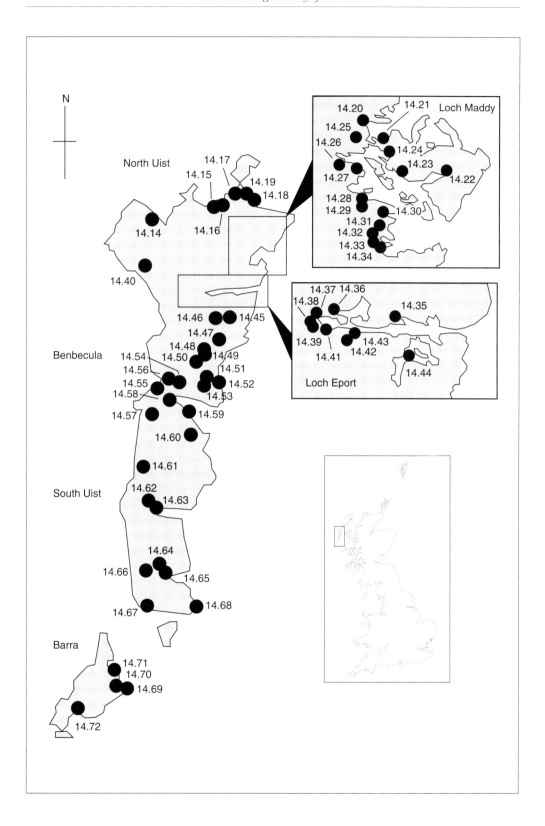

or variable salinity and a restricted connection with the open sea were surveyed by snorkelling. Survey consisted of standard MNCR field recording of each habitat within the lagoon and listing of the conspicuous species present, together with their abundance. Where possible, the geographic distribution of the habitats was also mapped.

Following surveys, data were entered on to the MNCR database (Mills, 1994) to enable comparisons to be made easily between all of the sites. Species data were analysed using TWINSPAN (Hill, 1979) to suggest groupings of species which formed recurring communities. Together with habitat information, this formed the basis of descriptions of 'biotopes' present in the lagoons.

Following data analysis, an assessment of the natural heritage importance of each of the lagoons was carried out using an assessment protocol developed by the MNCR (Connor and Hill, 1997).

13.3 Results

By direct survey or use of existing data, 139 lagoons have been reported on (Covey *et al.*, 1998; Thorpe, 1998; Thorpe *et al.*, 1998). The majority of the lagoons were situated in the Outer Hebrides (Figures 13.1 and 13.2) with smaller numbers in Shetland (Figure 13.3), Orkney (Figure 13.4) and mainland Scotland (Figure 13.5).

The survey recorded 41 biotopes (Covey *et al.* in prep.), which ranged from those characteristic of lagoons, such as soft sediments with beds of *Ruppia*, to those less frequently associated with lagoons such as tideswept bedrock with rich communities of sponges and seasquirts (Plate 45). A list of biotopes is provided in Table 13.1, of which 12 are considered to be unique to lagoon habitats (marked with * in Table 13.1).

The species present ranged from those typical of low-salinity environments such as estuaries and lagoons, to those found widely in fully marine conditions. Within this wide range of species were a smaller subset of species which may be considered to be lagoonal specialists. These included *Ruppia cirrhosa* (Plate 46), *R. maritima*, *Potamogeton pectinatus* and *Lamprothamnium papulosum*. The 11 new sites for *Lamprothamnium papulosum* have substantially increased the known range of this protected species.

The survey identified five physiographic lagoon types, which follow those of Sheader and Sheader (1989), and represent degrees of isolation from the open sea. Within these types, characteristic communities of flora and fauna were present.

13.3.1 Isolated lagoons

The Scottish isolated saline lagoons are cut off from the sea by an impermeable barrier above Mean High Water of Spring Tides. The barrier is composed of rock, or sediment in the case of some large pools, which occurs in high saltmarsh zones. In such lagoons water exchange with the open sea only occurs sporadically during high spring tides, or in periods of storm inundation. Conditions of salinity and

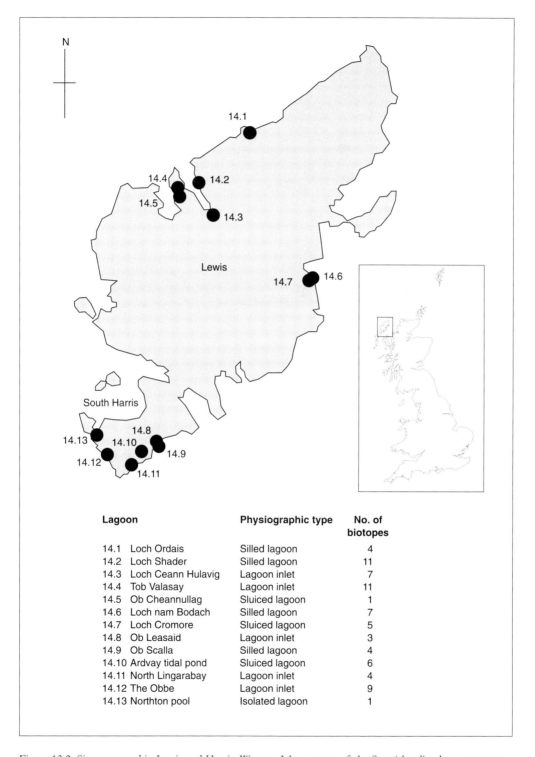

Lagoon	Physiographic type	No. of biotopes
14.1 Loch Ordais	Silled lagoon	4
14.2 Loch Shader	Silled lagoon	11
14.3 Loch Ceann Hulavig	Lagoon inlet	7
14.4 Tob Valasay	Lagoon inlet	11
14.5 Ob Cheannullag	Sluiced lagoon	1
14.6 Loch nam Bodach	Silled lagoon	7
14.7 Loch Cromore	Sluiced lagoon	5
14.8 Ob Leasaid	Lagoon inlet	3
14.9 Ob Scalla	Silled lagoon	4
14.10 Ardvay tidal pond	Sluiced lagoon	6
14.11 North Lingarabay	Lagoon inlet	4
14.12 The Obbe	Lagoon inlet	9
14.13 Northton pool	Isolated lagoon	1

Figure 13.2 Sites surveyed in Lewis and Harris, Western Isles, as part of the Scottish saline lagoon survey.

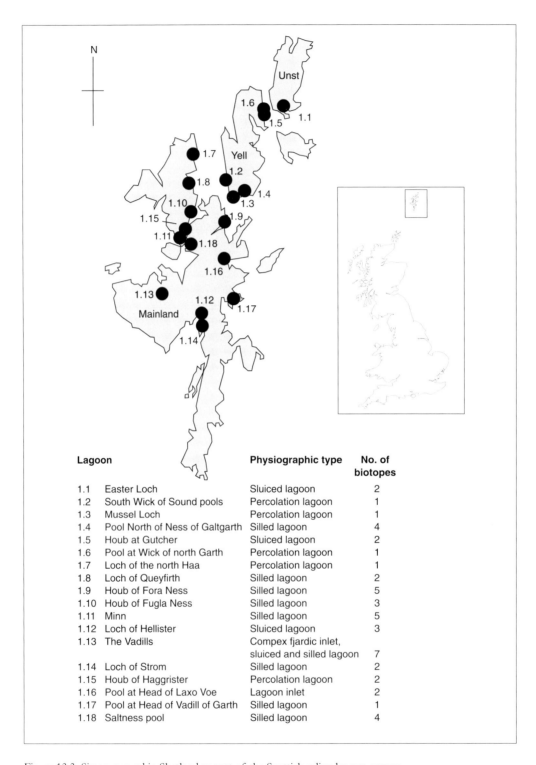

Lagoon		Physiographic type	No. of biotopes
1.1	Easter Loch	Sluiced lagoon	2
1.2	South Wick of Sound pools	Percolation lagoon	1
1.3	Mussel Loch	Percolation lagoon	1
1.4	Pool North of Ness of Galtgarth	Silled lagoon	4
1.5	Houb at Gutcher	Sluiced lagoon	2
1.6	Pool at Wick of north Garth	Percolation lagoon	1
1.7	Loch of the north Haa	Percolation lagoon	1
1.8	Loch of Queyfirth	Silled lagoon	2
1.9	Houb of Fora Ness	Silled lagoon	5
1.10	Houb of Fugla Ness	Silled lagoon	3
1.11	Minn	Silled lagoon	5
1.12	Loch of Hellister	Sluiced lagoon	3
1.13	The Vadills	Compex fjardic inlet, sluiced and silled lagoon	7
1.14	Loch of Strom	Silled lagoon	2
1.15	Houb of Haggrister	Percolation lagoon	2
1.16	Pool at Head of Laxo Voe	Lagoon inlet	2
1.17	Pool at Head of Vadill of Garth	Silled lagoon	1
1.18	Saltness pool	Silled lagoon	4

Figure 13.3 Sites surveyed in Shetland as part of the Scottish saline lagoon survey.

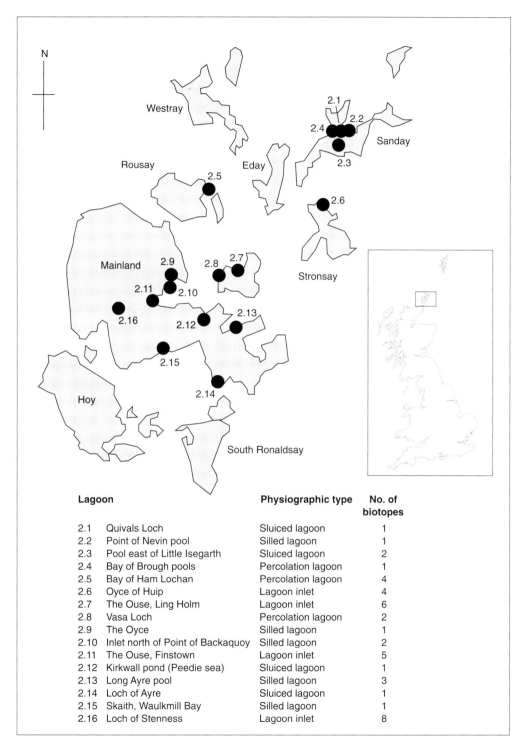

Lagoon		Physiographic type	No. of biotopes
2.1	Quivals Loch	Sluiced lagoon	1
2.2	Point of Nevin pool	Silled lagoon	1
2.3	Pool east of Little Isegarth	Sluiced lagoon	2
2.4	Bay of Brough pools	Percolation lagoon	1
2.5	Bay of Ham Lochan	Percolation lagoon	4
2.6	Oyce of Huip	Lagoon inlet	4
2.7	The Ouse, Ling Holm	Lagoon inlet	6
2.8	Vasa Loch	Percolation lagoon	2
2.9	The Oyce	Silled lagoon	1
2.10	Inlet north of Point of Backaquoy	Silled lagoon	2
2.11	The Ouse, Finstown	Lagoon inlet	5
2.12	Kirkwall pond (Peedie sea)	Sluiced lagoon	1
2.13	Long Ayre pool	Silled lagoon	3
2.14	Loch of Ayre	Sluiced lagoon	1
2.15	Skaith, Waulkmill Bay	Silled lagoon	1
2.16	Loch of Stenness	Lagoon inlet	8

Figure 13.4 Sites surveyed in Orkney as part of the Scottish saline lagoon survey.

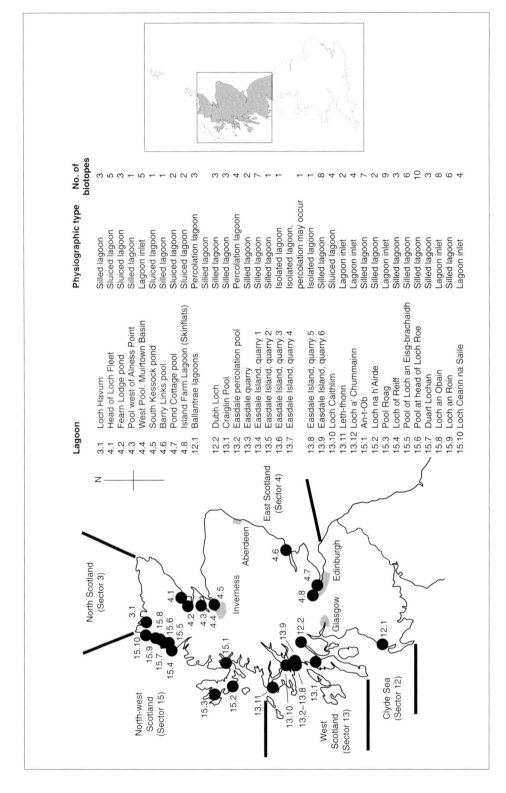

Figure 13.5 Sites surveyed in mainland Scotland and Inner Hebrides as part of the Scottish saline lagoon survey.

temperature within these lagoons are likely to vary immensely, both within single lagoons over time, and between lagoons. Salinity will be dependent on the relative rates of freshwater and seawater inputs. With high freshwater input and low salt-water input, low salinity results, with immense variability caused by freshwater input during winter rains, or evaporation during low rainfall conditions of summer. Because of the lack of water exchange, temperature and oxygen levels can vary substantially, often with periods of high temperature and resulting deoxygenation. This is a probable cause of the low species richness in these lagoons, compounded by the low chance of species' recruitment over the barrier during water exchange or by other agents. Scottish isolated lagoons are generally shallow (less than 2 m depth) and small (less than 1 ha). Typically, isolated saline lagoons have a muddy substratum dominated by ephemeral green algae. Because of the adverse conditions, lagoonal specialists are often able to thrive, and dense beds of spiral and beaked tasselweeds are present, along with stoneworts and *Potamogeton* spp. Biotope richness is generally low. The mean number of biotopes present is 1.

13.3.2 Percolation lagoons

The percolation saline lagoons identified in this study have a permeable barrier of shingle, sand or cobbles. Water exchange occurs through this barrier and, consequently, conditions are often more stable than those in isolated lagoons. Conditions of salinity and temperature can still vary immensely depending on freshwater input relative to the seawater exchange and the size of the lagoon. Similar to isolated lagoons, high temperatures and deoxygenation can often occur, resulting in species impoverishment. However, because water exchange occurs on most tides, recruitment of species is less of a chance event, although water is often subjected to a filtering process during passage through the sediment barrier, thus restricting larval transmission. The communities present in these lagoons vary according to the degree of water exchange. In Easdale (Argyll) the barrier is extremely permeable and salinity conditions resemble that of the open sea, allowing growth of kelps and a wide range of flora and fauna. In Ballantrae, a more restricted water exchange has favoured beds of eelgrass *Zostera marina* and beaked tasselweed *Ruppia maritima*. Biotope richness is generally low, however, with a mean of 2 biotopes recorded per lagoon.

13.3.3 Sluiced lagoons and silled lagoons

Sluiced saline lagoons have many features in common with silled saline lagoons, since both sluices and sills act as a restriction of water exchange with the open sea. Together, sluiced and silled saline lagoons are the commonest types present throughout Scotland (37 sluiced lagoons and 56 silled lagoons out of a total of 139 lagoons). With both sluiced and silled saline lagoons, the degree of water exchange varies according to the height of sluices or sills relative to mean high water or mean low water. Where sills are close to mean high water, limited water exchange takes place. This can lead to a stable, but low-salinity lagoon (salinity depending on the degree of freshwater input). Under such conditions, such as

Table 13.1 List of biotopes described from Scottish saline lagoon survey, with equivalent biotopes from the national classification (* considered unique to lagoons).

MNCR Scottish lagoon code	Biotope	Equivalent national code (Connor *et al.* 1997a, b – version 97.06)
LITTORAL ROCK		
Supralittoral (splash zone) rock		
Lag.1	Yellow and grey lichens on supralittoral rock	LR.YG
Lag.2	Black lichen *Verrucaria maura* on littoral fringe rock	LR.Ver.Ver
Sheltered eulittoral (intertidal) rock		
Lag.3	*Pelvetia canaliculata* on upper shore rock or mixed substrata	SLR.Pel
Lag.4	*Fucus spiralis* on upper eulittoral rock or mixed substrata	SLR.Fspi
Lag.5	Barnacles and *Patella vulgata* on vertical eulittoral bedrock	ELR.BPat
Lag.6	*Ascophyllum nodosum* on mid eulittoral rock or mixed substrata	SLR.Asc.Asc SLR.Asc.VS SLR.AscX
Lag.7	*Fucus vesiculosus* on mid eulittoral rock or mixed substrata	SLR.Fves SLR.FvesX
Lag.8	*Fucus serratus* on lower eulittoral rock or mixed substrata	SLR.Fserr SLR.FserX SLR.Fserr.VS
*Lag.9	Fucoids and *Mytilus edulis* in shallow tidal rapids	SLR.Asc.VS
Lag.10	*Fucus ceranoides* on low-salinity eulittoral rock or mixed substrata	SLR.Fcer SLR.FcerX
Lag.11	*Mytilus edulis* on eulittoral consolidated gravel	SLR.MytX
Lag.12	Mats of ephemeral green algae on eulittoral mixed substrata	SLR.EphX
LITTORAL SEDIMENT		
Lag.13	*Fucus muscoides* on supralittoral peaty turf	LMU.Sm
Lag.14	Blue-green algae on saltmarsh erosion steps or supralittoral rock around brackish pools	Not described
Lag.15	*Corophium volutator* and *Arenicola marina* in sandy mud shores. See also Lag.12	Not described
SUBLITTORAL ROCK		
Sheltered infralittoral (algal-dominated) rock		
Lag.16	*Laminaria saccharina* and *Chorda filum* on silted infralittoral rock	MIR.Lsac.Ft
Lag.17	Kelps and coralline algae in infralittoral tidal rapids	MIR.XKScrR SIR.Lsac.T
*Lag.18	Dense *Cladophora rupestris* on vertical infralittoral rock	SIR.FChoG
*Lag.19	*Polyides rotundus* or *Furcellaria lumbricalis* on reduced salinity infralittoral rock or mixed substrata	SIR.PolFur
*Lag.20	*Ascophyllum nodosum* with epibiota on fronds on infralittoral rock	SIR.AscSAs
*Lag.21	Fucoids on infralittoral rock in microtidal areas	SIR.FChoG
*Lag.22	*Fucus ceranoides* on infralittoral rock in brackish-water microtidal areas	SIR.FcerEnt
Lag.23	Filamentous algae on infralittoral rock or mixed substrata in microtidal areas of variable salinity	SIR.FiG IMX.Tra
Lag.24	Dense *Mytilus edulis* on vertical sublittoral rock	SIR.MytT
Lag.25	Sparse *Mytilus edulis* and a diatom film on vertical sublittoral bedrock	SIR.MytT

Table 13.1 continued

MNCR Scottish lagoon code	Biotope	Equivalent national code (Connor *et al.* 1997a, b – version 97.06)
Sheltered circalittoral (animal-dominated) rock		
Lag.26	*Alcyonium digitatum* on vertical circalittoral bedrock	Not described
*Lag.27	Sponges and ascidians on vertical circalittoral rock	Not described
SUBLITTORAL SEDIMENT		
Sublittoral plant-dominated mixed sediment		
Lag.28	Coralline algae on tide-swept infralittoral gravel, pebbles and cobbles	MIR.EphR IGS.Lgla
Lag.29	Dense *Trailliella* and other filamentous red algae on infralittoral muddy gravel	IMX.Tra
Sublittoral plant-dominated muds		
Lag.30	Filamentous green algae and ascidians on infralittoral sandy mud	IMS.Zmar
Lag.31	Filamentous green algae on infralittoral sandy mud	Not described
Lag.32	*Zostera marina* beds on infralittoral sandy mud	Not described
*Lag.33	*Ruppia* spp. beds on infralittoral mud and fine sand	IMS.Rup
*Lag.34	*Potamogeton* spp. on low-salinity infralittoral mud	IMU.NVC A12
*Lag.35	*Phragmites australis* on low-salinity infralittoral mud, peat and sand	IMU.NVC S4
Sublittoral animal-dominated sands		
*Lag.36	*Lanice conchilega* in tide-swept sublittoral sand	IGS.Lcon
Lag.37	An impoverished fauna in sublittoral sand	Not described
Sublittoral animal-dominated muddy sands		
Lag.38	*Arenicola marina* in sublittoral muddy sand and gravel	Not described
Sublittoral animal-dominated muds		
Lag.39	Holothurians in shallow sublittoral muddy sediment	Not described
*Lag.40	*Corophium volutator* in sublittoral mud	Not described
Lag.41	An impoverished fauna in sublittoral mud	Not described

*Unique to lagoon habitats.

found in Loch an Duin (North Uist), stable, low-salinity communities occur, with extensive beds of eelgrass *Zostera marina*, spiral and beaked tasselweed *Ruppia spiralis* and *R. maritima*, and stoneworts such as *Lamprothamnium papulosum*. Typically, sheltered conditions result in salinity stratification, where seawater, entering the lagoon over the sill or through the sluice, sinks below the less dense freshwater. This results in higher salinity conditions on the lagoon floor and low salinity in surface waters and shallower areas. With a sluice towards mean low-water level, good seawater exchange ensures that conditions tend towards fully marine, with communities typical of sheltered, fully saline water. Many of these communities are similar to those recorded at the head of some sea lochs (see, for example, Howson *et al.*, 1994), although where substantial freshwater input occurs, more brackish water communities are often present. Due to the good water exchange with the open sea, recruitment of species to these lagoons suffers few restrictions, resulting in generally high species richness. A particular feature of silled lagoons is the presence of a tidal waterfall or tidal rapids, caused by water draining from the lagoon over the sill during low tide periods or through a constricted channel as the tide recedes on the open coast. Such features have a very restricted European distribution due to the smaller tidal range in areas of Scandinavia where other suitable fjardic marine inlets occur. Biotope richness in sluiced lagoons varies immensely with a mean of 3 biotopes present, but ranging from 1 to 10 biotopes per lagoon. In silled lagoons it is generally higher with a mean of 4 biotopes per lagoon and a similar range of 1 to 11 biotopes per lagoon.

13.3.4 Saline lagoons

Saline lagoon inlets have no sill, or sub-tidal sill, but have limited water exchange with the open sea due to a restricted connecting channel. Strong tidal streams occur in the connection channel as water rushes into the lagoon as the tide rises, and out of the lagoon as the tide falls. Tidal range is restricted due to the inability of water to drain from the lagoon completely through the narrow channel. Brackish water conditions occur when high freshwater input is present. Communities within the Scottish saline lagoon inlets are similar to those of sheltered fully marine conditions, although with high freshwater influence, communities of brackish water are often present. The outstanding features of these lagoons are the species-rich, tideswept connecting channels, where increased water movement leads to the development of dense carpets of sponges and sea squirts. The rocky bed of these rapids is often dominated by pink encrusting coralline algae including rhodoliths attached to pebbles and/or free-living maerl. Scottish lagoon inlets have the highest biotope richness of all the physiographic types, with a mean of 5 biotopes recorded per site.

13.4 Discussion

A number of workers have suggested reasons to explain the variation in the development of lagoon biota. Barnes (1980) suggests that whilst lagoons can be classified on the basis of their salinity, substratum, physiographic type or mode of formation, the most useful distinction relates to their degree of isolation from the open sea. The degree of water exchange with the open sea was further examined by Guelorget and Perthuisot (1992), using the term 'paralic' to describe aquatic systems which have their origin with the sea but which are separated from it to varying degrees. They suggest a confinement scale, based on the degree of exchange with the open sea. The groups suggested range from zone 1, where there is free connection with the open sea, and where the biota is a continuation from the marine domain, to zone 6, where conditions are almost completely freshwater with associated freshwater biota, or hypersaline, with cyanobacterial mats. This approach is in broad agreement with the species groups described by Bamber *et al.* (1992) for British lagoons. They suggest six suites of species:

1. freshwater/low-salinity species
2. lagoonal species
3. euryhaline specialist lagoonal species which are also tolerant of estuarine conditions
4. stenohaline marine specialist lagoonal species
5 estuarine species which are pre-adapted to lagoonal conditions
6. estuarine species that occur incidentally in lagoons.

These divisions approximate to each species group's ability to colonise and survive varying degrees of confinement. In the current study the mean number of species recorded in a lagoon increased with increasing connection with the sea. Thus isolated lagoons had a mean of 3.6 species present, percolation lagoons 11.8, sluiced lagoons 27.1, silled lagoons 27.5 and lagoon inlets 54.5 species.

Sheader and Sheader (1989) suggest that larger lagoons are less susceptible to environmental perturbations and deleterious impacts, and thus should have higher species numbers. However, they found increased species numbers with increasing area only occurred in silled lagoons. Bamber *et al.* (1992) suggested that increasing area will lead to increasing exposure effects from wind, including wave action and turbulent mixing. This mixing will destroy any stratification and reduce any localised differences in the physical factors affecting habitats and thereby reduce the overall variability of the lagoon. They showed that increasing presence of lagoonal specialists with size only occurs with linear lagoons where the shape affords protection from wind fetch. This allows the development of stratification, and localised extreme conditions which favour lagoonal specialist species. Their conclusions were that large, narrow or convoluted shaped lagoons (including those that are broken up by islands) support the most diverse lagoonal communities. This is supported by the results of the natural heritage importance assessment carried out on the 139 lagoons surveyed during the current work. Those that were assessed as being of most importance were those which are large and have a convoluted shape with islands and numerous basins (such as the Vadills in Shetland, or Loch an Duin in North Uist), or have a linear shape (such as Tob Valasay in Harris).

13.5 Conclusions

The survey of 139 lagoon sites using standardised methodology provides the first comprehensive data set on this important natural resource. Use of MNCR survey and reporting techniques has resulted in the collection of information which can be directly compared with other marine surveys, including lagoon surveys carried out in England and Wales during the 1980s. The results of these surveys will enable Scottish Natural Heritage to assist the government in fulfilling its obligations under the Habitats Directive and will provide a basis for conservation of this fragile marine habitat.

Acknowledgements

These surveys would not have been possible without the cheerful support of the many survey staff from SNH and JNCC, and a number of contractors. Thanks also to Eleanor Murray of JNCC for assistance with outputs from the MNCR database.

References

Ardizzone, G.D., Catandella, S. and Rossi, R. 1988. *Management of coastal lagoon fisheries and aquaculture in Italy*. Technical Paper No. 295. FAO Fisheries, Rome.

Bamber, R.N., Batten, S.D., Sheader, M. and Bridgwater, N.D. 1992. On the ecology of brackish water lagoons in Great Britain. *Aquatic Conservation: Marine and Freshwater Ecosystems*, **2**, 65–94.

Barnes, R.S.K. 1980. *Coastal lagoons: the natural history of a neglected habitat*. Cambridge University Press, Cambridge.

Commission of the European Communities. 1992. *Relation between the Directive 92/43/CEC Annex I habitats and the CORINE habitat list 1991 (EUR 12587/3). Version 1 (Draft)*. Unpublished, Commission of the European Communities DG XI-EEA-TF.

Connor, D.W. and Hill, T.O. 1997. *Marine Nature Conservation Review: natural heritage assessment protocol – version 97.03*. Joint Nature Conservation Committee, Peterborough.

Connor, D.W., Brazier, D.P., Hill, T.O. and Northen, K.O. 1997a. Marine Nature Conservation Review: marine biotope classification for Britain and Ireland. Volume 1. Littoral biotopes. Version 97.06. *JNCC Report*, No. 229.

Connor, D.W., Dalkin, M.J., Hill, T.O., Holt R.H.F. and Sanderson, W.G. 1997b. Marine Nature Conservation Review: marine biotope classification for Britain and Ireland. Volume 2. Sublittoral biotopes. Version 97.06. *JNCC Report*, No 230.

Council of the European Communities. 1992. Council Directive 92/43/EEC of 21 May 1992: on the conservation of natural habitats and of wild fauna and flora. *Official Journal of the European Communities*, L206/7.

Covey, R., Fortune, F., Nichols, D. and Thorpe, K. 1998. *Marine Nature Conservation Review Sectors 3, 4, 12, 13 and 15. Lagoons in mainland Scotland and the Inner Hebrides: area summaries*. (Coasts and seas of the United Kingdom. MNCR series.) Joint Nature Conservation Committee, Peterborough.

Covey, R., Thorpe, K. and Nichols, D. Marine Nature Conservation Review Sectors 1–4 and 12–15. Lagoons in Scotland: biotope classification. *JNCC Report*, No. 233, in prep.

Guelorget, O. and Perthuisot, J.P. 1992. Paralic ecosystems. Biological organization and functioning. *Vie Milieu*, **42**, 215–251.

Hill, M.O. 1979. *TWINSPAN – a FORTRAN program for arranging multivariate data in an ordered two way table by classification of the individuals and attributes*. Cornell University, Ithaca, New York.

Hiscock, K. (ed.). 1996. *Marine Nature Conservation Review: rationale and methods*. (Coasts and seas of the United Kingdom. MNCR series). Joint Nature Conservation Committee, Peterborough.

Howson, C.M., Connor, D.W. and Holt, R.H.F. 1994. The Scottish sealochs. An account of surveys undertaken for the Marine Nature Conservation Review. (Contractor: University Marine Biological Station, Millport.) Marine Nature Conservation Review Report, No. MNCR/SR/27. *JNCC Report*, No. 164.

Joint Nature Conservation Committee. 1995. *Council Directive on the Conservation of natural habitats and wild fauna and flora (92/43/EEC) – The Habitats Directive. A list of possible Special Areas of Conservation in the UK. List for Consultation (31 March 1995)*. Joint Nature Conservation Committee for the Department of the Environment, the Welsh Office, the Scottish Office and the Department of the Environment (Northern Ireland), Peterborough.

Mills, D.J.L. 1994. A manual for the analysis of data held on the Marine Nature Conservation Review database. Marine Nature Conservation Review Report, No. MNCR/OR/18. *JNCC Report*, No. 173.

Sheader, M. and Sheader, A. 1989. The coastal saline ponds of England and Wales: an overview. (Contractor: University of Southampton, Department of Oceanography, Southampton.) *Nature Conservancy Council, CSD Report*, No. 1009.

Thorpe, K. 1998. *Marine Nature Conservation Review Sectors 1–2. Lagoons in Shetland and Orkney: area summaries.* (Coasts and seas of the United Kingdom. MNCR series.) Joint Nature Conservation Committee, Peterborough.

Thorpe, K., Dalkin, M.J., Fortune, F. and Nichols, D. 1998. *Marine Nature Conservation Review Sector 14. Lagoons in the Outer Hebrides: area summaries.* (Coasts and seas of the United Kingdom. MNCR series.) Joint Nature Conservation Committee, Peterborough.

14 THE STATE OF THE MARITIME NATURAL HERITAGE: MACHAIR IN SCOTLAND

S. Angus

Summary

1. Machair is more than a habitat; more than just plants, birds and sandy soil: it is a blend of low-lying coastline, sand, partly consisting of shell fragments, the effects of strong winds, combined with just the right amount of rainfall and, most crucially, the involvement of people and their grazing animals.
2. So unusual is the right combination of these features that machair is restricted worldwide to just the north-west of Scotland and the north-west of Ireland.
3. Machair is arguably as much a cultural phenomenon as a physical or biological one.

14.1 Introduction – what is machair?

Machair is a complex habitat, and a complex of habitats. Ritchie (1976) defined it as:

> a base of blown sand which has a significant percentage of shell-derived materials and lime-rich soils with pH values normally greater than 7.0. A level or low-angle smooth surface at a mature stage of geomorphological evolution and a sandy grassland-type vegetation with long dune grasses and other key dune species having been eliminated.

Core plants are red fescue (*Festuca rubra*), common bird's-foot-trefoil (*Lotus corniculatus*), white clover (*Trifolium repens*), yarrow (*Achillea millefolium*), lady's bedstraw (*Galium verum*), ribwort plantain (*Plantago lanceolata*), eyebright (*Euphrasia officinalis*), daisy (*Bellis perennis*) and the moss *Rhytidiadelphus squarrosus*. Biotic interference, such as is caused by heavy grazing, sporadic cultivation, trampling and sometimes artificial drainage should be a detectable influence within the recent historical period. Even with such detailed specifications, however, uncertainties remain regarding the geographical limits of the habitat in Scotland.

Machair is the only major habitat to be known solely by its Gaelic name, and the use of the term has been reviewed by Angus (1993). Strictly speaking, the term applies only to the plain, for which the term *machair grassland* has been suggested (Curtis, 1991). However, it is popularly employed to describe a wider range of habitats, including at least the dune and foredune. It has been suggested that the term *machair system* be adopted for this wider habitat complex based on blown shell sand. Angus (1994) defines this as:

> containing a core area of level or low-angle coastal plain (= machair grassland) fronted by beach and often dunes, and grading inland into hill machair, blackland, marsh, freshwater loch, saltmarsh, brackish loch or sandflats, or a combination of these, forming machair system, where altitude has a strong influence on habitat.

All parts of a machair system are subject to oceanic climate featuring strong winds and high rainfall and are influenced by blown sand, the sand composed of up to 90% shell fragments. Normally alkaline soils have been cultivated and/or grazed throughout the history of human settlement resulting in a *cultural* landscape. Vegetation of machair grassland significantly features the National Vegetation Classification *Ranunculus acris–Bellis perennis* (SD8d) and *Prunella vulgaris* (SD8e) sub-communities of the *Festuca rubra–Galium verum* community (SD8) (Dargie, 1993).

The nature of aquatic and transition habitats is often determined by slight variations in the underlying topography inland from the machair grassland. If the land slopes upwards, hill machair develops. Most larger systems, however, have a machair grassland which slopes downwards inland from the dunes, so that the inland boundary of the grassland takes the form of a marsh or, if lower-lying, a machair loch. In some situations, this marsh or loch may be connected to the sea, so that saltmarsh takes the place of marsh, and any loch becomes brackish, the salinity being determined by the altitude of the connection to the sea (though distance from the sea and freshwater flow may exert a strong influence on this relationship). If this inland area is particularly low-lying, the 'loch' will empty at low tide, forming sandflats, and sometimes isolating the machair grassland as an island, as in the case of Baleshare, Kirkibost and Vallay in North Uist. The transition area between blown sand and moorland, often occupied by human settlement, is *blackland*, a term which should not be applied to the moorland itself (Angus, 1997).

14.2 Extent

Recent work, as yet incomplete, carried out by Scottish Natural Heritage (Dargie and Duncan, Chapter 12) will provide a definitive figure for the area of blown sand in Scotland, while further analysis of this and other work, notably the beach surveys carried out by Aberdeen University for the Countryside Commission for Scotland (CCS) (Ritchie and Mather, 1984), may allow more precise identification of machair systems than is possible at present.

There remains uncertainty about the eastern limit of machair on the northern Scottish mainland. Many of the systems of the Northern Isles, described as machair in the beach reports (Mather *et al.*, 1974) were later said to 'resemble' machair (Ritchie, 1994). A provisional map of machair distribution in Scotland is given in Figure 14.1, based on a combination of the CCS beach reports and some of Dargie's work, but further detailed analyses will be required for a definitive map.

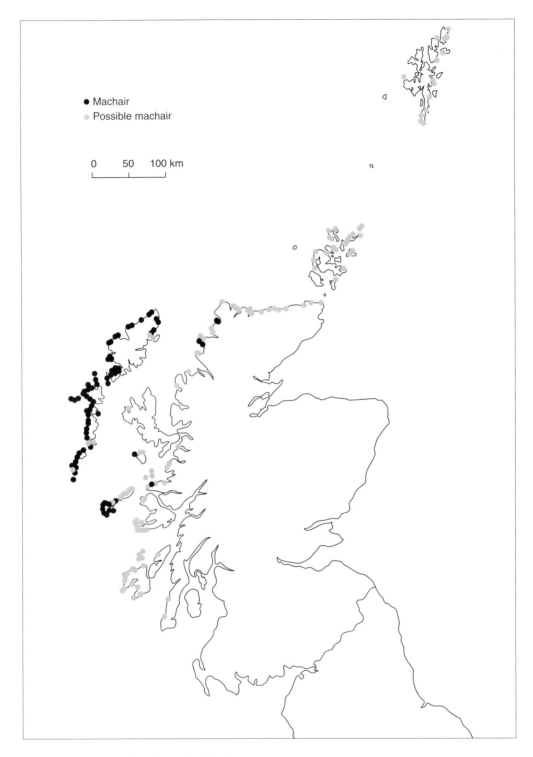

Figure 14.1 Location of machair in Scotland.

Even such detailed analyses, however, cannot provide exact figures for the total extent of machair systems in Scotland: problems will remain in allocating parts of lochs which are 'machair lochs' at their seaward end, and acid at their inland end (Angus, 1996). In addition, precise boundaries of all saltmarshes are not yet available, nor are the means of distinguishing all sand-based saltmarshes from other types. Likewise, the landward boundary of hill machair and blackland may be problematic. The extent of machair grassland in Scotland has been said to be of the order of 14 500 ha, with some 7500 ha in Ireland, a total resource of only 22 000 ha. The total extent of machair systems would probably double these figures (Angus, 1994). However, previous figures for the extent of blown sand in Scotland have been shown to be underestimates (Dargie and Duncan, Chapter 12), and it is probable that better estimates will give a larger extent, at least in Scotland.

Machair is restricted globally to north-west Scotland and north-west Ireland, though it has recently been claimed for New Zealand (Wilson *et al.*, 1993). Machair is listed on the EC Directive on the Conservation of Natural Habitats and of Wild Fauna and Flora (the 'Habitats Directive'), but is priority-rated only in Ireland, despite the greater extent (two-thirds of EU area) in Scotland and the higher conservation value of Scottish systems (see below).

14.3 Machair – its conservation value

The natural heritage value of machair systems has been reviewed by Angus (1994). Both Scottish and Irish systems have high value for landscape, geomorphology, botany and invertebrates, but Ireland lacks the wide range of aquatic communities seen in Scotland, as well as the very high numbers and densities of breeding birds known from Scottish machair. The links with the human heritage are arguably stronger in Scotland, certainly at the present day. It is fully acknowledged that the very high conservation value of at least the Scottish systems is entirely dependent on active management by crofters, especially in the Outer Hebrides and Tiree. Traditional, rotational cultivation, linked to cattle-rearing, is probably the main influence on maintaining the conservation interest. Where this has declined in recent times, as in Lewis and Harris, the wildlife has also declined, and these systems show a marked contrast to their counterparts in the southern Outer Hebrides.

A summary of nature conservation interest is given in Table 14.1. Though human history is omitted from the list, it should be noted that the human and natural heritage aspects of machair have always been very closely linked, and that historical studies can reveal a great deal about the habitat (Angus, 1997).

Machair in the Uists and Tiree supports densities of breeding waders which are unsurpassed in Europe. The traditional land use and the virtual absence of ground predators are key attributes of this breeding success. The main species are: dunlin (*Calidris alpina*), redshank (*Tringa totanus*), oystercatcher (*Haemotopus ostralegus*) and ringed plover (*Charadrius hiaticula*). There are also important numbers of breeding

Table 14.1 The natural heritage interest of machair.

Very high densities of breeding waders (not in Ireland)
Wintering birds
Rare species such as corncrake and corn bunting breeding
Wildfowl associated with open waters
Wide range of plant communities
Landscape
Invertebrates
Brackish waters (mainly Scotland)
Saltmarshes
Marshes
Freshwater lochs, some with contrasting water chemistry
Geomorphology
Environmental gradients/transitions

wildfowl on the machair lochs, and the winter lochs and beaches support large numbers of wintering birds.

Two key breeding species of the machair are the corncrake (*Crex crex*) and the corn bunting (*Emberiza celandra*), both in decline elsewhere in the UK.

Even though machair is very much a managed habitat, there are comparatively few alien species. As use of herbicide is rare, the patchwork of rotation encourages a rich and varied assemblage of agricultural wild flowers, which die back prior to harvest.

14.4 Agriculture

All the machair is grazed, mainly by sheep, but in Tiree and the Uists there are significant numbers of cattle. Winter fodder is grown by a traditional method which involves the collection and spreading of tangle, vast amounts of which are torn from the seabed by winter gales and deposited on the beaches for crofters to collect. This not only supplies nutrients, but binds the sand. Crops are grown in a rotation of about three years, with the land lying fallow in the other years. The patches are usually unfenced, and provide a great variety of cover and feeding areas for breeding birds.

Crofting is almost always a part-time occupation, and this labour-intensive type of agriculture is closely tied to the local economy, as other employment is required to retain a good range of age groups in the community. Where employment is now scarce, as in the remoter parts of Lewis and Harris, cattle have been abandoned in favour of more easily managed sheep, with a rapid decline in wildlife on the affected land.

Grazing is required to keep the grasses from out-competing flowering plants but, if overgrazed, the sward deteriorates, and, if broken, erosion may result.

14.5 Machair land-use issues

Human association with machair has a long history, and the machair has been a resource throughout the period of settlement.

Construction projects require sand and with few sources of glaciofluvial sand in north-west Scotland, machair and beach sand are exploited to varying degrees. Planning legislation now controls commercial extraction, and increasingly community control of small-scale agricultural extraction is exerted to conserve the wider resource.

Tourism is economically important throughout the machair areas. Noticeable effects are localised and active co-operation invariably solves the few problems. Car parking can be provided so as to avoid traffic damage to machair surfaces, as in the Western Isles Access to Beaches Programme. Targeted interpretation and education can usually alleviate other access difficulties, e.g. slope erosion caused by some windsurfers gaining access to beaches on Tiree by leaping down steep, eroding machair fronts.

Introduced predators can be a serious issue in areas with large numbers of ground-nesting birds, especially where there are no native ground predators, as in most of the machair islands. The Western Isles Mink Control Group is attempting to prevent mink released from farms in Lewis from crossing the Sound of Harris to North Uist; mink are also a problem in Argyll. The more recent introduction of hedgehogs to the islands is also a cause for concern, as they are known to consume birds' eggs.

The sandy machairs provide ideal burrowing and feeding territory for rabbits. Their burrowing and scraping can trigger or exacerbate erosion, while competition with stock for grazing can hinder management initiatives. Ferrets introduced to control rabbits can become a wider predator problem, as in North Uist. It is essential that islands such as Pabbay and Berneray in the Sound of Harris and Tiree in the Inner Hebrides be maintained in their rabbit-free state.

Rising sea level and associated increases in storm surges (Brampton *et al.*, Chapter 6) may pose long-term problems for machair systems, as much of their area is very low-lying, and protected (if at all) by only a narrow fringe of dunes. Though dynamism is an inherent feature of machair, and the habitat has an ability to accommodate large-scale change (Angus, 1997), such changes could flood large areas, threatening (at the very least) the present traditional cultivation which sustains important aspects of the natural heritage interest.

14.6 Conclusion

Scotland has a special responsibility for machair, being one of only two countries in the world supporting the habitat. Scotland has arguably superior bird populations to Ireland, and a wider range of habitats within the machair systems. Active management is essential to maintain these habitats, and this, in turn, is inextricably linked to economy and settlement. Though there are potential threats to the best machairs, there also exist opportunities for restoring the degraded machairs of islands such as Lewis and Harris.

References

Angus, S. 1993. The meaning and use of the word machair in Gaelic and English. *Hebridean Naturalist*, **11**, 41–49.

Angus, S. 1994. The conservation importance of the machair systems of the Scottish islands, with particular reference to the Outer Hebrides. *In* Baxter, J.M. and Usher, M.B. (eds) *The Islands of Scotland: A Living Marine Heritage*. HMSO, Edinburgh, 95–120.

Angus, S. 1996. Natural heritage conservation in the Southern Outer Hebrides. *In* Gilbertson, D., Kent, M. and Grattan, J. (eds) *The Outer Hebrides: the Last 14,000 Years*. Sheffield University Press, Sheffield, 227–251.

Angus, S. 1997. *The Outer Hebrides: the Shaping of the Islands*. White Horse Press, Harris and Cambridge.

Curtis, T.G.F. 1991. The flora and vegetation of sand dunes in Ireland. *In* Quigley, M.B. (ed.) *A Guide to the Sand Dunes of Ireland*. Compiled for the 3rd Congress of the European Union for Dune Conservation and Coastal Management, Galway, 42–66.

Dargie, T.C.D. 1993. *Sand dune vegetation survey of Great Britain: a national inventory. Part II: Scotland*. Joint Nature Conservation Committee, Peterborough.

Mather, A.S., Smith, J.S. and Ritchie, W. 1974. *Beaches of Orkney*. Unpublished report to Countryside Commission for Scotland by Geography Department, University of Aberdeen.

Ritchie, W. 1976. The meaning and definition of machair. *Transactions of the Botanical Society of Edinburgh*, **42**, 431–440.

Ritchie, W. 1994. Physical environments of the coastlines of the Outer Hebrides and the Northern Islands of Scotland and their potential for economic development. *In* Baxter, J.M. and Usher, M.B. (eds) *The Islands of Scotland: A Living Marine Heritage*. HMSO, Edinburgh, 13–29.

Ritchie, W. and Mather, A.S. 1984. *The Beaches of Scotland*. Countryside Commission for Scotland, Perth.

Wilson, J.B., Watkins, A.J., Rapson, G.L. and Bannister, P. 1993. New Zealand machair vegetation. *Journal of Vegetation Science*, **4**, 655–660.

15 SCOTLAND'S COASTAL BIODIVERSITY: WHAT, WHERE AND WHEN?

M. B. Usher

Summary

1. Scotland has a lengthy coastline of some 11 800 km, with a variety of environments, including cliffs, dunes, saltmarshes, intertidal lagoons, estuaries, etc. Four aspects of the biodiversity of this varied coastline are considered.

2. First, what does the biodiversity consist of? Highlights of Scotland's coastline are mentioned to demonstrate both the variety and the importance of this coastal resource. The discussion focuses on both species and habitats; insufficient is known about within-species variation.

3. Secondly, it is important to place this diversity in its geographical setting. Terrestrially, we can define biogeographical zones, but can these be extended into the coastal environment? The results of a study attempting to investigate the zonal structure of coastal Scotland indicates that four zones can be recognised, but these are poorly defined and do not have common boundaries across the coastline with the terrestrial zones.

4. Thirdly, ecosystem processes are dynamic and hence there is change over time. Scotland's coastal biodiversity is going to vary in both space and time. This ever-changing environment contributes to the variety of the coastline; speeding up or slowing down the changes could reduce biodiversity.

5. Finally, how should we view coastal biodiversity? There are many ecological processes contributing to the maintenance of species-richness, and these need to be understood if plans to safeguard biodiversity have a chance of success.

15.1 Introduction

Scotland has approximately 90 000 species (Usher, 1997), of which only a proportion are found along the coast. It is perhaps impossible to estimate what this proportion is because of the impossibility of defining where the coast begins and ends. Beside the deep sea lochs in the west of Scotland, oak (*Quercus petraea*) forest can come down virtually to the high-tide mark; are oak trees and all their associated fauna and flora to be counted as coastal? Similarly, species of the deeper sea, such as the sperm whale (*Physetes macrocephalus*), can occasionally be seen near to the shore; are these and their parasites also to be counted as coastal? If all of these are to be considered as coastal, then the proportion of species that are coastal must be large.

Even if a precise definition of what are coastal species is elusive, a 'common sense' definition cuts out the oakwoods (definitely terrestrial) and the sperm whale (an animal of the open ocean), and leaves the species and habitats that are really only found in the areas where the land meets the sea. Even such a common-sense approach leaves ambiguities; is thrift or sea pink (*Armeria maritima*) a species of the coast or of the mountain top? It occurs in both environments, but not in between!

However, counting the number of species is not the only way of measuring bio-diversity (Harper and Hawksworth, 1994). It should really include an element of intraspecific genetic diversity as well as a measure of habitat diversity. It is impossible to combine all of these elements into a single index of biodiversity, partly because they are inherently different concepts and partly because our knowledge base is so unequal (we know little about the genetic variability of most coastal organisms or about the species of bacteria in coastal soils, whereas we know a lot about the birds and vascular plant species as well as about the types of sand dune ecosystems). This inequality of the knowledge base is a major concern (Georgiadis and Balmford, 1992).

As well as enumerating the biodiversity, we also need to know the factors influencing it, and the way that we might manage that biodiversity in a sustainable, or, perhaps more strictly, a more sustainable, manner. It must be remembered that the coastline is naturally a highly dynamic system, eroding in some places and accreting in others. A whole variety of human activities impact on the coast (van der Maarel, 1997), but one that is often highlighted is the pressure of human trampling (Andersen, 1994). Why is this? Developments of docks, land claim for agriculture, and other large-scale projects change the coastal ecosystem entirely, replacing the more natural suite of microbial, plant and animal species with concrete, tarmac, crops and ruderal species. However, the effects of pollution (Leggett *et al.*, 1995), water abstraction or trampling modify the suite of natural species and ecosystems. This is much more open to observation, survey and experimentation, the tools of the ecologist. These factors, although having a lesser impact on coastal ecosystems, have been studied much more than the major factors that have totally altered the ecosystems.

This in turn leads on to a consideration of the management of the coast. Should this be targeted at management for a single purpose, such as flood defence (Leggett and Dixon, 1994), recreation (Duffus and Dearden, 1993; van der Maarel and Usher, 1997), water abstraction (van der Meulen, 1997), wildlife conservation (Jensen, 1994; Usher and Priest, 1997), or more futuristic uses such as seaweed extraction, fish farming or tidal power generation? Increasingly the answer to this question is 'no'. There is a greater realisation that the management of the coast is multi-disciplinary, involving an integrated approach (e.g. Kenchington and Crawford, 1993; Sorensen, 1993). Within this integrated framework, the question then arises as to whether the *status quo* is satisfactory for biodiversity, or whether restoration either to some former state or to some new state is desirable (e.g. Balciauskas and Angelstam, 1993).

The aim of this chapter is not to address these broader management issues, but rather to focus on biodiversity *per se*. What are the characteristics of the species and habitats of Scotland's long (approximately 11 800 km; Mackey, 1995) coastal zone? What is the spatial and temporal variability of these species and habitats? How should we plan the management of Scotland's coastal biodiversity? The coast is particularly important in Scotland because of its length of approximately 11 800 km; the equivalent figure for England and Wales is 4430 km (Steers, 1960), implying that Scotland has about 73% of the coastline of Great Britain, and of the order of two-thirds of the coastline of the United Kingdom.

15.2 Scotland's coastal biodiversity

Very little is known about the genetic variation within the wild species around Scotland. A striking exception is Todd *et al.*'s (1994) genetic research on two mollusc species, *Goniodoris nodosa* and *Adalaria proxima*. For *G. nodosa*, no significant genetic differentiation was found throughout the geographical range sampled (about 1500 km), whilst in *A. proxima* genetic differentiation could be detected over distances of less than 100 m. From results as different as these, it is impossible to make generalisations, and hence more studies of the genetic structure of coastal organisms, whether in the sea or on land, will be required. Another notable exception is the work on the grass *Puccinellia maritima*, summarized by Gray *et al.* (1979). In measuring heritable morphological characters, Gray *et al.* (1979) have shown that pioneer populations of this saltmarsh plant contain a wider range of biotypes than mature populations. They suggest that this accords with the hypothesis that genotypes adapted to conditions of high plant density are selected from the more variable colonising populations. It has also to be remembered that genetic differences may affect other species – herbivores, predators and parasites – that are higher in the food chain, even if the effects of genotypic variation are less than those of environmental variation (Stiling and Rossi, 1995).

Species are generally the most simply recognised 'building blocks' of biodiversity. Some species are totally confined to the coastal environment, such as the sea spleenwort (*Asplenium maritima*), which occurs on coastal rocks most commonly on the west coast, or the sea rocket (*Cakile maritima*), a plant of sandy beaches. Coastal habitats have their own array of species: sand dunes have the marram grass (*Ammophila arenaria*) and saltmarshes the grasses of the genus *Puccinellia* (especially the common saltmarsh grass, *P. maritima*). To find any of these four species of plants in Scotland, the coastal environments need to be searched. Similarly, large seaweeds such as kelp (*Laminaria* spp.) are attached to a substrate and, because of the need for light to photosynthesise, are confined to that narrow fringe between the low-water mark and only a few metres depth, depending on the clarity of the water (Connor, 1994). Smaller seaweeds, such as *Fucus* spp. and

Ascophyllum nodosum, are also attached to rock or boulders, and are commonly found in the intertidal zone. There are thus a number of species that are confined to the land within a zone affected by sea spray or to a zone of shallow water (probably less than 10 m) at low tide, and to the intertidal zone. These are the characteristic species of the coast; to find them you must search close to the line that separates the land from the sea.

However, some species will live in several habitats. A particular example of this is thrift (*Armeria maritima*) (Plate 47), that occurs abundantly around the coast of Scotland, and sporadically in the alpine flora of a number of inland mountains. Woodell and Dale (1993) discussed the possibility of ecological races and sub-species in *A. maritima*, but they put plants from 'coastal rocks, cliffs and shingle, and inland in Britain' into one ecotype of subspecies *maritima*; saltmarsh plants into a second ecotype that is associated with west European saltmarshes; and the Shetland saltmarsh plant into a third ecotype that is associated with the North Atlantic. Although the taxonomy of the thrift is fairly well understood, there remains much genetic work to undertake (for example, ssp. *intermedia* has been reported from northern England, and ssp. *elongata* is known inland in eastern England) before the distribution of the species is understood. There remains much greater taxonomic uncertainty about another genus of plants, the scurvy-grasses (*Cochlearia* spp.) which also occur in coastal and mountain environments: they are now frequently treated as a group of closely related species and sub-species (Rich, 1991).

It is therefore impossible to count the truly coastal species. Some species appear only to occur in coastal environments; some species occur in two or more environments, one of which is coastal; many species occur occasionally and generally accidentally in the coastal environment; and some species use the coast periodically, generally for a part of their life cycle. An example of the last type is provided by those seabirds which spend a considerable portion of the year at sea, but which return to the coast to breed, thereby providing a source of nutrients for some coastal soils, the so-called 'ornithogenic' soils, as in the maritime Antarctic (Lister, 1984), or near the Manx shearwater (*Procellaria puffinus*) burrows on the hills of Rum.

Scotland is not particularly rich in coastal vegetation communities (see the comparative data given by Usher, 1997) when compared with the rest of Great Britain. Given the diversity of dune types that are recognised in Europe (Olson and van der Maarel, 1989), Scotland appears poor, but more recent surveys by Dargie and Duncan (Chapter 12) are demonstrating a greater richness. Saltmarshes remain relatively unstudied in Scotland, as is the vegetation of cliffs and their ledges, although clifftop vegetation in Shetland is better known (Goldsmith, 1975). Given the length and complexity of the Scottish coastline, there are indications that the number of plant communities of the cliffs may be great, with Malloch (1993) listing nine types, largely based on his studies on the Isle of Lewis. Similarly, intertidally and sub-tidally the Scottish coast has a variety of environmental conditions, giving a huge variety of substrates to support plant and animal communities (e.g. Mackey, 1995). Whilst some of these have been documented in detail (e.g. in Baxter and Usher, 1994), ongoing survey work is demonstrating the richness of marine habitats around Scotland's shores. The survey described by Covey (Chapter 13) demonstrates the importance of Scotland, in a British context, for lagoon habitats. It is likely that Scotland could be particularly rich in reef communities, both physical and biogenic, but confirmation of this awaits further survey work.

A short description does not do justice to the genetic diversity, the large number of species, or the variety of plant and animal communities that occur in Scotland's coastal environment. There is, however, one factor that is important in understanding this diversity. In a very real sense southern (Lusitanian), northern (Arctic) and eastern (Boreal) influences meet in Scotland. Connor (1994) has described these influences in the marine environment. Terrestrially, many species that are far commoner in the south occur only along the coasts of Scotland where climatic extremes are less severe. The annual rest harrow (*Ononis reclinata*) or the natterjack toad (*Bufo calamita*) occur in Scotland only on the coast of the Solway Firth, whilst the small blue butterfly (*Cupido minima*) and a number of species of grasshoppers occur only on the sand dunes on the east coast as far north as St Cyrus or Forvie. The northern influence is seen with plants such as the oysterplant (*Mertensia maritima*) (Plate 48) or Scot's lovage (*Ligusticum scoticum*) (Plate 49) which, whilst occurring rarely south of the border, are most common in Scotland. With the North Atlantic Drift (Gulf Stream) to the west, and with Arctic waters dipping down into the North Sea, Scotland is at the meeting point of three major biogeographical zones, and this gives the coastal environment a particular interest and diversity. However, in the face of global warming, how will these influences affect the flora and fauna? Will the southern influences increase, and will the northern influences lessen? There is plenty of scope for developing scenarios and modelling their effects on the flora, fauna and communities.

15.3 Biogeographical considerations

The patterns of spatial distribution of plants and animals form the subject matter of biogeography. Studies generally take a defined geographical area – a nation, a continent, the Earth, etc. – and analyse distributions and attempt either to identify or to hypothesise about the causes of the observed patterns. The coast, being a narrow and convoluted zone, tends not to feature in such studies, though van der Maarel and van der Maarel-Versluys (1996) have attempted such an analysis for the vascular plants of European coasts. Interestingly they found that species of wet coastal habitats were concentrated in northern and northwestern Europe, and dune species in western and southwestern Europe. Does Scotland therefore tend to be rich, on a European scale, in saltmarsh and dune slack species, and poor in sand dune species? The analysis focused solely on the vascular plants of which few species grow below the high-tide mark – in Scotland marine vascular plants include two species of *Ruppia* (tasselweed) and three species of *Zostera* (eelgrass).

In order to analyse more clearly the coastal environment of Scotland, a parallel study of the terrestrial biogeographical zones (Carey *et al.*, 1995; Usher and Balharry, 1996) has been undertaken. The terrestrial study, similar to an earlier study by Bunce and Last (1981), demonstrated 12 zones, of which eight were lowland, including the terrestrial side of the land/sea divide. A map of these zones (Usher and Balharry, 1996) shows that the east coast of Scotland is less fragmented into zones than the west coast, where the maritime influence is strongest (Table 15.1). For the maritime environment it has been more difficult to find a basis for a similar analysis. Terrestrially, biological recording is based on the National Grid, and traditionally records are associated with a six-digit number, i.e. locating that record in a 100 m x 100 m square. In the marine environment records tend to have been given with reference to latitude and longitude. For reasons of convenience, the coastal environment has been gridded into cells of 5.5′ latitude by 10′ longitude, and presence/absence within these grid squares has been recorded (Kiemer *et al.*, 1998).

Environmental data, available in map form, include minimum and maximum depths of sea in each grid cell, as well as the depth range and the average depth.

Table 15.1 The 12 terrestrial biogeographical zones recognised by Usher and Balharry (1996) have been analysed in terms of the ten most characteristic species and ten most characteristic habitats in each. The table gives the number of those species that are essentially coastal in their occurrence in Scotland. Similarly, the table shows the number of National Vegetation Classification (NVC) communities that are coastal (data from Usher, 1997). The NVC communities counted are the MC (maritime), SD (driftline, etc.) and SM (saltmarsh) groups. Zones 2, 4, 5 and 6 are essentially intermediate and higher-altitude zones that would not be expected to have coastal species or habitats, especially as they are largely landlocked.

Biogeographical zone (number and name)	Characteristic coastal species	Characteristic coastal habitats
1 Central and Southern Lowlands	0	0
2 Grampian Fringe and Southern Uplands	0	0
3 East Coast	5	8
4 Cairngorm	0	0
5 Western Highlands	0	0
6 Western Highlands Fringe	0	0
7 Western Isles (North) and North Mainland	5	1
8 Barra and Tiree	6	9
9 Western Isles (South)	6	8
10 Northern Isles	6	7
11 Argyll and the Inner Hebrides	3	5
12 Galloway Coast	7	9

Maximum and minimum surface and benthic temperatures have also been included in the environmental dataset. It was not possible to find sufficiently detailed data for any other environmental variables such as salinity. Biological data have been gathered from many sources, including the Marine Nature Conservation Review of the Joint Nature Conservation Committee (largely data on more obvious species), seaweed data held by the Biological Records Centre, marine mollusc data held privately, and data held by Scottish Natural Heritage (e.g. the 1997 survey data from St Kilda). The analysis of the two datasets – environmental and biological – has used the same techniques as in the terrestrial analysis by Carey *et al.* (1995).

A major difficulty with the marine environment around Scotland is the apparent lack of species data (Plate 50). Some of the grid cells are apparently species-rich with over 300 species recorded. Many other cells, especially along the north and east coasts, are apparently without biota! The range of species richness clearly indicates a strong degree of recorder effort. It is therefore important in any analysis to use the environmental data to attempt to extrapolate the known species richness into cells with little or no data.

There is no way of saying exactly how many zones can be determined; this method of analysis can be used to generate any number of zones from 2 to 1347, i.e. when every cell is considered to be in a separate zone. Division into four and ten zones is shown in Plates 51 and 52. Focusing on the four-zone division, one of the zones (zone 3) is predominantly represented in south-west Scotland, as far north as the Ardnamurchan Peninsula and being represented along the Solway Firth. Another zone (zone 2) occurs close-in around the remainder of the coast, although it is further offshore in south-west Scotland. A third zone (zone 4) appears to be particularly associated with the coasts of the Hebrides, Orkney and Shetland. The final zone (zone 1) tends to occur more offshore in western Scotland and hence lies to the west and north of the Hebrides, and around the Shetland Islands.

The use of ten zones does not clarify the situation. All of the zones become fragmented without many discernible patterns. Pragmatically, having examined maps for 4, 5, 6, 8 and 10 zones, the four-zone map gives the clearest indication of a zonation; hence a pattern of four zones is suggested. These zones do not coincide spatially with the terrestrial zones listed in Table 15.1 except in so far as south-west Scotland appears distinct from the remainder of the country.

Work of this nature for the marine environment appears to be novel. On land, zones have been defined and conservation priorities have been assigned. 'Hotspots' have been defined (e.g. Prendergast *et al.*, 1993), being geographical areas of greatest species richness, and conservation actions can be targeted at these areas, as has been recommended by Williams *et al.* (1996). The concept has recently been extended by Troumbis and Dimitrakopoulos (1998) to 'threatspots', areas having an unusually large number of threatened species. Any such analysis requires excellent fundamental survey work so that a map, such as that in Plate 50, really represents species richness, rather than the survey effort. It is also true that statistical analyses of pattern, such as Birks' (1996) investigation of the Norwegian flora, can only be performed for the coastal habitats once a greater knowledge of the species and habitats has been acquired. In this respect, the recent cataloguing of species (Howson and Picton, 1997) and approaches to a biotope classification (Connor *et al.*, 1997a,b) are to be welcomed.

15.4 Change in time and space

The coast is a highly dynamic environment, and hence change can be expected, even ignoring changes that can be expected from global warming. From a physical point of view, the sea is eroding the coastline in some places, and accretion is occurring at others. Interestingly a number of coastal cells can be recognised, each reasonably independent of the others, and within each the redistribution of sediments is continually occurring (Anon., 1997). The 11 major coastal cells are shown in Figure 15.1, although, within each of these, sub-cells can be identified. The ecological importance of this is that new environments for species are continually being created, either by the erosion of existing habitats or by the establishment of new habitats from shingle, sand or shell deposits.

Processes of succession are continually occurring around Scotland's coasts. New rock ledges or crevices are being exposed as the cliffs slowly crumble; embryo dunes are being created that will be colonised speedily by micro-organisms, plants and animals, and sub-tidal sediments are being refreshed on a continuous basis. Apart from this continuous process of creation of new habitats, ecological succession, and the approach to a stable (climax) community of species, there are also periodic catastrophic changes, which can lead to (temporally) species-poor or even-aged communities.

Such changes may be natural. The effects of severe storms have been particularly well documented for coral reef communities (Connell, 1978; Karlson and Hurd, 1993), but it is important to distinguish local assemblages of species from the regional species pool. The effect of changing current strength has been implicated in the varying spawning stock of sandeel (*Ammodytes marinus*) in the coastal waters off Shetland, and hence in the breeding success of seabirds (Monaghan, 1992). Wind erosion following a severe gale will cause the formation of new dunes (Guilcher *et al.*, 1992) and hence the start of an ecological succession by microbes, including mycorrhizae, and plant species such as marram grass (*Ammophila arenaria*), sea rocket (*Cakile maritima*) and saltwort (*Salsola kali*). However, catastrophic change can also be anthropogenic. The predictions of sea-level rise with global warming are likely to mean that a fringe of terrestrial ecosystems will become dominated by marine organisms, and will have serious implications for people who live by the sea (Guilcher *et al.*, 1990). But such changes are imperceptible compared with the changes that followed the oil spill from the *MV Braer* in Shetland in January 1992 (Ritchie, 1995). Essentially all of the intertidal and imme-

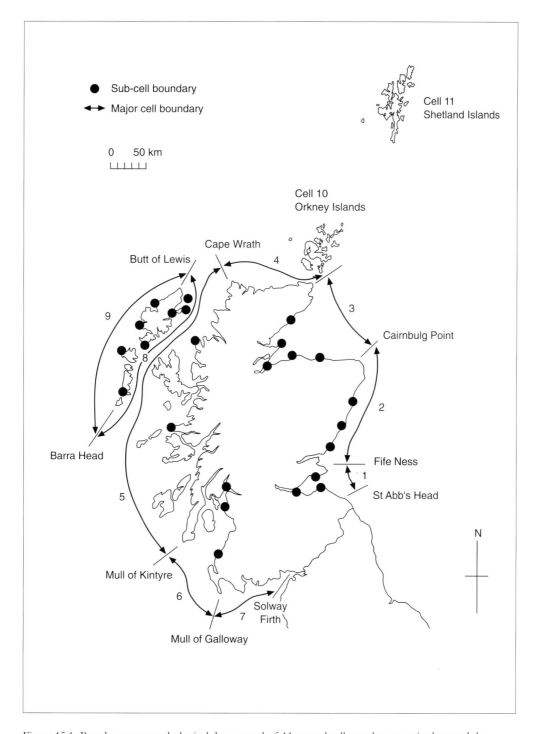

Figure 15.1 Based on geomorphological data, a total of 11 coastal cells can be recognised around the Scottish coast. The seven mainland cells are shown, but the situation is more complex in the Outer Hebrides (two cells) and in Orkney and Shetland (one cell each). The existence of sub-cells within the major cells is also indicated. The illustration is taken from Anon. (1997).

diate sub-tidal organisms were killed, leaving rocks and other substrates in an essentially sterile condition. Colonisation started, and a process of ecological succession created new assemblages of species, dominated in the early stages by algae, before the arrival of herbivorous invertebrate animals.

How do these processes affect biodiversity? At the genetic level, there is insufficient data to answer the question. Similarly, at the community level, it is impossible to answer the question, other than trivially to point out that if there are several successional sequences there will appear to be more 'communities', i.e. different assemblages of species, than in a less dynamic environment. It is, however, at the species level that the question can best be addressed. The 'Intermediate Disturbance Hypothesis' has been invoked to indicate that species richness rises with an increasing frequency of disturbance, and then starts to drop as the frequency increases further. Wilson (1994) analysed this hypothesis, recognising two cases that are of relevance to the coast – within patches and between patches.

Within a patch the species richness is related to the time since a disturbance (Figure 15.2a). Although the curve is usually portrayed as Gaussian (bell-shaped) there is no reason why it should be, and hence the illustration shows a curve that is monotonically increasing to a maximum, has a broad plateau, and is then followed by a monotonic decrease. Obviously, until real experimental evidence is collected the actual shape of this curve is unknown. The important point, demonstrated in many studies of secondary succession (e.g. Glenn-Lewin *et al.*, 1992), is that at some time following a disturbance the species richness is greatest; with more time the species richness decreases. If a single patch is studied, it is inevitable that the question will be asked about where the species came from during the increasing phase, and where the species go to during the decreasing phase.

The answer lies in an analysis of the species richness between patches. Here one needs to consider the disturbance frequency and the number of species over all patches. Similarly, it is customary to portray the change in species richness as a Gaussian curve, but there is no need to invoke such a symmetrical model (Figure 15.2b). Again, there is some intermediate value of the disturbance frequency that maximises species richness. The important point to gain from Figure 15.2 is that not all species will ever be present within a patch, but that in the wider area, of many patches of different successional age, it is possible to have a greater species richness. This implies that areas that are to be managed for their biodiversity should be large enough to encompass the whole of the ecological process; it is the preservation of processes, ecological and geomorphological, that is too often forgotten (Smith *et al.*, 1993).

The dynamism of the coast is important in maintaining its species-richness. If the processes that continually re-start ecological successions are altered, either by stopping them or making them more frequent, then species richness is likely to decline. It is the natural disturbance regime that generates biodiversity (Reice, 1994), and a study of biodiversity is essentially a study of a non-equilibrium world (Hengeveld, 1994). One of the major problems with biodiversity action plans for

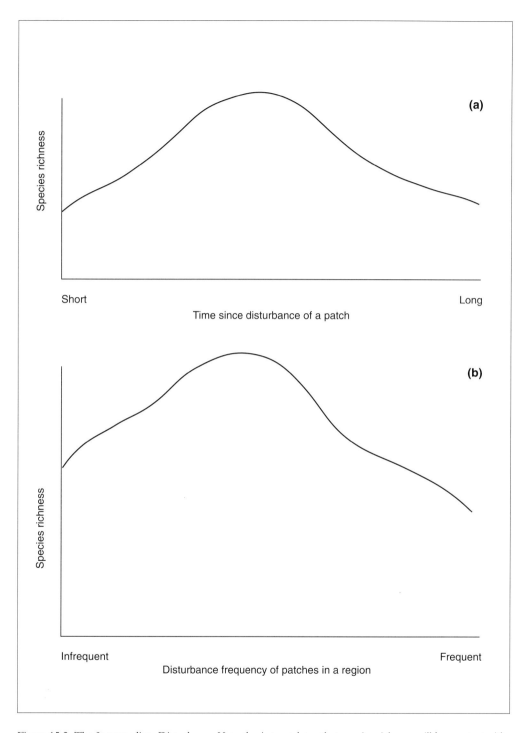

Figure 15.2 The Intermediate Disturbance Hypothesis postulates that species richness will be greatest within habitat patches when there is an intermediate time between patch disturbance (upper) and, on the larger spatial scale between patches (lower), that species richness will be greatest at an intermediate disturbance frequency (based on Wilson, 1994).

species (Anon., 1995) is that they tend to view the world at equilibrium, setting targets for sizes and numbers of populations. A major task is to gain recognition that there is no such thing as an equilibrium, other than in very controlled environmental conditions in the laboratory, and that action plans must cater for natural variability, for the natural disturbance regimes, and hence must incorporate the full range of ecosystem processes. Nowhere can these processes be more clearly seen than in the coastal environment.

15.5 Discussion: moving from research to management

Much of the discussion in the preceding sections, and the models in Figure 15.2, are essentially theoretical. As human population size increases, more pressures are placed on the coastal environment – be it for development (largely coming from the land), for aquaculture (which generally reduces biodiversity, as demonstrated by Beveridge *et al.*, 1994), or by various forms of pollution (see McNeely, 1992). It is important to ask if the biodiversity of Scotland's coast really matters. Do we need all of the species that we see today (Lockwood and Pimm, 1994), and does it really matter if some, or even most, of them disappear or go extinct? Do we really miss the great auk (*Pinguinus impennis*), the last pair of which was killed on the Icelandic island of Eldey in 1844 (Nettleship and Birkhead, 1988)? Is it right to have re-introduced the sea eagle (*Haliaeetus albicilla*) in the last decade or two; this is a species that became extinct in Scotland due to human persecution in 1918? These are anthropocentric questions, but it is important to maintain a wide view of the biological world (Nelson and Serafin, 1992). One wonders what questions a seal, a sea anemone or a sea rocket plant might ask – perhaps one might be 'Do we really need *Homo sapiens* (people) in our environment and would we notice a difference if the species became extinct?'

In maintaining a broad view of biodiversity, the question clearly arises as to priorities between within-species variation, species, communities and landscapes (Franklin, 1993). If a landscape (or perhaps in this context it should be a 'seascape' or 'underwater landscape') is the focus of attention, clearly all communities within that landscape are also attended to, and so on. There is an increasing number of perspectives on this problem of priorities. Samson and Knopf (1993) see hard decisions ahead in setting priorities in both research and management. They recommend four concepts as fundamental in the process – understanding diversity (both within and between habitats), emphasising biotic integrity, restoring ecological processes, and promoting ecological sustainability. This science-centred approach is in contrast with an approach adopted by Burton *et al.* (1992) who focused on the products provided by terrestrial species – wood, food, fibres, pharmaceuticals, etc. – or food, pharmaceuticals, oils and industrial raw materials from marine species. They recognised that we do not yet know all of the potential products, and they recommend that, as uncertainty exists about climate change and future socio-economic values, it is 'prudent to maximise flexibility by promoting a wide array of species and potential products'. Does this mean that everything must be conserved because it might have some value in the future?

One difficulty of applying research to practical management is that different ecosystems behave in different ways. Stone (1995) and Stone *et al.* (1996) compared coral reefs with forests. One of the most interesting differences relates to the extinction of species on a reef as a function of the proportion of the habitat that is destroyed. The relationships for both forests and coral reefs are not linear; for forests the curve is concave upwards so that a 50% habitat loss results in possibly less than a 20% extinction of species in the long term. For coral reefs, the curve is concave downwards; for a 50% habitat loss perhaps at least 80% of the species will become extinct in the long term. Such a relationship is clearly important; if incremental developments eat into a coral reef, they are going to affect its species richness disproportionately. We have no idea how widely these results hold, but they clearly present a warning for the reef communities around Scotland. The unique (in British waters) serpulid reefs of Loch Creran, or the *Lophelia* reefs thought to be fringing the continental shelf, may be more resilient, but, until we know, it is possibly best to apply 'the precautionary principle' to any activities that might affect them.

Scotland's coasts have a large number of species and habitats. Only a relatively small proportion of the 11 800 km has been developed, though virtually the whole of the coastline is being used to some extent. The use may be related to a harvest of fish, seaweed or aggregates; it may be for production as in aquaculture or agriculture on the machair; in local areas it may be for recreation; but the coastal waters are also used for waste disposal. With so many potential uses the problems of how to integrate the uses of this interface between land and sea arise (Ngoile and Horrill, 1993). It is for this reason that Sherman (1994) has introduced the concept of the 'health of coastal ecosystems'. Although there is no easy definition of the 'health' of an ecosystem, can appropriate indices be developed and agreed by all of the groups interested in the coastal environment?

For Scotland's coastal biodiversity, a number of research and management questions and conclusions need to be addressed. Six immediate ones are as follows.

- The inventory of coastal species and communities is still incomplete. As Magnusson (Foreword, this volume) and Kiemer *et al.* (1998) have reminded us, this is an important task that is expensive, but we cannot manage the coastal natural heritage if we do not know what is there.

- How dependent is the biodiversity of Scotland's coast on an intermediate level of disturbance? Is the cycle of erosion and accretion within the coastal cells (Figure 15.1), with the more devastating disturbance occasionally as a result of severe storms, flooding or tidal change, maintaining that biodiversity satisfactorily? How will disturbance regimes change with climate change?

- Can future changes be predicted? Work on scenarios of change, and the use of modelling techniques in the coastal environment has hardly been started. As well as documenting current changes, modelling to predict future changes is a powerful tool that has not yet been adequately used.

- In the management of the coastline, how can we work with the ecological processes rather than attempting to oppose them at considerable cost? The nearshore environment, with its extensive shallow water and, in places, kelp beds, protects the terrestrial environment. This protection could be lost in the face of some developments or in the face of sea-level rise. Understanding and working with the ecological processes that are at work could assist in the sustainable management of the coastline.

- How resilient are Scottish coastal ecosystems, especially the rarer ones, to damage? If they are like the tropical coral reefs, the loss of biodiversity is disproportionate to the amount of damage. Until we answer this question, it may be necessary to apply 'the precautionary principle'.

- Initiatives like Focus on Firths and The Minch Project (Atkins, Chapter 7) have been valuable in gaining consensus on how to manage the coast. Should this approach be extended to a greater length of Scotland's coast?

Surveys to ascertain what the resource is, monitoring to measure how the resource is changing, and research to test hypotheses about the causes of change, are all scientific aspects of Scotland's coastal biodiversity. An understanding of the uses of the coast, the dependence of people for their livelihood on coastal resources, and the recreational and educational opportunities of the coast, are all socio-economic aspects of Scotland's coastal biodiversity. That the biodiversity is rich is beyond doubt, even with our relatively limited knowledge of the coastal resource. It is important that Scottish Natural Heritage, with the other interest groups in the coastal environment, protect, and in places enhance, the coastal biodiversity, not only for this generation to use and enjoy, but also so that the ecosystems function fully for future generations.

Acknowledgements

I thank Professor Fred Last for commenting on a draft of this chapter. The work reported in section 15.3 was undertaken under an SNH contract to the Institute of Terrestrial Ecology, and I am particularly grateful to Dr Pete Carey for making available preliminary results of his analyses. I should also like to thank Jo Newman for her work on the manuscript.

References

Andersen, U.V. 1994. Resistance of Danish coastal vegetation types to human trampling. *Biological Conservation*, **71**, 223–230.

Anon., 1995. *Biodiversity: the UK Steering Group Report. Volume 2: Action Plans*. HMSO, London.

Anon., 1997. Coastal cells in Scotland. *SNH Research, Survey and Monitoring Report* No. 56.

Balciauskas, L. and Angelstam, P. 1993. Ecological diversity: to manage it or to restore? *Acta Ornithologica Lituanica*, **7/8**, 3–15.

Baxter, J.M. and Usher, M.B. (eds). 1994. *The Islands of Scotland: a Living Marine Heritage*. HMSO, Edinburgh.

Beveridge, M.C.M., Ross, L.G. and Kelly, L.A. 1994. Aquaculture and biodiversity. *Ambio*, **23**, 497–502.

Birks, H.J.B. 1996. Statistical approaches to interpreting diversity patterns in the Norwegian mountain flora. *Ecography*, **19**, 332–340.

Bunce, R.G.H. and Last, F.T. 1981. How to characterise the habitats of Scotland. *Annual Report of the Edinburgh Centre of Rural Economy*, 1–14.

Burton, P.J., Balisky, A.C., Coward, L.P., Cumming, S.G. and Kneeshaw, D.D. 1992. The value of managing for biodiversity. *The Forestry Chronicle*, **68**, 225–237.

Carey, P.D., Preston, C.D., Hill, M.O., Usher, M.B. and Wright, S.M. 1995. An environmentally defined biogeographical zonation of Scotland designed to reflect species distribution. *Journal of Ecology*, **83**, 833–845.

Connell, J.H. 1978. Diversity in tropical rain forests and coral reefs. *Science*, **199**, 1302–1310.

Connor, D.W. 1994. The sublittoral ecology of Scotland's islands. *In* Baxter, J.M. and Usher, M.B. (eds) *The Islands of Scotland: a Living Marine Heritage*. HMSO, Edinburgh, 144–159.

Connor, D.W., Brazier, D.P., Hill, T.O. and Northen, K.O. (eds). 1997a. Marine biotope classification for Britain and Ireland. Volume I. Littoral biotopes. *Joint Nature Conservation Committee Report* No. 229.

Connor, D.W., Dalkin, M.J., Hill, T.O., Holt, R.H.F. and Sanderson, E.G. (eds). 1997b. Marine biotope classification for Britain and Ireland. Volume 2. Sublittoral biotopes. *Joint Nature Conservation Committee Report* No. 230.

Duffus, D.A. and Dearden, P. 1993. Recreational use, valuation, and management, of killer whales (*Orcinus orca*) on Canada's Pacific coast. *Environmental Conservation*, **20**, 149–156.

Franklin, J.F. 1993. Preserving biodiversity: species, ecosystems, or landscapes. *Ecological Applications*, **3**, 202–205.

Georgiadis, N. and Balmford, A. 1992. The calculus of conserving biological diversity. *Trends in Ecology and Evolution*, **7**, 321–322.

Glenn-Lewin, D.C., Peet, R.K. and Veblen, T.T. (eds). 1992. *Plant Succession: Theory and Prediction*. Chapman and Hall, London.

Goldsmith, F.B. 1975. The sea-cliff vegetation of Shetland. *Journal of Biogeography*, **2**, 297–308.

Gray, A.J., Parsell, R.J. and Scott, R. 1979. The genetic structure of plant populations in relation to the development of salt marshes. *In* Jefferies, R.L. and Davy, A.J. (eds) *Ecological Processes in Coastal Environments*. Blackwell Scientific, Oxford, 43–64.

Guilcher, A., Bodéré, J.C. and Hallégouët, B. 1990. Coastal evolution in western, south western and northern Brittany as a regional test of impact of sea level rise. *Journal of Coastal Research*, Special Issue No. 9, 67–90.

Guilcher, A., Hallégouët, B., Meur, C., Talec, P. and Yoni, C. 1992. Exceptional formation of present-day dunes in Baie d'Audierne, south western Brittany, France. *In* Carter, R.W.G., Curtis, T.G.F. and Sheehy-Skeffington, M.J. (eds) *Coastal Dunes, Geomorphology, Ecology and Management for Conservation*. Balkema, Rotterdam, 15–23.

Harper, J.L. and Hawksworth, D.L. 1994. Biodiversity: measurement and estimation. *Philosophical Transactions of the Royal Society of London*, **B345**, 5–12.

Hengeveld, R. 1994. Biodiversity – the diversification of life in a non-equilibrium world. *Biodiversity Letters*, **2**, 1–10.

Howson, C.M. and Picton, B.E. (eds). 1997. *The Species Directory of the Marine Fauna and Flora of the British Isles and Surrounding Seas*. Ulster Museum, Belfast.

Jensen, F. 1994. Dune management in Denmark: application of the Nature Protection Act of 1992. *Journal of Coastal Research*, **10**, 263–269.

Karlson, R.H. and Hurd, L.E. 1993. Disturbance, coral reef communities, and changing ecological paradigms. *Coral Reefs*, **12**, 117–125.

Kenchington, R. and Crawford, D. 1993. On the meaning of integration in coastal zone management. *Ocean & Coastal Management*, **21**, 109–127.

Kiemer, M.C.B., Carey, P.D., Palmer, S.C.F. and Roy, D.B. 1998. The biogeographical zones and biodiversity of the coastal waters of Scotland. *SNH Research, Survey and Monitoring Report* No. 103.

Leggett, D.J. and Dixon, M. 1994. Management of the Essex saltmarshes for flood defence. *In* Falconer, R. and Goodwin, P. (eds) *Wetland Management*. Institute of Civil Engineers, London, 151–164.

Leggett, D., Bubb, J.M. and Lester, J.N. 1995. The role of pollutants and sedimentary processes in flood defence. A case study: salt marshes of the Essex coast, UK. *Environmental Technology*, **16**, 457–466.

Lister, A. 1984. *Studies on the Antarctic Predatory Mite* Gamasellus racovitzai. D.Phil. Thesis, University of York.

Lockwood, J.L. and Pimm, S.L. 1994. Species: would any of them be missed? *Current Biology*, **4**, 455–457.

Mackey, E.C. (ed.). 1995. *The Natural Heritage of Scotland: an Overview*. Scottish Natural Heritage, Perth.

Malloch, A.J.C. 1993. Dry coastal ecosystems of Britain: cliffs. *In* van der Maarel, E. (ed.), *Ecosystems of the World 2A: Dry Coastal Ecosystems – Polar Regions and Europe*. Elsevier, Amsterdam, 229–244.

McNeely, J.A. 1992. The sinking ark: pollution and the worldwide loss of biodiversity. *Biodiversity and Conservation*, **1**, 2–18.

Monaghan, P. 1992. Seabirds and sandeels: the conflict between exploitation and conservation in the northern North Sea. *Biodiversity and Conservation*, **1**, 98–111.

Nelson, J.G. and Serafin, R. 1992. Assessing biodiversity: a human ecological approach. *Ambio*, **21**, 212–218.

Nettleship, D.N. and Birkhead, T.R. 1988. *The Atlantic Alcidae*. Academic Press, London.

Ngoile, M.A.K. and Horrill, C.J. 1993. Coastal ecosystems, productivity and ecosystem protection: coastal ecosystem management. *Ambio*, **22**, 461–467.

Olson, J.S. and van der Maarel, E. 1989. Coastal dunes in Europe: a global view. *In* van der Meulen, F., Jungerius, P.D. and Visser, J.H. (eds) *Perspectives in Coastal Dune Management*. SPB Academic, The Hague, 3–32.

Prendergast, J.R., Quinn, R.M., Lawton, J.H., Eversham, B.C. and Gibbons, D.W. 1993. Rare species, the coincidence of diversity hotspots and conservation strategies. *Nature*, **365**, 335–337.

Reice, S.R. 1994. Nonequilibrium determinants of biological community structure. *American Scientist*, **82**, 424–435.

Rich, T.C.G. 1991. *Crucifers of Great Britain and Ireland*. Botanical Society of the British Isles, London.

Ritchie, W. 1995. Maritime oil spills – environmental lessons and experiences with special reference to low-risk coastlines. *Journal of Coastal Conservation*, **1**, 63–76.

Samson, F.B. and Knopf, F.L. 1993. Managing biological diversity. *Wilson Society Bulletin*, **21**, 509–514.

Sherman, K. 1994. Sustainability, biomass yields, and health of coastal ecosystems: an ecological perspective. *Marine Ecology Progress Series*, **112**, 277–301.

Smith, T.B., Bruford, M.W. and Wayne, R.K. 1993. The preservation of process: the missing element of conservation programs. *Biodiversity Letters*, **1**, 164–167.

Sorensen, J. 1993. The international proliferation of integrated coastal zone management efforts. *Ocean & Coastal Management*, **21**, 45–80.

Steers, J.A. 1960. *The Coast of England and Wales in Pictures*. Cambridge University Press, Cambridge.

Stiling, P. and Rossi, A.M. 1995. Coastal insect herbivore communities are affected more by local environmental conditions than by plant genotype. *Ecological Entomology*, **20**, 184–190.

Stone, L. 1995. Biodiversity and habitat destruction: a comparative study of model forest and coral reef ecosystems. *Proceedings of the Royal Society of London*, **B261**, 381–388.

Stone, L., Eilam, E., Abelson, A. and Ilan, M. 1996. Modelling coral reef biodiversity and habitat destruction. *Marine Ecology Progress Series*, **134**, 299–302.

Todd, C.D., Lambert, W.J. and Thorpe, J.P. 1994. The genetic structure of intertidal populations of two species of mollusc on the Scottish west coast: some biogeographic considerations and an assessment of realized larval dispersal. *In* Baxter, J.M. and Usher, M.B. (eds) *The Islands of Scotland: a Living Marine Heritage*. HMSO, Edinburgh, 67–87.

Troumbis, A.Y. and Dimitrakopoulos, P.G. 1998. Geographic coincidence of diversity threatspots for three taxa and conservation planning in Greece. *Biological Conservation*, **84**, 1–6.

Usher, M.B. 1997. Scotland's biodiversity: an overview. *In* Fleming, L.V., Newton, A., Vickery, J. and Usher, M.B. (eds) *Biodiversity in Scotland: Status, Trends and Initiatives*. The Stationery Office, Edinburgh, 5–20.

Usher, M.B. and Balharry, D. 1996. *Biogeographical Zonation of Scotland*. Scottish Natural Heritage, Perth.

Usher, M.B. and Priest, S.N. 1997. Conservation of dry coastal ecosystems. *In* van der Maarel, E. (ed.) *Ecosystems of the World 2C: Dry Coastal Ecosystems – General Aspects*. Elsevier, Amsterdam, 557–571.

van der Maarel, E. (ed.). 1997. *Ecosystems of the World 2C: Dry Coastal Ecosystems – General Aspects*. Elsevier, Amsterdam.

van der Maarel, E. and Usher, M.B. 1997. Recreational use of dry coastal ecosystems. *In* van der Maarel, E. (ed.), *Ecosystems of the World 2C: Dry Coastal Ecosystems – General Aspects.* Elsevier, Amsterdam, 519–529.

van der Maarel, E. and van der Maarel-Versluys, M. 1996. Distribution and conservation status of littoral vascular plant species along the European coasts. *Journal of Coastal Conservation*, **2**, 73–92.

van der Meulen, F. 1997. Dune water catchment in the Netherlands. *In* van der Maarel, E. (ed.) *Ecosystems of the World 2C: Dry Coastal Ecosystems – General Aspects.* Elsevier, Amsterdam, 553–556.

Williams, P., Gibbons, D., Margules, C., Rebelo, A., Humphries, C. and Pressey, R. 1996. A comparison of richness hotspots, rarity hotspots and complementary areas for conserving diversity of British birds. *Conservation Biology*, **10**, 155–174.

Wilson, J.B. 1994. The 'Intermediate Disturbance Hypothesis' of species coexistence is based on patch dynamics. *New Zealand Journal of Ecology*, **18**, 176–181.

Woodell, S.R.J. and Dale, A. 1993. *Armeria maritime* (Mill.) Willd. (*Statice armeria* L.; *S. maritima* Mill.). *Journal of Ecology*, **81**, 573–588.

16 BIODIVERSITY ACTION PLANS: CHALLENGES FOR SCOTLAND'S COAST

M. Scott

Summary

1. This chapter summarises the process leading to the preparation of Biodiversity Action Plans for species and habitats of particular relevance to Scotland.
2. These plans provide a focus for action to protect and restore the biodiversity of Scotland's coasts, but concerted action will be needed to achieve the plans' ambitious targets.
3. This chapter points to some of the challenges in meeting these targets, with reference to species action plans for the otter (*Lutra lutra*), harbour porpoise (*Phocoena phocoena*) and eyebrights (*Euphrasia* spp.).
4. It also considers the habitat action plans for seagrass (*Zostera* spp.) beds, saline lagoons, machair and unattached beds of egg wrack seaweed (*Ascophyllum nodosum* ecad *mackaii*), and the significant challenges presented for their implementation.

16.1 Introduction

The production of Biodiversity Action Plans for the main habitats and a range of priority species in Scotland provides an important opportunity to address some of the coastal conservation issues that have been identified in earlier chapters. The innovative partnership that has been brought together, as the Scottish Biodiversity Group (SBG), to take forward these plans provides hope that the ambitious objectives in the plans can be translated into constructive action. However, to succeed, the task ahead will need clear vision, strong leadership and a commitment to concerted action from everyone with an interest in managing the coast. This chapter illustrates some of the challenges that must be addressed in realising the vision of the action plans.

16.2 The scope of biodiversity

It is important to recognise the breadth of issues encompassed in the term 'biodiversity', which were considered in the previous volume in this series (Fleming *et al.*, 1997). A recent SBG publication (Scottish Office, 1998) provides a comprehensive briefing on biodiversity as 'the planet's most valuable resource', analysing the arguments for its conservation and summarising current action to protect it.

The standard definition of biodiversity, now enshrined in government policy (Anon., 1994), is that which appears in the United Nations Convention on Biological Diversity:

> Biological diversity' means the variability among living things from all sources, including, *inter alia*, terrestrial, marine and other aquatic ecosystems and the ecological complexes of which they are part; this includes diversity within species, between species and of ecosystems.

A more 'user-friendly' definition is offered by Murphy in Wilson (1988), in which he defines biological diversity as encompassing:

> …the variety of life forms, the ecological roles they perform and the genetic diversity they contain.

The important point from the perspective of this volume is to recognise that biodiversity cannot be measured simply by a species count. Indeed, in some species-poor coastal ecosystems, human activities can increase species diversity artificially, at the cost of damage to the value of the natural ecosystem and an overall loss of biodiversity. An example is shown by Dargie and Duncan (Chapter 12) in sand dunes, where the grazing of rabbits, introduced and encouraged by humans, has stimulated weed species at the expense of the natural sand-dune community. The emphasis that is sometimes placed on so-called 'biodiversity hotspots' does not help this appreciation. Some 'lowspots' of species diversity are in fact extremely important components of biodiversity – as is recognised in several habitat action plans.

16.3 The biodiversity process in Scotland

The process of action for biodiversity in Scotland is described fully in the Scottish Office guide (Scottish Office, 1998) but a few key points should be summarised here.

The Convention on Biological Diversity was one of the outputs from the United Nations Conference on Environment and Development (the 'Earth Summit') in Rio de Janeiro in 1992. The UK government ratified the convention in June 1994, having, five months previously, published *Biodiversity: the UK Action Plan* (Anon., 1994). One of its key recommendations was the establishment of a Biodiversity Action Plan Steering Group 'to oversee the development of a range of targets for biodiversity'. This group was duly convened, and in December 1995 it published *Biodiversity: the UK Steering Group Report* (Anon., 1995). This report contained proposed, fully costed action plans for 116 of Britain's most threatened species and 14 habitats, as well as shorter, outline 'habitat statements' for other habitats. The report also listed species and habitats for which action plans should be considered as a medium- or long-term priority (the so-called 'medium' and 'long lists').

In May 1996, the government endorsed the Steering Group proposals, effectively adopting these action plans as a programme for government action. It also

Table 16.1 Action plans of particular relevance to Scotland's coastline in the UK Steering Group Report (Anon., 1995) or (*) in draft in February 1999.

Habitat action plans	Habitat statements	Species action plans
Saline lagoons	Maritime cliff and slope	Otter (*Lutra lutra*)
Coastal grazing marsh	Shingle above high-tide mark	Harbour porpoise (*Phocoena phocoena*)
Seagrass (*Zostera* spp.) beds	Boulders/rocks above high tide	Corncrake (*Crex crex*)
Machair*	Coastal strandline	Natterjack toad (*Bufo calamitai*)
Ascophyllum nodosum ecad *mackaii* beds*[a]	Machair	Allis shad (*Alosa alosa*)
Cliff and slope*	Saltmarsh	Twaite shad (*Alosa fallax*)
Vegetated shingle*	Sand dune	Eyebrights (some species)
Saltmarsh*	Estuaries	Narrow mouthed whorl snail (*Vertigo angustiori*)
Sand dune*	Islands and archipelagos	Atlantic lejeunea (*Lejeunea mandonii*)
Tidal rapids*	Inlets and enclosed bays	Petalwort (*Petalophyllum ralfsii*)
Maerl beds*	Open coast	Mossy stonewort (*Chara muscosa*) – possibly extinct
Serpula vermicularis reefs*		Foxtail stonewort (*Lamprothamnium papulosum*)*
Deep mud*		Baleen whales (especially Minke)*
Lophelia pertusa reefs*		Northern hatchet shell (*Thyasira gouldi*)*
		Fan mussel (*Atrina fragilis*)*

[a]Since submitting this chapter the action plan for *Ascophyllum nodosum* ecad *mackaii* has been converted from a habitat action plan to a species action plan.

acted on the recommendation to set up a UK Biodiversity Group and country focus groups to guide the implementation of the action plans and to develop plans for a further 286 species and 24 habitats. Table 16.1 lists the action plans of particular relevance to Scotland's coastline, completed or in draft in February 1999.

The membership of the SBG is shown in Table 16.2; it represents a broad cross-section of those with an active interest in Scotland's countryside and coastline. The SBG has begun commissioning further action plans for species and habitats of which more than 75% of the UK resource is found in Scotland. The plans are commissioned by Scottish Natural Heritage (SNH), refereed by the SBG, then passed to the UK Biodiversity Group for adoption.

Government has expressed its strong support for this biodiversity process, which was reinforced in the publication *Biodiversity in Scotland – The Way Forward* (Scottish Office, 1997).

Each action plan species in the UK Steering Group Report has been assigned a contact point and a lead partner (including several voluntary conservation organisations) to guide work. The government has also begun finding commercial 'champions' to assist with the funding and implementation of action plans. While

Table 16.2 Initial membership of Scottish Biodiversity Group.

Chair:	The Scottish Office
Membership:	Confederation of British Industry Scotland
	Convention of Scottish Local Authorities
	Forestry Commission
	Ministry of Defence
	National Farmer's Union of Scotland
	Plantlife
	Royal Botanic Garden Edinburgh
	Royal Society for the Protection of Birds
	Scottish Crofter's Union
	Scottish Environment Protection Agency
	Scottish Fishermen's Federation
	Scottish Landowners Federation
	Scottish Natural Heritage
	Scottish Office Agriculture, Environment and Fisheries
	Department: various divisions
	Scottish Sports Council
	Scottish Wildlife Trust
	University of Edinburgh

sponsors have come forward quickly for the water vole and skylark, species such as the endemic eyebright *Euphrasia heslop-harrisonii*, or petalwort, *Petalophyllum ralfsii*, a liverwort found in damp calcareous dune slacks in Easter Ross, may not find champions so readily.

16.4 Biodiversity action plans

16.4.1 The challenges of the action plans

Against a general background of attrition of biodiversity in Scotland, action to reverse the pressures causing these losses is never likely to be easy. However, some of the action plans throw up particular difficulties, a few of which are discussed here. The central requirement of each action plan is that it contains objective and testable targets, so that progress against these targets can be monitored at intervals, although inevitably some plans must also take account of the inherent variability of natural ecosystems described by Usher (Chapter 15).

Running throughout the plans, inevitably, is the issue of cost. The steering group estimated that the cost of implementing the 116 species action plans in its report would be £3.8 million in 1997, falling to £2.4 million per year by 2010. It expected half of this to be found from government sources, with the rest to come from other sources, including voluntary conservation bodies and champions from business and industry. It also estimated that total public expenditure for the 14 habitat plans would be £12.9 million in 1997, rising to £37.2 million in 2010.

These are substantial sums, but to put them in perspective, the group noted that the total projected cost of all their plans was only about 3% of the £3 billion per year which the government pays in support payments for farming. Furthermore, in many cases, the actions proposed in the plans do not require new funding, but a more careful disposition of existing funding, to take better account of biodiversity in measures already being undertaken.

16.4.2 *Action for the otter and harbour porpoise*

Widely dispersed, mobile species present problems of geographic scale that are not encountered with rarer but localised species. The otter action plan, for instance, has a target of restoring breeding otters by 2010 to all coastal areas and river catchments from which they have been recorded since 1960. To achieve that, the plan proposes that action for otters should be included in catchment management plans for all rivers containing otter populations by 2005. However, it stops short of making a similar proposal action for shoreline otters, perhaps because, as earlier chapters have shown, we are at only the earliest stages of developing equivalent coastal management plans.

Similarly, the harbour porpoise plan calls for measures to improve coastal water quality by reducing the discharges of substances which are toxic, persistent and liable to bioaccumulate. This is a desirable target, not just for harbour porpoises but for the health of the wider marine environment, but it is an issue with which the Scottish Environment Protection Agency is just beginning to grapple. The fish-farming industry insists that a number of bioaccumulative chemicals are essential for the control of sea-lice. The organophosphates used by sheep dips on land also provide a significant input into coastal waters, but it seems unlikely that measures to phase them out will be introduced in the near future, especially as the pyrethroid alternatives are so toxic to aquatic invertebrates.

The harbour porpoise plan also calls for the Scottish Office Agriculture, Environment and Fisheries Department to work with fishermen with the aim of reducing and avoiding by-catches in fishing gear, and to dispose of discarded gear safely. A number of non-governmental environmental organisations continue to argue that the government's 1996 decision to lift the ban on the carriage of monofilament gill nets in coastal waters contradicts this action plan objective.

As in other action plans, it is difficult to separate the measures proposed from other conservation measures being undertaken by the government and its agencies. Both the otter and the harbour porpoise are listed in Annex II of the Community's *Council Directive on the Conservation of Natural Habitats and of Wild Fauna and Flora* (the 'Habitats Directive') (Council of the European Communities, 1992), as species of community interest whose conservation requires the designation of Special Areas of Conservation (SACs), and in Annex IV as species in need of strict protection. A start has been made in proposing SACs for otters in Loch Sunart and the coast of part of Shetland. However, there is still debate about the appropriateness of site-based measures, such as SACs, as a way of ensuring the required 'favourable conservation status' for such widely dispersed and mobile species as otters and harbour porpoises, and, even if appropriate, on how best to select sites for this purpose. This emphasises the important role of the 'wider countryside (and coastal) measures' in the species action plans in achieving the UK's international conservation obligations.

16.4.3 Action for endemic eyebrights

The endemic eyebright action plan covers at least three 'microspecies' recorded from coastal habitats in Scotland: *Euphrasia rotundifolia* and *E. campbelliae* in maritime heaths and grasslands in northern Scotland, and *E. heslop-harrisonii* in dune grass and saltmarsh in the north and west (Plates 54–6). All are hemi-parasitic plants with miniature flowers, whose attractiveness can only be seen on close inspection. The action plan suggests using these species to highlight the threat to UK biodiversity from the destruction of heathland and coastal habitats, but, in truth, it would be difficult to win much public support for plants whose identification is so critical, especially when the larger eyebrights are widespread.

The biggest 'threat' to the status of these species is taxonomic. The action plan notes that the taxonomic status of *E. rotundifolia* is uncertain, and some, or all, of the records might turn out to be a hybrid, while Stace (1991) suggests that *E. heslop-harrisonii* is perhaps not distinct from *E. micrantha* and *E. scottica*. It is difficult to imagine a champion volunteering to support an action plan for a species which might cease to exist at any time as a result of taxonomic revision.

Yet it is here that the definition of biodiversity becomes vitally important. As the Convention definition (Anon., 1994) makes clear, biodiversity includes variation *within* species, and the process of evolution is, in itself, a key component of biodiversity. The challenge therefore must be to protect the entire range of genetic variability within any taxon, as the raw material from which natural selection might, in time, allow for the emergence of new species. The action plan recognises this in its target 4.2 which states: 'Protect known populations until taxonomic status clear'.

16.4.4 Action for seagrass beds

The seagrasses or eelgrasses (*Zostera* spp.) (Plate 57) are covered by a costed action plan, not as species but for the habitat they form. Seagrass beds develop in sheltered intertidal and shallow sub-tidal areas. The eelgrass leaves are often colonised by algae, stalked jellyfish and anemones, while the sheltered beds provide nursery areas for flatfish, and the protected substrates within the beds are the home for amphipods, polychaete worms, bivalves and echinoderms. The eelgrass leaves are also important food for wildfowl, particularly brent geese and wigeon.

A substantial and commercially significant sub-tidal community therefore depends on the survival of dense stands of eelgrass, but the action plan makes clear that the species is highly susceptible to marine pollution, nutrient enrichment, increased turbidity, physical disturbance by trampling, dredging and the use of mobile bottom fishing gear, land claim and adjacent coastal developments.

Yet many of the sites for the species are subject to precisely these pressures.

The action plan notes that, for example, the Cromarty Firth supports probably the largest area of the narrow-leaved species (or forms) in Britain, extending to 1200 ha. But the Cromarty Firth is already under high development pressure, and current proposals to designate the firth as a Special Protection Area under the European Commission Directive on the Conservation of Wild Birds (Council of the European Communities, 1979) are arousing considerable controversy. The challenge for the government, local authorities, enterprise companies and industry is to find ways to encourage truly sustainable development in areas of this sort, and the fundamental test of sustainability is that it must not deplete biodiversity.

The eelgrasses raise another intriguing conundrum for biodiversity. In the 1930s, many populations were decimated by a 'wasting disease'. This is generally attributed to the micro-organism *Labyrinthula macrocystis*, but other human-induced environmental factors may have put populations under stress, allowing the parasite to flourish (Stewart *et al.*, 1994). The natural occurrence of a parasite is itself an element of biodiversity, but when anthropogenic factors may have exacerbated its impact, it is arguable whether the recovery of the parasitised species should be left to natural processes. The action plan proposes an interim target of restoring 1000 ha of damaged or degraded seagrass beds, but suggests that work is first needed to identify suitable areas for re-introduction or restoration and to draw up a strategy to guide such work.

16.4.5 Action for saline lagoons

Saline lagoons (Plate 44) are another coastal habitat to benefit from a costed action plan in the UK Steering Group report. Covey (Chapter 13) has described these lagoons, and shown their importance as habitats for algae, charophytes, invertebrates, and a variety of birds. Many suffer extreme eutrophication from sewage. In several, the sills have been raised to form causeways, blocking exchanges with the sea. Some are viewed as candidates for infilling, and others as convenient sites for fish or shellfish farms, despite the fact that the low water exchange with the open sea makes them highly susceptible to the accumulation of nutrients and chemical wastes.

All these problems are symptoms of the low esteem in which lagoons are held by their adjacent human communities. The action plan recognises that the highest priority therefore is to promote the value of these lagoons. It proposes providing schools, colleges and universities with educational materials and training on saline lagoon habitats.

16.4.6 Action for machair

A habitat action plan for machair is being developed. As Dargie and Duncan (Chapter 12) have already noted, machair is the distinctive coastal grassland of northern and western Scotland, formed where calcareous shell sand is blown inland by the strong prevailing winds from beaches and mobile dunes (Plate 43). The draft action plan estimates that the approximately 14 500 ha of machair grassland in Scotland represents some 66% of the global extent of this habitat.

Despite its calcareous nature, machair grassland has modest species diversity, but this has been enhanced by several millennia of management by humans. The addition of peat and seaweed provides added humus and nutrients to the soil. Seasonal grazing and rotational cropping, based on low chemical inputs, sustains varied dune, fallow and arable weed communities and enhances the natural biodiversity. Machair grassland is therefore strongly anthropogenic, and the maintenance of its biodiversity depends on the maintenance of the social, economic and cultural diversity of the crofting communities that support it.

There has been a recent upsurge of interest in crofting, but it remains economically marginal. Financial exigencies and ill-targeted support mechanisms in recent years have led to a progressive shift from arable to stock grazing and from cattle to sheep on many machair areas. Undergrazing and poor management of seasonal grazing encourages rank, species-poor grassland, while the increase in rabbit numbers, poor recreation management and sand and shingle extraction have greatly accelerated the natural processes of erosion.

Protecting the biodiversity of machair grassland is as much a matter of social governance as of ecological management, and the challenge is to find ways of adopting crofting into a multifaceted economy, appropriate to the aspirations of rural Scotland in a new millennium. The Scottish Office consultation on a replacement to the Environmentally Sensitive Areas scheme (Scottish Office Agriculture, Environment and Fisheries Department, 1998) provides the opportunity to widen agri-environment support to all machair areas, but it must not reduce the funding that supports sound agricultural management of machair areas.

Other human influences on the machair may prove more intractable. The action plan notes that coastline retreat due to the rising sea level and falling isobase, already referred to by Hansom (Chapter 3) and by Pethick (Chapter 4), together with increasing storminess as a result of climate change, produce extensive slow erosion of the outer dune edge, which can be accelerated by stock damage. As the pace of these changes quickens, the scale of damage to the machair is likely to accelerate, until such time as the equilibrium between the sea and the land that creates the machair might itself break down. Addressing this issue is a priority, not just for machair, but for many other ecosystems and, indeed, for many aspects of the modern human economy.

16.4.7 *Action for* Ascophyllum nodosum *ecad* mackaii *beds*

Extensive beds of *Ascophyllum nodosum* ecad *mackaii* (Plate 53), the unattached and bladderless ecological form of knotted wrack, develop in conditions of extreme shelter and fluctuating salinity on sea-loch shores across which freshwater runs or seeps. The tumbleweed-like mats provide a protected, humid habitat for many mid-shore animals. The ecad – and therefore the habitat – is only found in sheltered Scottish sea lochs and a few sites in Northern Ireland, Eire and North America.

Such sheltered shores are inevitably susceptible to pollution, land claim and damage from road and bridge construction. The action plan calls for the most extensive beds to be incorporated into designated conservation sites. It also advocates measures to ensure that road building schemes and other developments do not damage the conservation interest of beds of this seaweed, and proposes that the Scottish Office and SNH should provide advice to local authorities and others on minimising the impacts of their activities on these beds.

As with so many of the action plans, this latter objective is essentially one of focus, not of public expenditure. In most cases, relatively small modifications to proposed developments can remove almost entirely the damaging effects on biodiversity, often at no additional cost, other than in time and planning. More than anything else, the challenge of biodiversity action plans is to ensure a refocusing of development priorities, so that biodiversity conservation is taken into account at the planning stage.

However, the action plan includes a salutary example of where this process can go wrong. An environmental impact assessment into the planned route of the Skye Bridge identified small beds of *Ascophyllum nodosum* ecad *mackaii*. The contractors were made aware of the importance of these beds, and requested to scrape aside the unattached mats from shores on which they planned construction. This they did, leaving the beds undamaged throughout the construction process. However, prior to the bridge-opening ceremony, another contractor was employed to tidy up the area, but was not informed of the importance of these beds. The contractor removed one entire bed, which was perceived as 'untidy', and more than two years later it shows no sign of recovery.

16.5 The way forward

There are two further benefits arising from the implementation of these action plans, which, in the long term, may prove especially beneficial. The first is the proposal that each targeted species and habitat should have a co-ordinating group to take forward the proposed actions. Assembling the key enthusiasts for these species and habitats should provide a new focus for action and is likely, in itself, to be a powerful incentive for pro-activity. Secondly, it is proposed to establish groups to develop local Biodiversity Action Plans. In the pilot areas, these groups already have stimulated greatly enhanced understanding of, and considerable pride in, locally distinctive elements of biodiversity. The resulting sense of local identification with biodiversity may be the strongest incentive for its future protection.

References

Anon. 1994. *Biodiversity: the UK Action Plan*, Command 2428. HMSO, London.

Anon. 1995. *Biodiversity: the UK Steering Group Report* (2 volumes). HMSO, London.

Council of the European Communities. 1979. Council Directive 79/409/EEC of 2 April 1979: *On the Conservation of Wild Birds*.

Council of the European Communities. 1992. Council Directive 92/43/EEC of 21 May 1992: on the conservation of natural habitats and of wild fauna and flora. *Official Journal of the European Communities*, L206/7.

Fleming, L.V., Newton, A.C., Vickery, J.A. and Usher, M.B. 1997. *Biodiversity in Scotland: Status, Trends and Initiatives*. The Stationery Office, Edinburgh.

Scottish Office. 1997. *Biodiversity in Scotland – The Way Forward*. The Stationery Office, Edinburgh.

Scottish Office. 1998. *Biodiversity for All: A Toolkit*. Scottish Biodiversity Group, Edinburgh.

Scottish Office Agriculture, Environment and Fisheries Department. 1998. *Merger of Scottish agri-environment schemes*; consultation document.

Stace, C. 1991. *New Flora of the British Isles*. Cambridge University Press, Cambridge.

Stewart, A., Pearman, D.A. and Preston, C.D. 1994. *Scarce Plants in Britain*. Joint Nature Conservation Committee, Peterborough.

Wilson, E.O. (ed.). 1988. *BioDiversity*. National Academy Press, Washington, DC.

INDEX

Page numbers in *italics* refer to illustrations. Numbers preceded by *pl* refer to plates.